Progress in Thin-Layer Chromatography and Related Methods

Volume II

A. Niederwieser and G. Pataki

Editors

a|a
s|p ann arbor science publishers inc.

© 1971 by Ann Arbor Science Publishers, Inc.
600 South Wagner Road, P.O. Box 1425, Ann Arbor, Michigan 48106

Library of Congress Catalog Card No. 73-94256
SBN 250-39969-5
Printed in the United States of America

Ann Arbor Science Publishers, Ltd.
5 Great Russell St., London, W. C. 1, England

The Editors

A. Niederwieser, Department of Chemistry, Universitäts-Kinderklinik, Zürich, Switzerland

G. Pataki Pharmaceutical Department, Sandoz AG, Basle, Switzerland

Contributors to Volume II

F. J. Detterbeck, Howell State Hospital, Michigan, Department of Mental Health, Howell, Michigan, USA

R. W. Frei, Department of Chemistry, Dalhousie University, Halifax, Nova Scotia, Canada

J. Janák, Institute of Instrumental Analytical Chemistry, Czechoslovak Academy of Sciences, Brno, Czechoslovakia

H. A. Lillevik, Department of Biochemistry, Michigan State University, East Lansing, Michigan, USA

O. Renkonen, Department of Biochemistry, University of Helsinki, Finland

E. Röder, Department of Pharmacy, University of Bonn, West Germany.

F. Snyder, Medical Division, Oak Ridge, Associated Universities, Oak Ridge, Tennessee, USA

E. Tyihák and **G. Held,** Research Institute for Medicinal Plants, Budapest, Hungary

Preface

Thin-layer chromatography is now one of the most widely applied methods of separation. A tremendous number of publications in almost all fields of chemistry, biochemistry and the medical sciences demonstrate the advantages of TLC for qualitative and quantitative analysis and for micropreparative purposes. There are several handbooks on this technique in general[1] and also on more specialized subjects.[2] However, it is impossible, particularly for the nonspecialist, to keep step with the present development since the number of publications increases exponentially. It was felt that a series of monographs written by specialists could reflect the continual advances more adequately and would be very useful to everybody interested in TLC. Because different chromatographic techniques are used simultaneously as well as in connection with many other physico-chemical methods, the series also includes combinations of TLC with other analytical techniques, *e.g.*, with radioactive techniques, gas chromatography, and reflectance spectroscopy.

The second volume of this series, international in scope, contains seven contributions. Three papers deal with general problems: reflectance spectroscopy (R. W. Frei), the combination of TLC with gas chromatography (J. Janák), and the use of azeotropic mixtures as solvents (E. Röder). Four contributions treat more specialized subjects: the chemistry, physical properties, and chromatography of lipids containing ether bonds (F. Snyder), the analysis of molecular species of polar lipids (O. Renkonen), the application of TLC in pharmacognosy (E. Tyihák and G. Held), and TLC of amino acids in urine (F. J. Detterbeck and H. A. Lillewik). Because all the authors are working, in general, at the forefront of their specialized field, they are able to treat their subjects critically and authoritatively. Some of the chapters are review-like while others treat the literature less comprehensively as they describe important techniques in detail.

The editors hope that this volume, as well as the first and third, will aid chemists, biochemists, biologists, clinical chemists, and medical scientists in keeping step with the techniques of TLC and that it will help in the practical performance of their work.

Basle/Zurich   A. Niederwieser
September, 1970   G. Pataki

---

1. E. Stahl (Ed.). *Thin-Layer Chromatography* (New York: Academic Press, 1965); K. Randerath, in *Thin-Layer Chromatography* (New York: Academic Press, 1965); J. M. Bobbitt. *Thin-Layer Chromatography* (New York: Reinhold, 1963); E. V. Truter. *Thin-Film Chromatography* (London: Cleaver-Hume, 1963); and J. G. Kirchner. *Thin-Layer Chromatography* (New York: Interscience, 1967).
2. R. Neher. *Steroid Chromatography* (Amsterdam: Elsevier, 1964); G. Pataki. *Techniques of Thin-Layer Chromatography in Amino Acid and Peptide Chemistry* (Ann Arbor, Michigan: Ann Arbor Science Publishers, 1968).

Contents

R. W. FREI

Reflectance Spectroscopy in Thin-Layer Chromatography

O. RENKONEN

*Thin-Layer Chromatographic Analysis of Subclasses and
Molecular Species of Polar Lipids*

TLC-Nomenclature
Used in This Volume

The nomenclature used in TLC differs widely from author to author. Several expressions may give rise to misunderstandings, for example "development" which stands for "chromatography" as well as for "detection." Such expressions should be avoided completely. Other terms used in literature are not correct from the standpoint of physico-chemistry: "mobile phase" is sometimes used for the liquid in the chromatographic chamber but should be restricted for the liquid moving within the chromatographic layer. Due to the existing nonequilibrium between the layer material and the solvent as well as the gas phase in the chamber, the composition of the mobile phase usually does not correspond to the composition of the solvent in the chamber and changes locally and temporarily on the chromatogram. Similarly, the composition of the surface of the chromatographic layer material, the "stationary phase" in the chromatographic sense, usually is not known. It seems to be more adequate to use terms like layer material, adsorbent, impregnated adsorbent, etc. To avoid any misunderstanding we list in the following some expressions used in this volume.

Term	Definition
adsorbent	a powder of at least about 50 m²/g specific surface area. In adsorption chromatography the adsorbent surface forms the stationary phase by interaction with the mobile phase and the gas phase in the chamber.
adsorption chromatography	chromatography on an adsorbent.

Term	Definition
to apply	to apply the test solution to the chromatographic layer.
bed	a layer or column of (porous) material containing the stationary phase, the interstices being filled with mobile phase.
chamber	the vessel in which chromatography takes place, usually a closed trough-chamber of a relatively large volume (see also sandwich-chamber).
chamber saturation	equilibration of the gas phase in the chamber with the solvent. By convention, chamber saturation is achieved by lining the walls of the trough-chamber with filter paper being in contact with the solvent. The time needed for saturation is reduced from about 1 hour to about 5 minutes by vigorously shaking the closed chamber for about 10 seconds. Chamber saturation prevents an appreciable evaporation of mobile phase from the chromatogram, but leads to an impregnation of the nonwetted part of the adsorbent layer with solvent vapors.
chromatogram	thin-layer during and after chromatography, or its reproduction.
to chromatograph	to make a chromatogram; to undergo chromatography.
chromatographic system	the whole physicochemical state under which chromatography occurs: adsorbent, solvent, chamber saturation, temperature, relative air humidity, technique (ascendent, horizontal, descendent), etc.
chromatographic technique	special arrangement used for chromatography, *e.g.*, descending solvent flow, multiple chromatography, running through technique, etc.
chromatography	multiple physiochemical equilibrium distribution of dissolved or vaporized substances between a stationary and a mobile phase, for the purpose of separation or characterization.
detection	visualization of chromatographed substances.
diluent	volatile liquid used for spreading a nonvolatile liquid stationary phase on a solid support.
elution	extraction of substances from layer material after chromatography.

Term	Definition
flow direction	direction of migration of the solvent in the layer.
front	the *visible* boundary between solvent wetted layer and "dry" layer material. It should be emphasized that the "dry"-appearing layer material may contain appreciable amounts (about 30% w/w) of solvent or solvent components if a trough chamber is used with chamber saturation.
GC, gas chromatography	chromatography using a gas as the mobile phase.
GLC, gas-liquid chromatography	chromatography using a gas as mobile phase and a liquid as stationary phase.
hRf	$100 \times$ Rf-value.
immersion line	line of application of the solvent to the layer.
impregnation	loading of the layer material with a solid or liquid (impregnant) to effect a change in the chromatographic properties of the layer.
iteration chromatography	multiple chromatography in the same direction using the same solvent.
layer	uniform sheet of porous material containing the stationary phase.
length of run	distance between starting point and solvent front.
to migrate	traveling of the sample or of the solvent front in flow direction.
mobile phase	liquid transporting the sample through the chromatographic bed (*e.g.*, layer), being in interaction with the stationary phase and the gas phase in the chamber. Therefore not a priori identical with the solvent.
multiple chromatography	chromatography repeated several times using the same or different solvents.
partition chromatography	chromatography on a layer material impregnated with a liquid which is not completely miscible but equilibrated with the solvent.
precoated sheets (plates)	commercially available thin-layer plates or sheets ready for chromatography.

Term	Definition
resolution	the degree of separation of two substances, measurable, *e.g.*, as $R = d/(w_1 + w_2)$, where d is the distance of the peak maxima, and w_1 and w_2 are the peak widths (at half height) of substance 1 and 2. Resolution is practically complete if $R \gtreqqless 1.5$.
reversed phase chromatography	chromatography on a solid support impregnated (*e.g.*, using a volatile diluent) with a nonpolar and nonvolatile liquid as stationary phase. Chromatography is effected by a polar solvent equilibrated with the nonpolar liquid.
Rf-value	distance starting point to center of substance spot divided by the distance starting point to solvent front.
R_M-value	$\log\left(\dfrac{1}{Rf} - 1\right)$. Conversion table $Rf - R_M$ see Appendix in Volume I of this series.
to run, run	to chromatograph, chromatography.
sample	substance(s) to be chromatographed.
sandwich-chamber	thin-layer plate covered by a cover plate at a distance of up to about 2 mm. Several devices are commercially available.
solvent	one- or multi-component liquid employed for chromatography, forming the mobile phase by interaction with the stationary phase and the gas phase in the chamber. Not a priori identical with the mobile phase.
start, starting point	point of application of the substance to be chromatographed, usually at a distance of 10 mm from the immersion line.
stationary phase	the surface region of an adsorbent or a stationary liquid dispersed on an inert support, being in interaction with the mobile phase.
TLC, thin-layer chromatography	liquid-solid or liquid-liquid chromatography on a layer up to 2 mm thick in a chamber containing a gas phase.
two-dimensional TLC	successive runs in directions orthogonal to each other.

The Editors

Chapter 1

Reflectance Spectroscopy in Thin-Layer Chromatography

by R. W. Frei

With the advent of commercially available reflectance attachments for practically all the standard spectrophotometers on the market, diffuse reflectance spectroscopy has become an increasingly important tool for workers in fields such as solid state chemistry, adsorption, structural analysis and analytical chemistry. Diffuse reflectance and the transparency of light-scattering and light-absorbing layers have been investigated by numerous workers because of their great significance in such areas as the paint, paper and ceramics industries. The renaissance of interest in reflectance spectroscopy during the last few years is seen in the appearance of the first text specifically on this subject[1] and the organization of a symposium on all aspects of reflectance spectroscopy held in Chicago in 1967.[2]

Although the thin-layer chromatographic technique offers many distinct advantages, its analytical utility is restricted by two shortcomings. In the first place, the difficulty experienced in obtaining reproducible Rf-values on thin-layer plates usually makes it necessary to run standards for comparison with the samples. Second, the quantitative removal and extraction of individual spots from plates is a tedious process which often cannot be accomplished without decomposition. These shortcomings would be eliminated if it were possible to effect the *in situ* identification and determination of chemical species separated on thin-layer plates.

The use of spectral reflectance for the *in situ* evaluation of thin-layer chromatograms was suggested by various studies[3-6] which demonstrated its utility with respect to paper chromatography. Furthermore, it has been shown that the reflectance spectra of substances concentrated on particulate adsorbents can be used for their identification[7] and that spectral reflectance can be employed to determine the concentration of dyes scavenged from solution by the addition of starch.[8] A critical evaluation of the application of reflectance measurements to the direct analysis of solid mixtures has established the fact that analytically useful data can usually be obtained with samples in powdered form.[9] In view of these results, the analytical applications of spectral reflectance to thin-layer chromatography were investigated.

THEORY

Kubelka-Munk Equation

The most generally accepted theory concerning diffuse reflectance and the transparency of light-scattering and light-absorbing layers was developed by Kubelka and Munk.[10, 11] When applied to an infinitely thick, opaque layer, the Kubelka-Munk equation may be written as

$$\frac{(1 - R'_\infty)^2}{2R'_\infty} = \frac{k}{s} \tag{1}$$

Where R'_∞ is the absolute reflectance of the layer, k is its molar absorption coefficient, and s is the scattering coefficient (for the derivation of the equation see Appendix). Instead of determining R'_∞, however, it is customary in practice to work with the more convenient relative diffuse reflectance, R_∞, which is measured against a standard such as MgO or $BaSO_4$. In these cases it is assumed that the k values for the standards are zero and that their absolute reflectance is one. But since the absolute reflectance of the standards exhibiting the highest R'_∞ values never exceeds 0.98–0.99, one is actually dealing in such instances with the relationship

$$\frac{R'_\infty \text{ sample}}{R'_\infty \text{ standard}} = R_\infty \tag{2}$$

and it is essential that the standard employed be specified. If this expression is introduced into the initial equation it will assume the form

$$F(R_\infty) \equiv \frac{(1 - R_\infty)^2}{2R_\infty} = \frac{k}{s} \tag{3}$$

This indicates that a linear relationship should be observed between $F(R_\infty)$ and the absorption coefficient k, provided s remains constant;

s is rendered independent of wavelength by the use of scattering particles whose size is large relative to the wavelength being used.

When the reflectance of a sample diluted with a non- or low-absorbing powder is measured against the pure powder, the absorption coefficient *k* may be replaced by the product 2.30εc, where ε is the extinction coefficient and *c* is the molar concentration.[12] Kubelka-Munk Equation 3 can then be written in the form

$$F(R_\infty) = (1 - R_\infty)^2/2R_\infty = c/k'$$ (4)

where *k'* is a constant equal to s/2.30ε. Since $F(R_\infty)$ is proportional to the molar concentration under constant experimental conditions, the Kubelka-Munk relationship is analogous to the Beer-Lambert law of absorption spectrophotometry. At high enough dilutions, the regular reflection from the sample approximates that from the standard and is thus cancelled out in any comparison measurement.

A straight-line relationship between $F(R_\infty)$ and *c* is observed, however, only when dealing with weakly absorbing substances and only when the grain size of the powders employed is less than 1μ in diameter (Kortüm[13-15]). Furthermore, any significant departure from the state of infinite thickness of the adsorbent layer assumed in the derivation of the Kubelka-Munk equation results in background interference, which in turn is responsible for nonideal diffuse reflectance. When adsorbents having a large grain size or when large concentrations of the absorbing species are used, plots of $F(R_\infty)$ versus concentration deviate from straight lines in that there is a decrease in slope at higher concentrations.

In his explanation of this phenomenon, Kortüm[13-16] postulates that the reflected radiation is the result of both regular and diffuse reflectance. The first can be described as a mirror reflection whereas the second occurs when impinging radiation is partly absorbed and partly scattered by a system so that it is reflected in a diffuse manner; that is to say, with no defined angle of emergence. Regular reflectance for cases involving normal incidence is described by the Fresnel equation:

$$R_{reg} \equiv \frac{I_{REFL}}{I_0} = \frac{(n - 1)^2 + n^2k^2}{(n + 1)^2 + n^2k^2}$$ (5)

where *k* is the absorption coefficient and *n* is the refractive index. Diffuse reflectance is described by the Kubelka-Munk function given earlier. Since regular reflectance is superimposed on diffuse reflectance, a distortion of the diffuse reflectance spectrum results, which is responsible for the anomalous relationship observed between $F(R_\infty)$ and *k* at high concentrations of the absorbing species. It is essential, therefore, to eliminate as far as possible the interference caused by regular reflectance, R_{reg}. This can be accomplished by selecting appropriate experimental conditions. Especially effective are the use of powders having a small grain size and the dilution of the light-absorbing species with suitable diluents.

Most equations derived by other investigators have proved to be special cases or adaptations of the Kubelka-Munk equation.[16–19] Kortüm and Vogel[16] have also summarized the theory and the derivation of the Kubelka-Munk function for special cases involving infinitely thick, opaque layers, which in the case of fine powders would be those having a depth of approximately one millimeter. Judd and Wyszecki[19] have compiled most of the different forms of the Kubelka-Munk function and have pointed out some of their specific uses and applications.

Zeitlin and Niimoto[20] found that the particle size of the adsorbent or diluent can affect reflectance spectra, and that the absorption bands tend to broaden as the particle size increases. Various attempts have been made to account for the deviations from the Kubelka-Munk law that are observed with increased concentration and particle size. Kortüm[16] ascribed them to the interference of regular (Fresnel) reflection and verified his explanation experimentally[14] by measuring the reflectance spectra of powders between crossed polarization foils. In this manner he was able to separate diffuse from direct reflection.

Goldman and Goodall[21] recently proposed some theoretical relationships based on the Kubelka-Munk function, specifically designed to fit the conditions for diffuse reflectance measurements on thin-layer plates. The theory is based on two separable effects, "hyperchromaticity" and "curvature of response." These two effects have been evaluated experimentally on silica gel layers.

Particle Size and Sample Thickness

Commercially available adsorbents for TLC with particle sizes usually between 5 and 40μ are suitable for use as diluents in both visible and ultraviolet regions of the spectrum. With these powders, simple mixing of the sample in a small mortar produces a sufficiently homogeneous mixture of reproducible texture. The resulting system usually conforms to the Kubelka-Munk equation over a concentration range that has analytical utility.[22–24]

Although Kortüm reported that a layer 1 mm thick of a powder of 1μ particle size is needed to achieve infinite layer thickness and hence adherence to the Kubelka-Munk equation, it was found[22] that the portion of visible light that is able to penetrate a compressed silica gel layer of 0.4-mm thickness is negligibly small for analytical purposes. Cells employing white, gray, and black backing paper were used to investigate background interference, and the reflectance values for silica gel samples of 0.4-mm thickness packed in each of these cells differed by not more than 1%. Jork[23] has also investigated the relationship between the layer thickness of adsorbent and the amount of light transmitted through the layer. The ultraviolet region was included in his study. With a 300μ layer thickness, for example, he found a transmission of 2.2% at =500 nm, and of 1% at =300 nm. The amount of transmitted light ($\lambda > 300$ nm) at the more realistic plate-layer thickness of 160μ is, however, already quite appreciable ($> 5\%$), and the author has repeatedly recommended the use of a white backing paper inserted behind the plate as a reflecting background if spectra are to be recorded directly from the plate and in the visible region of the spectrum. One tends to agree with Klaus[25, 26] that the use of the Kubelka-Munk function is not justified under these circumstances and that empirical functions resulting in linear calibration curves should be used.

Optimum Concentration Range and Calibration Curves

For systems exhibiting no deviation from the Kubelka-Munk equation, the optimum conditions for accuracy can be deduced by computing the relative error, dc/c. In terms of Kubelka-Munk Equation 4, the error in c is

$$dc = k'(R_\infty^2 - 1)dR_\infty/2R_\infty^2 \qquad (6)$$

and the relative error in c is

$$dc/c = (R_\infty + 1)\ dR_\infty/(R_\infty - 1)R_\infty \qquad (7)$$

Assuming a reading error in reflectance amounting to 1%, that is, $dR_\infty = 0.01$,

$$(dc/c)100 = (R_\infty + 1)/(R_\infty - 1)R_\infty = \% \text{ error in } c \qquad (8)$$

To determine the value of R_∞ which will minimize the relative error in c, $d(\% \text{ error in } c)/dR_\infty$ is equated to zero. The positive solution of the resulting equation

$$R_\infty^2 + 2R_\infty - 1 = 0 \qquad (9)$$

indicates that the minimum relative error in c occurs at a reflectance value of 0.414, corresponding to a reflectance reading of 41.4% R. This is presented graphically in Figure 1, where the per cent of error, computed by Equation 8, is plotted as a function of the per cent of reflectance. The minimum in the resulting curve corresponds to the 41.4% R-value obtained by the solution of Equation 9.

Reflectance spectrophotometric methods of analysis usually involve the use of a calibration curve prepared by measuring the reflectance of samples containing known amounts of the substance of interest. Conformity to the Kubelka-Munk equation is indicated if the data, when

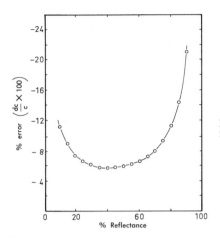

Figure 1. Percentage error, computed with the use of Equation 8, as a function of percentage reflectance.

plotted in the form $F(R_\infty)$ vs. c, follow a straight line. From the standpoint of utility in analysis, however, it is immaterial whether the system in question conforms to the Kubelka-Munk equation or not. Provided some sort of near linear relationship is found to exist between reflectance and concentration, it is more important, if the method is to be used for analysis, to select a suitable concentration range for the analysis and to evaluate its accuracy. To illustrate how this might be done, two systems were selected as models. These were Rhodamine B, which absorbs in the visible region, and aspirin, which absorbs in the ultraviolet, both adsorbed on silica gel. The experimental data of the first system are presented in Figure 2 as curve 1 and of the second as curve 3. When these data are plotted in the form $F(R_\infty)$ vs. c (Figure 3), curve 1 results for Rhodamine B and curve 3 for aspirin. Although both curves are linear over a considerable portion of the concentration ranges investigated, neither conforms to the Kubelka-Munk equation. This becomes more evident when the pair of curves obtained with Rhodamine B (curves 1

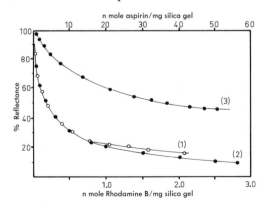

Figure 2. Percentage of reflectance as a function of concentration:

(1) Experimental } values
(2) Theoretical } of Rhodamine B at 545 nm.

(3) Experimental values of aspirin at 302 nm.

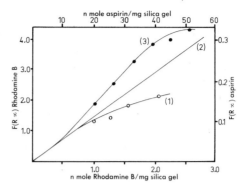

Figure 3. Kubelka-Munk values as a function of concentration:
(1) Experimental ⎫ values of
(2) Theoretical ⎭ Rhodamine B at 543 nm.
(3) Experimental values of aspirin at 302 nm.

of Figures 2 and 3) is contrasted with the pair of hypothetical curves that would have been obtained had the system behaved ideally (curves 2 of Figures 2 and 3). The departure from linearity observed with both Rhodamine B and aspirin at higher concentrations may be ascribed to the approaching saturation of the adsorbent surface by the first monomolecular layer of the adsorbed species.[12] Variations in the optical properties of the reference standard were at least partly responsible for the nonlinearity that was also observed at lower concentrations in the case of aspirin. When the relative error in concentration arising from a 1% error in R is plotted against per cent of reflectance (Figure 4), there is close agreement between the experimental curve of Figure 2 and the hypothetical values curve for the Rhodamine B system. The scatter in curve 2 arises from the method of calculation. There is poorer agreement with the experimental curves for Rhodamine B and aspirin, because of the

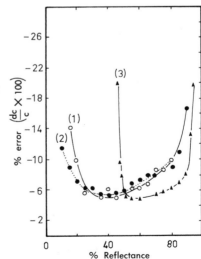

Figure 4. Per cent of error arising from a reading error of 1% R (estimated graphically) as a function of per cent reflectance:
(1) Experimental Rhodamine B values
(2) Hypothetical Rhodamine B values
(3) Experimental aspirin values.

departure from the Kubelka-Munk equation. Nevertheless, the curves
do show the range of reflectance that gives minimum error.

Another approach to the selection of the optimum range for reflectance analysis is one suggested by Ringbom,[28] and later by Ayres,[29] who
evaluated relative error and defined the suitable range for absorption
analysis by plotting the absorbance (1-transmittance) against the logarithm of the concentration. When the reflectance data obtained with
Rhodamine B and aspirin and the hypothetical data computed for
Rhodamine B are plotted as per cent of reflectance versus the logarithm
of concentration (Figure 5), the advantages of this method become

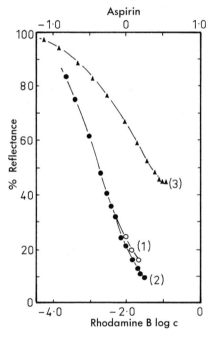

Figure 5. Per cent reflectance as a
function of the logarithm of concentration:
  (1) Experimental   Rhodamine   B
values
  (2) Hypothetical   Rhodamine   B
values
  (3) Experimental aspirin values.
Log concentration (μmole $\times 10^5$ Rhodamine B/mg adsorbent; μmole aspirin/
70 mg adsorbent).

manifest. The optimum range for analysis corresponds to that portion
of each curve exhibiting the greatest slope. Since a considerable portion
of each of the curves shown in Figure 5 is also fairly linear in this region,
it is apparent that reasonable accuracy can be expected over a wide concentration range. The maximum accuracy can be estimated from the
equation

$$\frac{dc}{c}100 = 2.303 \, d(\log c) \, 100 = 2.303 \frac{d(\log c)}{dR}100 \, dR \qquad (10)$$

Assuming a constant reading error of 1% R, *i.e., dR* = 0.01,

$$\% \text{ error} = 2{,}303\frac{d(\log c)}{dR} \qquad (11)$$

For the three systems under consideration the optimum range for analysis can be arrived at by a consideration of the curves in Figure 5, and the per cent of error resulting from a reading error of 1% R can be computed with the use of Equation 11 and the slope of the appropriate curve. When this is done, the data obtained (presented in Table I) are found

Table I
Optimum Range of Reflectance and Error of Analysis in Per Cent

Curve number (see Figure 5)	System	Optimum range of reflectance (% R)	% Error of analysis per 1% reading error
1	Rhodamine B (experimental)	25–65	6.0
2	Rhodamine B (hypothetical)	20–65	6.0
3	Aspirin (experimental)	55–85	6.0

to be in accordance with those resulting from the application of the graphic method. Values for the hypothetical Rhodamine B system also agree with the figures obtained for an ideal system and computed with the use of Equation 11. It would seem, therefore, that the minimum error in reflectance spectrophotometric analysis is about 6% per 1% R reading error, regardless of whether the system conforms to the Kubelka-Munk equation or not. This value can obviously be decreased by reducing the reading error. Although a reading error amounting to 0.5% R should not be too difficult to attain, it would be unrealistic to expect a precision better than 0.1–0.2% R, and therefore a minimum error smaller than 1–2%. Similarly, regardless of whether or not a system conforms to the Kubelka-Munk equation, the optimum range for analysis can be arrived at after plotting the reflectance data according to either of the two procedures described. The Ringbom method has the advantage not only of making available the optimum range and maximum accuracy but also of providing a plot usable as a calibration curve.

Multicomponent Systems

The validity of the theoretical principles discussed was further investigated with respect to multicomponent systems,[27] of interest in cases of incomplete chromatographic separation.

For a powder mixture containing n light-absorbing components whose reflectance functions are additive, the Kubelka-Munk function $F(R_\infty)$ can be adapted for simultaneous analysis. The function of the total reflectance $R_{\infty T}$ of the mixture at some wavelength i may be represented as the sum of all individual reflectance functions:

$$F(R_{\curlywedge T})i = \sum_{j=i}^{n} \tau_{ij}C_j \qquad (12)$$

where j refers to components and τ is the slope of the Kubelka-Munk plot of $R(R_{\curlywedge})$ vs. C.

Equation 12 can be written in a more explicit manner by writing as many equations as there are components in the mixture.

$$F(R_{\curlywedge T})_1 = \tau_{11}C_1 + \tau_{12}C_2 + \ldots \tau_{1n}C_n \qquad (13)$$

$$F(R_{\curlywedge T})_2 = \tau_{21}C_2 + \tau_{22}C_2 + \ldots \tau_{2n}C_n \qquad (14)$$

These equations are, of course, valid only for a concentration range within that prescribed by the Kubelka-Munk law. At higher concentrations interference due to saturation of the first monomolecular adsorption layer[12] results in marked deviations from linearity, and in extreme cases gives a calibration curve asymptotic to the horizontal axis. The useful concentration range can be extended, however, by use of the semiempirical relationship

$$(1 - R_{\curlywedge})^2/2R_{\curlywedge} = k \log C \qquad (15)$$

suggested in an earlier paper,[22] which results in an almost fivefold extension of the range. Other functions which tend to give linear calibra-

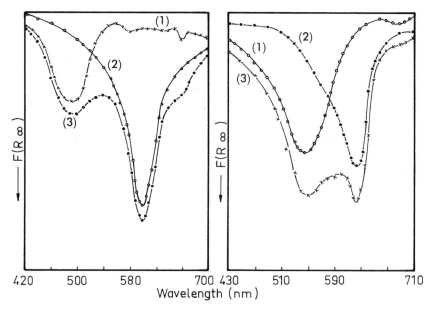

Figure 6. Reflectance spectra of (1) Orange G, (2) Crystal Violet, (3) a mixture of the two.

Figure 7. Reflectance spectra of (1) Fuchsin, (2) Brilliant Green, (3) a mixture of the two.

tion curves under suitable conditions [log R_∞ *vs.* C^2, R_∞ *vs.* $^3\sqrt{C}$ or $\sqrt{C/(1-C)}$] have been proposed by Lermond and Rogers[30] and could be applied for simultaneous analysis as well.

The dye pairs Orange G–Crystal Violet and Fuchsin–Brilliant Green were chosen for study. Figures 6 and 7 show the individual spectra of the dyes and the spectra of the mixtures of the two pairs; the theoretically computed total spectra of the pairs (by addition of the individual reflectance functions) are essentially identical with the measured spectra. Throughout the entire concentration range studied, the absorption maxima for all four dyes do not vary significantly. Figure 8 shows absorption

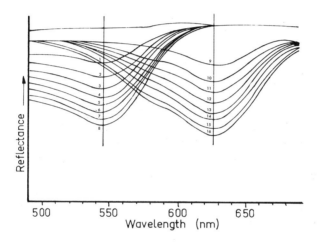

Figure 8. Reflectance spectra of dilution series of Fuchsin (1–8) and Brilliant Green (9–16) adsorbed on Silica Gel G, recorded against a barium sulfate reflectance standard. The zero line is for pure Silica Gel G. The concentration of dye in μg per sample is as follows. Fuchsin: (1) 0.3, (2) 0.6, (3) 0.9, (4) 1.2, (5) 1.5, (6) 1.8, (7) 2.4, (8) 3.0. Brilliant Green: (9) 0.3, (10) 0.6, (11) 0.9, (12) 1.2, (13) 1.5, (14) 1.8, (15) 2.4, (16) 3.0.

characteristics of Fuchsin and Brilliant Green and mixtures of the two dyes; these results show the absence of interferences due to molecular dissociation, association, and abnormal adsorbent-adsorbate interactions and show that the dye systems are satisfactory for further investigation. The absorption maxima determined from Figures 6–8 (626 nm for Brilliant Green, 600 nm for Crystal Violet, 545 nm for Fuchsin, and 490 nm for Orange G) were used for quantitative analysis. Calibration plots for the Fuchsin–Brilliant Green pair are shown in Figure 9. Within the concentration ranges studied, the Kubelka-Munk relationship was valid

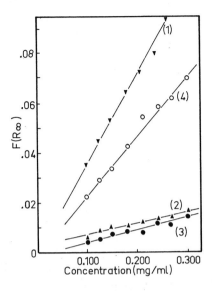

Figure 9. Kubelka-Munk plots for Brilliant Green at 626 nm (1); Fuchsin at 626 nm (2); Brilliant Green at 545 nm (3); Fuchsin at 545 nm (4).

for all four dyes, and the τ-values for the slopes of the Kubelka-Munk curves required for Equations 13 and 14 were readily obtained. To test the reliability of the method, sample mixtures were prepared and analyzed as unknowns by students at the junior and senior level. The dilution series were processed simultaneously with the unknowns to avoid fluctuations due to temperature, humidity changes, and bleaching effects. Six concentrations were measured for each calibration curve and four samples of each dye pair were prepared. The students results are shown below.

Precision (average standard deviation for four sets of
four samples) $= \pm 2.4\%$

Accuracy (average deviation of four samples from true value)

Dye pair 1		*Dye pair 2*	
Orange G	Crystal Violet	Fuchsin	Brilliant Green
1.9%	3.3%	2.1%	3.1%

As expected, the precision is somewhat lower than for single component analysis; the factors limiting precision for such simple systems were found to be the packing reproducibility and the homogeneity of the samples.

APPARATUS

Instrumentation

Although reflectance attachments are now available for a wide range of commercial spectrophotometers, only the instruments which have actually been used by the author or which have been specifically designed for thin-layer chromatography are dealt with here. For a detailed discussion of reflectance spectroscopic instrumentation the reader is referred to Wendlandt and Hecht.[1]

Perhaps the best known and most widely used spectrophotometer for reflectance work is the Beckman Model DU single beam instrument equipped with a standard reflectance attachment for the measurement of diffuse reflectance (Figure 10). Monochromatic radiation from slit D is made less divergent by quartz lens L, and after reflection from the front-surface plane mirror M it irradiates the sample S. A portion of the diffusely reflected light from the sample, in the geometry of a hollow cone centered at an angle of 45° to S, is reflected from the ellipsoidal metal mirror R onto the diffusing envelope H of a phototube and then to the photosensitive surface. The hollow cone of light includes an angle of approximately 20° about the line SR. In this way, light rays from the center of the sample surface (or reference) making angles of 35° to 55° with the perpendicular are measured.

The sample and reference materials are placed in a sliding drawer located at the bottom of the accessory. The various reflectance cells described later in this section were originally designed to fit into the sliding drawer of the Beckman DU attachment, but were later used with other attachments without alteration.

The reflectance accessory for the Model DK-1A or DK-2A spectrophotometers (spectroreflectometers) (Figure 11) utilizes an integrating sphere in which the sample and reference materials are illuminated by monochromatic radiation from the monochromator by means of an oscillating mirror. Either the total or the diffuse reflectance of a sample may be measured; the former is obtained by mounting the sample and reference materials at an angle of 5° to the incident lightbeam. By using a 1P28 photomultiplier tube and/or a lead sulfide cell as detectors, the range of the reflectance accessory is from 210 to 2700 nm. Another diffuse reflectance attachment, recently introduced, can be used with the Beckman Model DB or DG recording spectrophotometer.

Diffuse reflectance attachments for the Bausch and Lomb Spectronic 20 and Spectronic 505 instruments have also been used for the investigations. In the Spectronic 20 attachment monochromatic light is reflected by a mirror, lens, and filter onto the sample or reference material placed at the top of an integrating sphere. The reflected diffuse light is detected by a photomultiplier tube placed at a 90° angle to the sample. A rectangular spot of light, 2×8 mm in area, strikes the sample surface so that fairly small samples may be examined (see also Reference 1). A modified attachment with a lightbeam area of 12×12 mm is also available, employing a band width of 20 nm in the 400–700 nm wavelength range. The reflectance attachment for the Bausch & Lomb Spec-

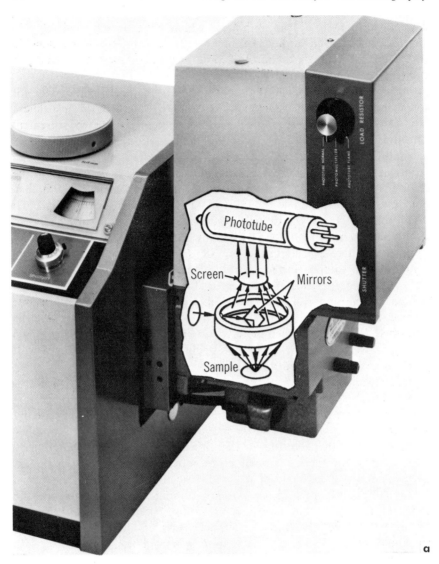

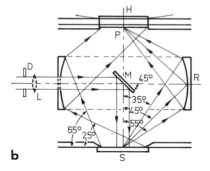

Figure 10. Reflectance accessory for the Beckman Model DU Spectrophotometer. (10a) Overall view, with cutaway detailed below. (10b) Schematic cross section of reflectance attachment showing geometry of irradiation and reception. D, slit; L, lens; M, mirror; S, specimen; R, ellipsoidal reflector; P, diffusing quartz plate; H, phototube envelope.

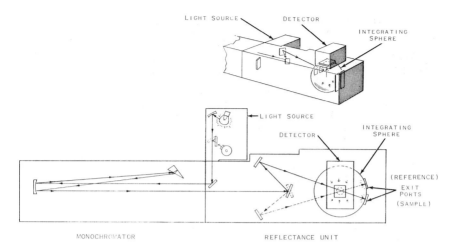

Figure 11. Optical diagram of the Beckman Model DK-2 Spectrophotometer.

tronic 505 spectrophotometer consists of an integrating sphere equipped with a suitable end-on photomultiplier tube, sample and reference holders, and a lens system. Light from the monochromator is focused by the lens system onto the sample and reference surfaces. The incident light spot is circular in shape and is about 16 mm in diameter. Diffuse reflected light is detected by the photomultiplier tube located at the top of the sphere. The specular component of the sample reflectance may be rejected by using the light traps located at an angle of 90° to the sample and reference materials. Band width of the monochromatic light is 50 Å in the wavelength range of 400–700 nm. A reflectance attachment which extends the wavelength lower limit to about 200 nm is also available.

The first commercially available attachment for the direct mechanical scanning of thin-layer plates for reflectance measurements has recently appeared. It was developed by Zeiss Ltd., in Germany in cooperation with Stahl and Jork, and is described in several papers.[32–38, 59] The Zeiss Chromatogram-Spectrophotometer is shown in Figure 12.

For the quantitative determination of chromatographically separated substances by means of their light absorption, the chromatogram is illuminated with practically monochromatic light at an angle of 90° with respect to the sample surface (the radiation of the light source is spectrally dispersed in the monochromator and then strikes the sample), and the diffusely reflected, nonabsorbed light is measured at an angle of 45° [Figure 13, setup M–Pr (M = monochromator; Pr = probe = sample)]. In the actual measurement the chromatogram is placed horizontally on a mechanical stage which can be moved in two directions at

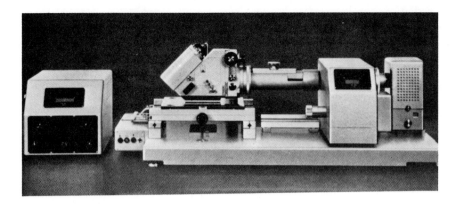

Figure 12. Zeiss Spectrophotometer PMQ-II equipped with thin-layer chromatography attachment for diffuse reflectance spectroscopy.

right angles to each other. The stage is driven by a motor at preselected speed in one direction and adjusted manually in the other direction. With small alterations in the optical system, the same instrument can be used for fluorescence measurements. Recently, the Camag-Z-Scanner, based on the Zeiss Spectrometer PMQ-II, has become available commercially. Klaus[25, 26] has described another modification of the Zeiss attachment. De Galan *et al.*[39] have reported on a device for measuring spectral reflectance on thin-layer plates, making use of the standard diffuse reflectance attachment for the Zeiss PMQ-II spectrophotometer, which contains an integrating sphere. In the new Zeiss chromatography attachment the use of an integrating sphere (Ulbricht Kugel) for the collection of the diffuse

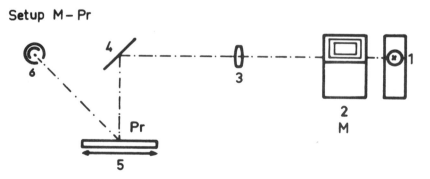

Figure 13. Simplified optical diagram of the Zeiss Chromatogram-Spectrophotometer. Setup M-Pr (M = monochromator, Pr = probe = sample). (1) light source: hydrogen lamp, incandescent lamp, or high-pressure xenon lamp; (2) monochromator; (3) intermediate optical system (simplified); (4) deviating mirror; (5) chromatogram; (6) detector.

radiation has been abandoned. Consequently, one might assume that a large portion of the diffusely reflected energy would be lost. From experimental data this does not, however, seem to be the case.

Beroza *et al.*[40] have devised a new and promising instrument for the automatic recording of spectral reflectance from thin-layer chromatograms, which seems to be a simple and low-cost alternative to the Zeiss instrument. Fiber optics are used for both the ultraviolet and the visible region of the spectrum, and the instrument permits single beam as well as double beam operation. With a few simple alterations transmission measurements can also be carried out on the chromatogram. In dual-beam operation, the instrument utilizes two fiber optic assemblies fabricated by Dolan-Jenner Industries, Inc., of Melrose, Massachusetts (Types ER 14024 and EFR 14024). One assembly (the scanning head) is used to scan the TLC spots and the other (the reference head) to scan the adjacent blank area. Each assembly contains a Y-shaped bundle of randomly arranged glass fibers 24 inches long. One arm of each Y conducts light from a 10-volt incandescent bulb to the surface of the TLC plate while the other arm conducts reflected light to a cadmium sulfide (CdS) photocell (equivalent to Clairex CL 705HL; its response is similar to that of the human eye). The glass fibers of the two arms are interspersed randomly in the lower portion of the Y to form a common bundle 0.25 inch in diameter. The scanning head common bundle terminates in a 2 × 20-mm rectangular array of fibers, and the reference head terminates in a circular array 0.25 inch in diameter. Each CdS cell forms one leg of a Wheatstone bridge while a 10-turn 500-ohm potentiometer and two 100-ohm resistors serve as the other two legs. Figure 14 is a schematic diagram of the circuit. The unbalanced output from the bridge is attenuated by a 10K-ohm linear taper potentiometer and fed to a strip chart recorder. Power for the bridge and light bulbs is supplied by

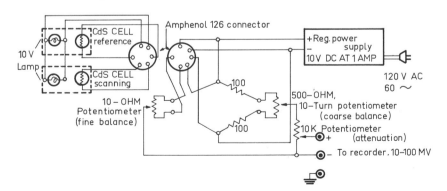

Figure 14. Schematic diagram of scanner bridge circuit.

a 10-volt regulated solid state power supply rated at less than 500-mV ripple (Lectroteck Model 1015). The motor-driven carriage for the thin-layer plate is adapted from the one used with the Aminco-Bowman Spectrophotofluorometer (American Instrument Co., Silver Springs, Maryland) by removing the lid and optical assembly. The fiber-optic scanning and reference heads are fastened side by side at the end of a freely pivoting aluminum rod supported by conventional laboratory clamps and rods; when scanning, the heads are stationary while the TLC plate moves under them at the rate of three inches per minute. Covering the TLC plates with a $200 \times 250 \times 1.5$-mm piece of quality plate glass (free of scratches, bubbles, and dust) and allowing the scanning head to slide on the surface of the cover glass as the plate moves under it maintains the heads at a constant distance above the adsorbent. Sliding friction is reduced by covering the scanning head with a 20-mm wide, 3-mm thick Teflon (Du Pont) strip attached with black plastic tape. The reference head is clamped slightly higher than the scanning head and therefore does not slide on the cover glass, nor is it covered with a Teflon strip. As an alternative, the scanning head could be held a small distance above the glass by having it slide on a block of Teflon positioned next to the head.

For scanning colored spots with light of a narrow wavelength range, the instrument is modified by replacing the light source of the scanning head with light from a Beckman Model DU spectrophotometer and by removing the reference head to give single beam operation. The reference head is removed from its bracket and its beam is aimed at a wall sufficiently distant to preclude significant reflection. The cell holder and photocell compartment of the spectrophotometer are removed to expose a circular port, and the arm of the scanning assembly normally leading to the light source is fitted firmly into the port with a one-hole rubber stopper. The arm is carefully aligned to receive the light output of the spectrophotometer. With this arrangement and a maximum slit width setting on the spectrophotometer, the bridge circuit can be balanced from 480 to 700 nm when the scanning head is placed over a white reflecting surface.

The fiber optics make it possible to bring the light to a small defined area on the chromatoplate. By maintaining the light-gathering fiber optic very close to the illuminated area, the loss through scattering of reflected energy can be minimized. The validity of the Kubelka-Munk function and hence proof that the collected energy consists of diffusely reflected light was determined on the basis of ultraviolet reflectance data from some pesticide spots. The Leitz Mikrophotometer is another low-cost precision instrument available for reflectance as well as transmission spectrophotometry on thin-layer chromatograms. Equipped with a KNOTT-Elektronik, a Beckman 1-mV lin-log Recorder, and a motor-driven microscope table, highly stabilized one-beam scans along a distance of about 70 mm can be made without readjustment. The rectangular area of measurement is continuously adjustable between about 1 mm and 1 μm allowing unusual resolution of high reproducibility. For reflectance measurement the object is illuminated by a tungsten (or deuterium) lamp at an angle of 45° and observed by the photomultiplier at an angle of 0°. Interference filters are employed. The use of the Schott-Verlauf Filter for 380–650 nm is of advantage. First examples of this instrument's application for TLC are described in Reference 95.

Reflectance Cells

Three types of reflectance cells, each capable of accommodating samples weighing up to 100 mg, have been devised to carry out reflectance measurements on spots following their removal from thin-layer plates.

Glass Window Cell[22]

This cell consists of white paperboard to which a 3.7 × 2.5 × 0.1-cm microscope cover glass is affixed with two pieces of masking tape. The white backing paper is cut to a size (4.0 × 3.0 × 0.1 cm) which permits its introduction into the sample holder of the reflectance attachment of

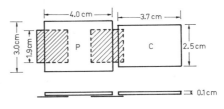

Figure 15. Glass window cell. Dimensions of cell elements and sketch of assembled cell. P, backing paper; C, microscope cover glass; S, sample.

the Beckman DU spectrophotometer. A sketch of the cell is presented in Figure 15. The analytical sample consisting of adsorbent plus the resolved compound is carefully compressed between the cover glass and the paperboard until a thin-layer is obtained.

Quartz Window Cell[42]

This cell (Figure 16) consists of a circular quartz plate 22 mm in diameter, superimposed on a 40 × 40 × 1-mm piece of white paperboard. The quartz disc is held in place by means of a 40 × 40 × 3-mm

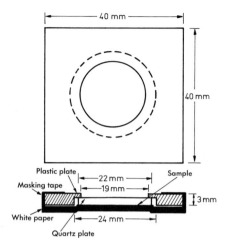

Figure 16. Quartz window cell. Dimensions of cell elements and sketch of assembled cell.

plastic plate which is affixed to the backing paper with two pieces of masking tape. A circular window 19 mm in diameter in the upper surface of the plate opens into a concentric circular well 24 mm in diameter that is deep enough to accommodate the quartz disc. The analytical sample, after being introduced into the cell, is carefully compressed between the quartz disc and the paperboard by rotating the former until a thin-layer is obtained.

Windowless Cell[42]

This cell (Figure 17) consists of a 35 × 40-mm plastic plate affixed to white paperboard of the same dimensions with two pieces of masking

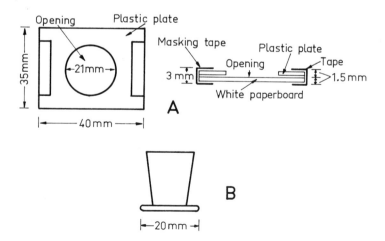

Figure 17. Windowless cell. (A) dimensions of cell elements and sketch of assembled windowless cell; (B) tamp used to pack cell.

tape. As shown in Figure 17, the plastic plate has a circular opening 21 mm in diameter in its center. The cell is packed by introducing the sample into the opening and then compressing it with a fitted tamp made of an aluminum planchet affixed to a cork stopper.

Obviously the glass window cell can be employed only with samples that absorb in the visible, while the other two are suitable for use in both the visible and ultraviolet regions of the spectrum. Of the latter two, the windowless cell, though it is simpler in design and costs almost nothing to make, provides less protection to the analytical sample.

GENERAL EXPERIMENTAL PROCEDURE

Detection of Spots

Techniques for detection of spots in reflectance work do not differ greatly. Unless the compounds are colored, spraying with a chromogenic reagent is necessary. If the resulting colored spots are to be analyzed by spectral reflectance, the instantaneous and quantitative formation of a stable and reproducible color is of prime importance, as can be seen from a study of color stabilities of ninhydrin complexes of amino acids on thin-layer chromatograms using the reflectance technique.[43] Occasionally it is possible to form a colored product by heating the plate.[41] If the compound fluoresces, the plate is observed under ultraviolet light (*cf.* Reference 44). Compounds absorbing in the ultraviolet spectrum can be detected on a fluorescent background produced by incorporating a luminous pigment into the adsorbent (*cf.* References 42, 45, and 46). They also lend themselves to direct scanning procedures. Compounds absorbing in the ultraviolet have been located by scanning the thin layer with a Beckman Model DK-2 spectrophotometer set at the absorption maximum of the compound of interest.[42] The scanning is carried out by holding the chromatoplate, which is taped to a protective plastic shield, against the sample exit port of the reflectance attachment unit in such a way that the adsorbent along the path of chromatographic separation is exposed to the impinging beam of light. A 3-mm thick plastic shield is employed, whose other dimensions match those of the chromatoplates but which has a 3 × 18-cm window about which are spaced four 1 × 2-mm strips of plastic. A sudden decrease in reflectance occurs when the beam of light falls upon a spot containing the compound of interest. During the scanning process, the reflectance attachment is covered with a dark cloth to exclude outside light. When a particular compound has been located, its position is marked on the reverse side of the glass plate. The same approach has also been used quite successfully with a Spectronic 505 equipped with a reflectance attachment.

More sophisticated devices for mechanical scanning (*e.g.*, the Zeiss Chromatogram-Spectrophotometer), recording of reflectance, and detection of zones on chromatoplates have been used by Stahl and Jork,[23, 31–38] or devised by Klaus[25, 26] and De Galan et al.[39] These devices are considerably more expensive than that used in the technique recommended by Lieu et al.[42]

Recording of Reflectance Spectra

Once the resolved compounds have been located, their reflectance spectra are recorded in one of two ways. The direct recording of spectra is made possible by positioning chromatoplates against the sample exit port of the reflectance attachment of a Beckman Model DK-2 or a Spectronic 505 spectrophotometer in such a way that the lightbeam is centered on the spot of interest. A glass plate of identical size is taped on top of the thin-plates to protect the adsorbent surface during the recording process. For work involving ultraviolet radiation, it is necessary to replace the glass plate with a protective plastic plate or with a paper mask of identical size having punched holes where the spots are located. A sheet of thick, nontransparent paper resembling the plate coating in color is inserted behind the plate to serve as a reflecting background. Spectra can also be recorded with the use of glass and, where necessary, quartz window reflectance cells.[47] When this procedure is followed, the spot of interest is excised and placed on top of 30 to 50 mg of adsorbent which has been removed from the same plate and introduced into an appropriate cell. After this sample has been compressed as described earlier, its reflectance is recorded in the usual manner. The reference standard in both procedures consists of adsorbent from the plate under investigation packed into the appropriate cell. For the procedure used in recording spectra with the Zeiss Chromatogram-Spectrophotometer, see References 32, 35, and 59.

Quantitative Measurement of Reflectance

Quantitative data have been obtained by the direct examination of chromatographic plates. By carefully adjusting the lightbeam of a Spectronic 505 or Beckman DK-2 spectrophotometer to the center of the spots, semiquantitative results with an accuracy of about 10% can be obtained. Tailing of the spots results in a drastic drop in accuracy.[48] Recently, spots not more than 0.75 cm in diameter chromatographed on Eastman chromatogram sheets have been cut out and placed in the lightbeam of a Beckman DU or Spectronic 20 reflectance attachment. The area of the impinging lightbeam is large enough to cover the entire spot and permits the measurement of reflectance in a single reading.[49] The accuracy and reproducibility of this fast technique are superior to those of the method mentioned above.

The quantitative measurement of reflectance by mechanical scanning and recording devices has been discussed in detail.[31-38] Jork[23] and Pataki[59] have reported relative per cent errors of between 3 and 5% for measurements in the ultraviolet regions using this technique.

As a rule, it has been found by the author that a greater degree of precision results when the measurements are carried out on spots removed from the thin-layer plates.[48] The substance being analyzed is removed from the plate together with enough adsorbent to make up an analytical sample of predetermined weight. (Depending on the adsorbent, 20 to 80 mg provide an optimum thickness for reflectance measurements.) The reflectance of this mixture is then measured after it has been ground in a small agate mortar for a given period of time to ensure homogeneity and has been packed in an appropriate cell. The reference standard consists of adsorbent from the same plate which has been treated in the same way as the analytical sample. The analysis can be expedited by removing the analytical sample from the thin-layer plate with a circular aluminum planchet which is manipulated by means of a cork stopper affixed to the planchet.[50] The size of the planchet employed is dictated by the thickness of the adsorbent layer and by the area to be excised. An assembly that has been used for this purpose is shown in Figure 18. Once the sample has been cut from an adsorbent layer by exerting a slight pressure on the inverted planchet, the most direct path between it and the nearest plate edge is cleared of adsorbent

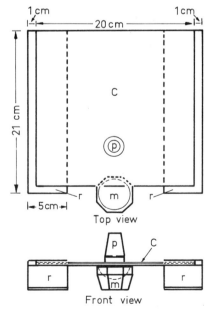

Figure 18. Assembly employed to exercise samples from chromatoplates. C, chromatoplate; m, agate mortar; p, planchet affixed to cork stopper; r, wooden rack.

with a brush; the planchet is moved along this path until the sample is
deposited in the agate mortar. By means of this procedure, it is possible
to remove a spot for analysis in less than a minute.

The suitability of this planchet technique as a means of expediting the
analyses of substances resolved on chromatoplates and of absorbing in the
visible or in the ultraviolet was tested by determining the deviation in the
per cent reflectance of samples of Eosine B and salicylic acid prepared
from center plates 2, 3 and 4. Plates 1 and 5, which in the coating procedure were the starting and the end plates, were eliminated because of
poorer quality. For four- and five-membered sets of samples on individual
plates of all thicknesses, average relative standard deviations of 0.3%
and 0.4% reflectance unit were obtained for Eosine B and salicylic acid,
respectively. A value of 0.5% R was obtained for both compounds when
the precision was computed for all plates of all thicknesses. The first
values represent the level of precision obtained in the application of the
reflectance technique to thin-layer chromatography using the weighing
procedure, while the latter exceeds this level only slightly. It can therefore
be concluded that the surfaces laid down by a commercial applicator are,
within certain limitations, uniform enough to permit this procedure to
be employed in routine analyses without sacrificing the precision inherent
in the reflectance technique.

If direct scanning techniques are used, it is important to standardize
coating procedures in order to obtain uniform and reproducible plate
coatings. Reflectance spectroscopy, however, is somewhat less sensitive
to variations in layer thickness than are transmission techniques.[33, 34]
The effects of fluctuations in layer thickness, layer quality and other
experimental conditions on the reproducibility of reflectance measurements have been investigated recently by Klaus[51] and Huber.[52]

In general, the disadvantage of the somewhat longer time of analysis
involved in using the spot removal technique is offset by its improved
precision. The major advantage, however, particularly in comparison
with mechanical scanning techniques, is its simplicity. Commercial TLC
scanning devices which can be adapted to the standard reflectance
attachments are difficult to obtain, and the construction of custom-made
units is tedious and time-consuming. Although only Beckman and
Bausch & Lomb instruments have been used by the author, the cells
and procedures described earlier can, without doubt, be easily adapted
to any other commercially available diffuse reflectance attachment.

APPLICATIONS

Spectral reflectance has been used for the *in situ* identification and
determination of many substances following resolution on thin-layer

plates.[53] For the sake of convenience, applications are discussed below in the chronological order of their development: visible and ultraviolet reflectance spectroscopy of organic systems, and reflectance spectroscopy of inorganic systems.

Visible Reflectance Spectroscopy of Organic Systems

Dyes

It is not surprising that the first application of reflectance spectroscopy to thin-layer chromatography was in the field of dyes.[48] This system, stable and not requiring detection that would involve spraying or scanning procedures, readily lent itself to the technique.

Stock solutions containing 50 mg of the dyes studied (Aniline Blue, Eosine B, Basic Fuchsin, Malachite Green, Naphthol Yellow S, and Rhodamine B) per 100 ml of solvent were applied as spots by means of a 10-μl Hamilton microsyringe. Except for the aqueous Eosine B, the solvent used was 95% ethanol. The $10 \times 7 \times 0.15$-cm plates were cut from ordinary window glass and were coated with adsorbent by distributing the adsorbent–water mixture with a glass rod which rested on one thickness of masking tape affixed to the ends of the plates. This technique gave a uniform coating 0.2–0.3 mm thick. The plates were dried at 180°C for 2 hours and were stored in a desiccator. Merck Aluminum Oxide G and Silica Gel G were used as adsorbents.

The dyes were chromatographed in *n*-butanol–ethanol–water (80:20: 10) by the ascending technique according to Mottier,[54] and the plates were then dried at 110°C for 15 minutes. Direct spectral examination of these plates was carried out with a Beckman DK-2 spectrophotometer according to the experimental procedure discussed previously. Figure 19 shows the reflectance spectra of these dyes adsorbed on alumina. With proper precautions it is possible to obtain spectra suitable for identification purposes. The general shape of reflectance and transmittance spectra is similar. Some peak broadening is observed for reflectance spectra and a shift of the absorption maxima (See Figure 20) generally occurs, depending on the adsorbent. The operation is capable of providing semiquantitative results. A precision of about 3% can be attained by carrying out the reflectance measurements on spots removed from the chromatoplate and packed in appropriate cells (see General Procedure).

When this procedure was employed as the basis for a student experiment[55] in an undergraduate course in quantitative analysis, the data obtained indicated that the same technique can be used successfully even by individuals having no specific training or prior experience in it. The data reported in Table II were obtained either by using a calibration curve or by an algebraic method. Since the concentrations of the un-

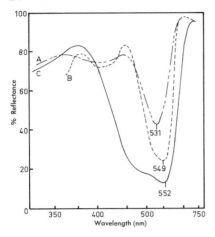

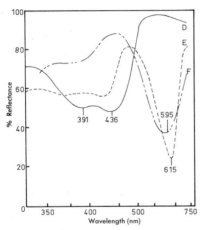

Figure 19. (19a) Reflectance spectra of dyes adsorbed on alumina. (A) Eosine B; (B) Rhodamine B; (C) Fuchsin. (19b) Reflectance spectra of dyes adsorbed on alumina. (D) Naphthol Yellow S; (E) Malachite Green; (F) Aniline Blue.

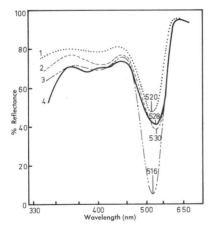

Figure 20. Reflectance spectra of Eosine B adsorbed on filter paper, alumina, and silica gel compared with the transmittance spectrum of an aqueous solution of the dye. (1) silica gel (Merck thin-layer chromatography grade); (2) filter paper (Whatman No. 42); (3) alumina (Merck thin-layer chromatography grade); (4) transmittance spectrum.

Table II
Accuracy and Precision of Student Determinations
by Spectral Reflectance of Dyes on Thin-Layer Plates

		Crystal Violet	Fuchsin	Rhodamine B
GRAPHIC METHOD	Average accuracy in % deviation from the true value	5.7	5.7	3.8
	Range % deviation for a set of eight results	3.5–9.5	0.3–9.6	1.3–8.0
ALGEBRAIC METHOD	Average accuracy in % deviation from the true value	7.8	7.1	5.8
	Range % deviation for a set of eight results	0.0–15.0	0.6–15.0	2.0–10.8

knowns all fell on the linear portion of the calibration curve, it was possible to determine their concentration by means of the equation

$$C_u = \frac{C_s F(R)_u}{F(R)_s}$$

where C_u and C_s represent the concentrations of the unknown and standard solutions, and $F(R)_u$ and $F(R)_s$ stand for the Kubelka-Munk functions of the unknown and standard. Ninety per cent of the dyes were correctly identified by the students on the basis of reflectance spectra, without resorting to Rf-values.

The usefulness of reflectance spectroscopy for the examination of various effects (such as humidity, regeneration temperatures, and pH) on the behavior of dye systems adsorbed on chromatographic adsorbents has been demonstrated.[56] A shift to higher wavelength accompanied by an increase in color intensity is observed at higher regeneration temperatures for Eosine B adsorbed on alumina. This is attributed to a higher adsorbent–adsorbate interaction and is consistent with earlier observations.[57] The importance of a standardization of activation procedures before chromatography is further supported by Figure 21, which demonstrates the variations of Kubelka-Munk plots for dilution series of Rhodamine B adsorbed on alumina of different activity. The advantage

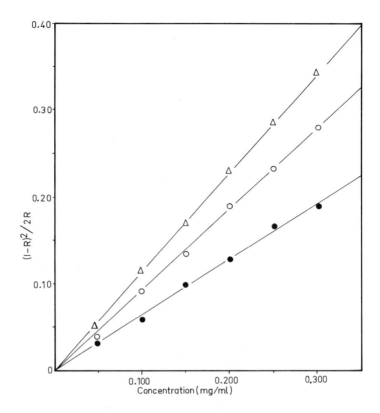

Figure 21. Kubelka-Munk plots for a dilution series of Rhodamine B adsorbed on ●, alumina (air-dry state); O, alumina (preheated to 200°C); △, alumina (preheated to 1100°C).

of using dye systems for the experimental verification of some fundamental studies in this field has been realized in several other investigations.[21, 22, 24, 25, 27, 39, 50]

Amino Acids

Reduced tailing, increased sensitivity, and greater speed and resolution have made thin-layer chromatography an important tool in amino acid analysis.[71] Improved *in situ* evaluation techniques of such chromatograms were desirable and reflectance spectroscopy showed much promise. The various studies of reflectance spectroscopy applied to amino acids resolved on thin-layer plates have recently been reviewed.[58, 59] With the use of a standard ninhydrin spray reagent, no significant differentiation was observed for the reflectance spectra of a group of amino acids. The use of a modified spray reagent recommended by Moffat and Lytle,[60] however, permitted the author to identify complex mixtures of amino acids rapidly by making use of a combination of reflectance spectra, visual appearance, and Rf-values of the spots.[47] The solvent used by the author to separate two mixtures totaling 18 amino acids on silica gel layers was suggested by Brenner and Niederwieser[61] and consisted of *n*-butanol–acetic acid–water (60:20:20). The spray reagent[60] was a combination of two solutions:

(1) 50 ml 0.2% ninhydrin solution in absolute EtOH, 10 ml AcOH, 2 ml 2,4,6-collidine
(2) 1% $Cu(NO_3)_2 \cdot 3H_2O$ solution in absolute EtOH.

The solutions are mixed in the ratio 50:3 shortly before spraying. The sensitivity is increased by substituting 0.4% for 0.2% ninhydrin solution. The spots are removed for reflectance measurement with a Beckman DK-2 spectrophotometer. The preparation of the samples has been described above. Observations are reported in Tables III and IV.

A reflectance spectroscopic study of color stabilities of ninhydrin complexes of adsorbed amino acids[43] revealed that a ninhydrin reagent recommended by Bull *et al.*[62] gave the most stable color formation. A time study carried out at room temperature showed a fading of about 30% within three days. The spray reagent consisted of 90 g of *n*-butanol, 10 g of phenol and 0.4 g of ninhydrin and was chosen for a quantitative investigation of amino acids on thin-layer plates by spectral reflectance.[63] The color intensity produced by this spray was superior to that produced by other reagents, as can be seen from calibration plots in Figure 22. The absorption maxima of the reflectance spectra were approximately 510–520 nm over a large concentration range for the 14 amino acids investigated. Very little peak shift was observed with various concentrations. The same calibration curve could be used for amino acids of similar structure, such as valine, norvaline, leucine, isoleucine and norleucine, without affecting the precision significantly. Limiting factors for the precision attained with this procedure included the incomplete reaction of the amino acids with the ninhydrin reagent and the leaching out of the acids during the spraying operation.

Since the degree of precision achieved was less than that attained when the same procedure without the chromogenic step is applied to a stable system,[48] it was felt that substantial improvement in the method would result if the color were developed without sprays. Accordingly, it was decided to investigate the possibility of adapting a nonspray method such as that suggested by El-Khadem *et al.*,[64] for example, for the identification of amino acids and sugars separated on paper chromatograms. By adding the detecting reagents to the solvent mixtures, the authors[65] succeeded in notably increasing the precision of the method,

Table III

Color, Absorption Maxima and Rf-Values for Amino Acids of Group I

Amino acids	Concen- tration (μg/spot)	Color	Absorption maxima (nm)	Detection limits (μg/spot)		Rf-values
				DK2	Visual	
Aspartic acid	5	light blue with yellow ring changes to blue violet after 5 minutes				0.21
	4	as above			0.2	
	3	pale violet				
Glycine	5	intensive orange with violet center	484			0.22
	4	orange	475			
	3	orange	475			
	2	orange	475	1	0.1	
Isoleucine	5	dark violet	539,478,413			0.46
	3	violet	534,477,413			
	2	violet, pink after 24 hours	532,478	1	0.3	
Leucine	5	dark violet	543,480			0.47
	3	violet, pink after 7 days	542,480			
	2	violet-pink	540,474			
	1	pink		2	0.3	
Lysine · HCl	5	intensive yellow-brown, brown after 7 days	536,480,397			0.05
	3	as above		3	1	
	1	light brown				

Phenylalanine	5	brown with yellow ring, yellow-pink after 24 hours				0.49
	2	brown-yellow			2	
Proline	5	intensive brown-yellow, brown after 7 days			1	0.19
Threonine	5	violet with yellow ring, pink after 5 days	537,478,417			0.25
	3	as above	529,475,412	3		
Tryptophan	5	brown with light blue ring, blue fades after 5 minutes	422			0.56
	3	as above				
	2	pale blue, brown after 5 minutes				
	1	brown			1	
Valine	5	dark violet	537,480,409			0.35
	3	blue-violet, pink-violet after 7 days		3	0.2	

Table IV
Color, Absorption Maxima and Rf-Values for Amino Acids of Group II

Amino acids	Concentration (µg/spot)	Color	Absorption maxima (nm)	Detection limits (µg/spot) DK2	Visual	Rf-values
Alanine	5	blue-violet, fades to red-violet after 24 hours	540,480,412			0.26
	2	as above	532,486,416	2		
	1	as above	528,473		0.2	
Arginine · HCl	10	light violet, fades to pink	547,483,419			0.08
	5	as above	535,484	5	3	
Cystine	8	pink-gray	447			0.16
	6	pink-gray	455			
	5	pink-gray		5	3	0.06
Glutamic acid	5	dark violet with pale orange ring, brown after 24 hours	532,482,409			0.27
	3	as above	536,481,416	3		
	2	as above			1	
Histidine · HCl	5	gray with yellow ring	455			
	3	yellow, brown-gray after 24 hours	455			
	0.5	as above	455	0.5	0.5	

Methionine	10	violet with yellow ring, pink after 24 hours	535,478,421			0.40
	8	as above	538,483,410			
	5	as above	537,480	5		
	2	as above			1	
Serine	5	dark violet with yellow ring, fades to pink	540,478,415			0.47
	3	as above	540,478,415	2		
	2	as above	537,479,429			
	1	as above			0.3	
Tyrosine	5	orange with yellow ring, light yellow after 24 hours		2		0.47

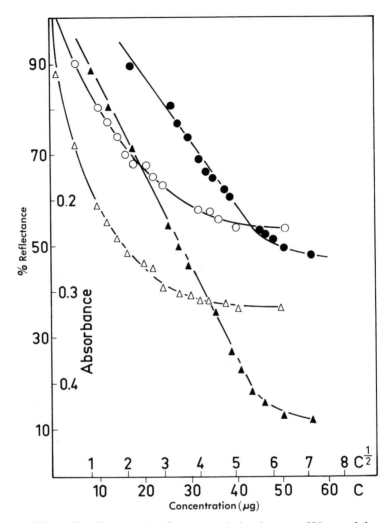

Figure 22. Per cent of reflectance and absorbance at 520 mμ of the leucine–ninhydrin reaction product adsorbed on silica gel as a function of concentration. Modified Moffat-Lytle[60] spray: O–O, per cent reflectance vs C; ●–●, absorbance vs C½. Bull *et al.*[62] spray: △–△, per cent reflectance vs C; ▲–▲, absorbance vs C½.

and in eliminating not only the spraying operation but also the drying step preceding it.

Merck Silica Gel G was used to coat the $20 \times 5 \times 0.35$-cm plates employed for one-dimensional analysis as well as the $20 \times 20 \times 0.35$-cm plates utilized for the two-dimensional resolutions. After resolution had been achieved, the plates were heated in a mechanical convection oven at 60°C for 30 minutes to dry them and develop the colors. Both one-

and two-dimensional chromatograms were used in investigating the applicability of four solvent mixtures: (1) *n*-propyl alcohol–water–acetic acid (64:36:20), (2) *n*-butyl alcohol–water–acetic acid (60:20:20), (3) phenol–water (75:25 w/w), and (4) *n*-propyl alcohol–34% ammonia (67:33 w/w). The first three solvent systems were employed in conjunction with one-dimensional analyses carried out by the ascending technique. A pairing of systems 3 with 2 and 4 with 1 was performed during the two-dimensional analyses; the first of each pair was used for the initial dimension. Chromatograms were dried at 60°C for 30 minutes prior to chromatography in the second dimension. For two-dimensional separation, 0.2% ninhydrin was added to the second solvent system. The ninhydrin-containing solvents had to be absolutely free of ammonia. If an ammonia-containing solvent had been used for the first dimension, all ammonia had to be removed by sufficient drying before the second development; otherwise, a brownish or purplish tinge was imparted to the entire plate. Successful resolutions of mixtures of the ten amino acids were achieved in 10 hours or less, during which the solvent fronts were permitted to move 18 cm in each dimension by the ascending technique. The amino acids were identified by using Rf-values or, in ambiguous situations, by simultaneously running standards for comparison purposes. A Beckman Model DU spectrophotometer fitted with a standard attachment for the measurement of diffuse reflectance was employed for the quantitative evaluation of the spots, which were scraped from the chromatographic plates and prepared as 40-mg analytical samples. The cells used to hold the samples and reference material as well as the procedure followed in preparing material for examination have been described above (see General Procedure).

The reproducibility that can be expected with the method was determined by chromatographing four 5-μg replicates of each amino acid over a distance of 15 cm in one dimension using the ascending technique and by preparing them for analysis according to the procedure outlined in the section on General Procedure. When solvent mixture 1 with 0.2% ninhydrin was employed to develop the plates, an average standard deviation of 0.49% R was obtained for the ten sets. As may be seen in Table V, which summarizes the results of this experiment, the largest standard deviation found for any one set was the 0.84% R-value observed with lysine. Similar data were obtained using solvent mixture 2, also with 0.2% ninhydrin. These results represent a considerable increase in precision over that attained by spray methods. An average standard deviation of 1.45% R and a maximum standard deviation for a single set of 2.32% R were found in a previous study conducted with three 3-μg replicates of the same amino acids. The two studies differ principally in the solvent systems used and in the fact that in one, the ninhydrin was applied as a spray. Since the results of this research indicate that precision changes of the magnitude being discussed are not observed when the solvent systems are varied, one must ascribe the increase in reproducibility to the elimination of the spraying operation. By increasing the ninhydrin concentration to 0.4% in phenol–water (75:25 w/w), the average standard deviation for the ten sets was 0.53% R and the sensitivity improved from 1.0 μg to 0.5 μg per spot.

Table V

Reproducibility of Reflectance Readings Obtained
at 515 nm for Different Spots of the Same Concentration
(5 μg per spot) of Amino Acids Chromatographed in
One Dimension Using Solvent Mixture No. 1 (0.2% ninhydrin)
(Number of Determinations n = 4 in each Case)

Amino acid	Range (% R)	Mean (% R)	Std. dev. (% R)
Alanine	72.8–73.6	73.0	0.39
Arginine·HCl	80.3–81.6	80.8	0.59
Glutamic acid	80.5–81.7	81.2	0.51
Glycine	77.3–77.9	77.5	0.27
Leucine	73.8–74.5	74.2	0.30
Lysine·HCl	79.0–80.9	79.8	0.84
Methionine	78.3–79.4	78.8	0.58
Phenylalanine	81.3–82.6	82.3	0.71
Serine	75.5–76.4	76.1	0.41
Valine	74.2–74.7	74.4	0.27
		Av. std. dev.	0.49

As expected, there was some decrease in reproducibility when the amino acids were chromatographed in two dimensions, though the precision was still considerably better than that achieved in one dimension with the use of sprays. The results obtained when four 5-μg replicates were chromatographed in the first dimension with solvent mixture 3 and in the second dimension with solvent mixture 2—to which 0.2% ninhydrin had been added—gave a 0.77% R average standard deviation, with the standard deviation of no one set being in excess of 1.18% R. The probable relative error in the measurement of the concentrations of alanine, leucine, serine and valine was determined by making use of the precision data obtained with four 5-μg replicates of the amino acids (listed in Table V) and of the calibration curves for these same acids. A similar investigation was carried out to ascertain the relationship between the probable relative error and the concentration of glycine. In this instance, solvent 1 with 0.2% ninhydrin was employed in conjunction with four replicates of amino acid at each concentration investigated.

Table VI

Probable Relative Error in the Measurement of the
Concentrations of Some Amino Acids (Number of Determinations n = 4)

	Alanine	*Leucine*	*Serine*	*Valine*
Range (% R)	72.8–73.6	73.8–74.5	75.5–76.4	74.2–74.7
Mean (% R)	73.0	74.2	76.1	74.4
Standard deviation (% R)	0.39	0.30	0.41	0.27
Equivalent change in measured concentration of acid (μg)	0.18	0.15	0.25	0.14
Probable % relative error	3.6	3.8	5.0	2.8

Data relative to these two studies are presented in Tables VI and VII, respectively. The change in measured concentration equivalent to the deviations observed for the various amino acids was obtained from the appropriate calibration curves and expressed as a probable per cent of relative error in concentration. For the five amino acids at 5-μg concentration this figure ranged from a low value of 2.8% for valine to a high of 5.0% for serine. In the case of glycine, minimal values were obtained in the intermediate concentration range. The relatively large 9.0% value observed at the 2-μg concentration may be attributed to the fact that this concentration approaches the 1-μg sensitivity limit for glycine. At the opposite end of the scale, the 7.0% figure found for 20-μg concentrations can be ascribed to the flattening of the calibration curve that occurs at high concentrations. Of the amino acids investigated, this effect is particularly noticeable in the case of glycine.[65] Quantitative analysis by reflectance spectroscopy of amino acids resolved on thin-layer plates has also been investigated by Pataki,[59] using the Zeiss Chromatogram-Spectrophotometer.

Table VII

Probable Relative Error in the Measurement of the
Concentration of Glycine as a Function of Concentration
(Number of Determinations n = 4)

	Concentration of glycine (μg per spot)			
	2	*5*	*10*	*20*
Range (% R)	84.3–86.0	77.3–77.9	63.6–65.1	55.3–57.1
Mean (% R)	85.1	77.5	64.4	56.3
Standard deviation (% R)	0.92	0.27	0.66	0.76
Equivalent change in measured concentration of glycine (μg)	0.18	0.20	0.50	1.40
Probable % relative error	9.0	4.0	5.0	7.0

Sugars

The feasibility of this approach was also demonstrated by the successful determination of mixtures of sugars.[66, 67] For aldopentoses the following procedure is recommended:

1. Chromatographic resolution of sugar mixtures on cellulose thin-layers by the procedure set forth by Vomhof and Tucker[68]
2. Chromogenesis by dipping the chromatogram in ethyl acetate containing 2% each of aniline and trichloroacetic acid
3. Air-drying the plates for 30 minutes followed by heating at 110°C for 6 minutes
4. Removal of the spots and preparation of samples and standards for reflectance measurements at 500 nm, as described earlier.

The dipping technique provides more uniform distribution of spray reagent over the entire chromatoplate. The reproducibility obtained under these conditions for arabinose is depicted in Table VIII. An accuracy of about 5% is reported for this method; the sensitivity is 5 μg per spot. The sugar-aniline compounds are stable for periods of at least one week.

A 0.2% naphthoresorcinol–85% phosphoric acid mixture (9:1 v/v) which has been described by McCready and McComb[69] has been found useful for hexoses as well as for pentoses.[67] Using the dipping technique, stable red spots were obtained for fructose, and blue-green and blue spots for rhamnose, arabinose and glucose.

Table VIII

Reproducibility of Reflectance Readings Obtained
for Equal Concentrations of Arabinose Adsorbed on
Cellulose and Detected with Aniline. A Reference Cell Containing
Background Material Scraped from Sample 1 Chromatoplate Was Used.
(All samples 25 μg: readings taken at 500 nm)

Sample	Per cent reflectance	Deviation from mean
1	91.2	+1.2
2	88.0	−1.4
3	89.7	+0.3
4	90.6	+1.2
5	88.9	−0.5
6	88.0	−1.4
7	88.8	−0.6
8	88.3	−1.1
9	91.0	+1.6
Mean value	89.4	Std. dev. +1.3

Ultraviolet Reflectance Spectroscopy of Organic Systems

Aspirin and Salicylic Acid

Because of the large number of substances having characteristic ultraviolet spectra that may be employed in their analysis, it was felt that the application of ultraviolet reflectance spectroscopy to thin-layer chromatography would prove to be invaluable, especially for those in the pharmaceutical and biochemical sciences. The feasibility of this approach was ascertained by employing it to determine the composition of mixtures of aspirin (acetylsalicylic acid) and salicylic acid which had been separated on silica gel plates. This particular system was selected for study not only because the spectra of the two compounds are suitable, but also because it presents no difficulties in locating the compounds after resolution. Both appear as yellowish-brown spots when the plates are dried.

Aspirin and salicylic acid, of Merck U.S.P. and Chase U.S.P. purity respectively, were dried over sulfuric acid for 24 hours before use. Stock solutions of the compounds in chloroform, 0.10M, were used to prepare the dilution series employed in this study. Chromatography was carried out by ascending technique in hexane–chloroform–glacial acetic acid (85:10:15 v/v). Rf-values observed for salicylic acid and aspirin were 0.35 and 0.2, respectively. Although in preparative work the spots may be removed from the layer directly after chromatography, in the analysis of the mixtures the plates were dried in an oven at 90°C for 2 hours.

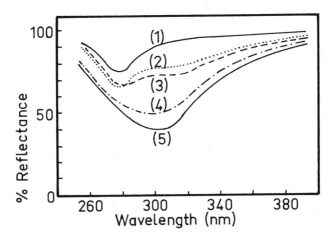

Figure 23. Reflectance spectra obtained for aspirin adsorbed on Silica Gel G at indicated intervals after spotting: (1) After 15 minutes at room temperature; (2) after 2 more hours at room temperature; (3) after an additional 5 minutes at 90°C; (4) after an additional 10 minutes at 90°C; (5) after still another 10 minutes at 90°C.

Under these conditions, a quantitative conversion of aspirin to salicylic acid takes place. This can be seen from Figure 23, which shows the gradual conversion at various drying conditions. A shift in absorption maximum from 278 nm (for aspirin) to 302 nm (for salicylic acid) is observed. The aspirin is determined as salicylic acid at 302 nm; precisions of 0.37% R and 0.47% R standard deviation for salicylic acid and aspirin, respectively, have been reported. Linear calibration curves (absorbance versus $\sqrt{\text{conc.}}$) have been obtained over a concentration region of 0.2–1.7 μmole per spot.

Aspirin has also been used as a model system in an extensive error analysis of ultraviolet reflectance spectroscopy.[24]

Amino Acid Derivatives and Nucleotides

The suitability of DNP-amino acids for determination by reflectance spectroscopy has been recognized and confirmed;[59, 70–72] the estimation of PTH-amino acids investigated by Pataki[59, 70] has revealed that variables due to chromogenesis are eliminated. The method is also capable of giving spectra suitable for identification purposes, particularly after treatment of the spots with hydrochloric acid or sodium hydroxide.[59, 70] Analysis of nucleotides has been described by Lieu *et al.*,[44] Pataki,[59] and Frei *et al.*[96]

In Lieu's technique, after spotting, the cellulose plates are dried at 85°C for 15 minutes. Chromatography is performed by the ascending technique in isopropyl alcohol–1M sodium acetate–saturated ammonium sulfate (2:18:8 v/v) according to Randerath.[73] The plates are then dried at 85°C for 60 minutes. Since the resolved compounds appear as light- to dark blue spots under ultraviolet light (maximum at 254 mμ), no difficulty is experienced in locating them on the plates. For qualitative analysis each spot is excised. Then it is centered in a windowless reflectance cell atop a uniformly thick layer of 40 mg of cellulose powder that has been packed in the cell with the use of a fitted tamp (see Apparatus).

The reflectance spectra of the various nucleotides adsorbed on cellulose permit the ready identification of the adsorbed species. However, this is not possible between the isomers of AMP and GMP, as identical spectra are obtained for the members of each isomer pair. By making use of both spectral data and Rf-values, however, all the resolved nucleotides can be identified unequivocally. It is noteworthy that in most cases the absorption maximum of the reflectance spectrum virtually coincides with the absorption maximum of the corresponding transmittance spectrum obtained with an aqueous solution of the nucleotide (however, see Reference 59). This would seem to indicate that these data (Table IX)

Table IX
Rf-Values and Absorption Maxima of Nucleotides Adsorbed
on MN-Cellulose, and Absorption Maxima of Nucleotides
in Aqueous Solution
(Chromatography according to Randerath)[73]

| Nucleotide | Isomer | Rf-value | | Absorption maximum (nm) | |
		MN-300	MN-300G	Reflectance	Transmittance
AMP	2′	0.35	0.35	260	260
AMP	3′	0.21	0.28	260	260
ADP	5′	0.45	0.48	259	259
CMP	2′ + 3′	0.73	0.73	281	280
GMP	2′	0.51	0.58	256	252
GMP	3′	0.39	0.49	256	252
UMP	3′ + 2′	0.68	0.73	264	262

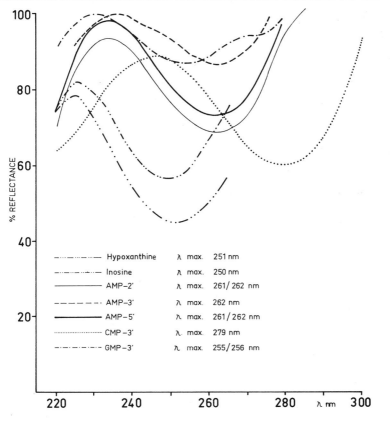

Figure 24. Reflectance spectra of some nucleoderivatives adsorbed on cellulose.

can be used interchangeably for most purposes. Spectra of nucleic acid derivatives according to Frei *et al.*[96] are shown in Figure 24.

With regard to the precision of this method, standard deviations ranging from 0.39 to 0.78 reflectance unit have been reported by Lieu *et al.* The accuracy is 2–6%. Calibration curves (% R vs. log C) for concentration ranges of about 50–400 μg were used.

A group of nucleic acid derivatives has also been investigated by Pataki,[59] using reflectance spectroscopy in connection with the Zeiss instrument.

Vitamins

In this study, the ultraviolet reflectance technique was applied to the nondestructive analysis of five B-group vitamins—thiamine hydrochloride, pyridoxine hydrochloride, nicotinic acid, nicotinamide, and *p*-aminobenzoic acid.[42] Detection of these vitamins was possible either by addition of a luminous pigment to the Silica Gel G adsorbent and examination of the chromatoplates under ultraviolet illumination, or by the direct scanning technique described under General Procedure.

The vitamins were employed in the form of aqueous stock solutions, 0.10M except for *p*-aminobenzoic acid which was 0.020M. Silica Gel G (Merck) with and without 2% w/w zinc silicate (ZS Super, Riedel de Haën AG, Seelze-Hannover, West Germany) was used as fluorescent pigment. TLC was carried out in benzene–acetone–methanol–glacial acetic acid (70:5:20:5 v/v) according to Gänshirt and Malzacher.[74] The plates were then dried at 45°C for 20 minutes. Each of the vitamins with the exception of nicotinic acid and nicotinamide was shown to have a unique reflectance spectrum (see also Frei *et al.*[96]). Spectra and Rf-values are essentially identical on silica gel with and without luminous pigment (Table X). Of the two methods, the one employing only Silica Gel G as an adsorbent provides the greater sensitivity. However, the other is somewhat less time-consuming in that it does not require the use of a spectrophotometer to locate the spots on the chromatograms. Both methods are rapid and nondestructive and have been employed successfully in the analysis of multivitamin preparations. For quantitative analysis samples are prepared and packed in the windowless cells as described before. The calibration curves [% R vs. log C (μg/spot)] are not linear and the use of the Kubelka-Munk function may be advisable. The reproducibility of reflectance measurements of nicotinic acid and nicotinamide at 264 nm was between ±0.33 and ±0.39%R mean standard deviation for four samples each (conc. 2.0 μmole per 80 mg). An accuracy of 2.3% was found.

Other work on reflectance spectroscopy of nicotinic acid and nicotine amide has been reported by Pataki.[59]

Table X

Absorption Maxima, Rf-Values, and Sensitivities of Vitamins Adsorbed on Silica Gel G and on Silica Gel G-Luminous Pigment Mixture

Vitamin	Absorption maximum (nm)		Rf-value		Sensitivity (μmole)	
	Silica Gel G-lum. pgmt. mixture	Silica Gel G	Silica Gel G-lum. pgmt. mixture	Silica Gel G	Silica Gel G-lum. pgmt. mixture	Silica Gel G
Thiamine hydrochloride	278	278	0.00	0.00	0.01	0.01
Pyridoxine hydrochloride	298	298	0.17	0.18	0.05	0.01
Nicotinamide	263–268	264	0.51	0.51	0.02	0.01
Nicotinic acid	262–268	264	0.66	0.65	0.02	0.01
p-Aminobenzoic acid	295	295	0.85	0.86	0.01	0.005

Hormones

A procedure for the determination of Δ^4-androstene-3,17-dione and testosterone has been described by Struck *et al.*[36] It is one of numerous studies that have been carried out with the use of the Zeiss Chromatogram-Spectrophotometer mentioned earlier. It is reported that 0.2–0.5 μg of the studied compounds can be estimated with an accuracy of ±10% standard deviation on different two-dimensional chromatograms.

Herbicides and Pesticides

Because fluorescence quenching detects compounds without destroying them,[45] the investigation of ultraviolet reflectance techniques for the evaluation of triazines from thin-layer plates was possible.[46] Triazine stock solutions (2 mg per ml) were prepared in spectroscopic grade methanol. The $20 \times 5 \times 0.35$-cm plates were coated with a layer of Camag Silica Gel DF-5 with organic fluorescence indicator 0.25 mm thick. The triazines were applied on the chromatoplates by means of a 10-μl Hamilton microsyringe. After separation by the ascending technique in 2% methanol in chloroform, the plates were dried at 60°C for 10 minutes and the spots were observed under an ultraviolet lamp. The reflectance spectra were recorded with a Spectronic 505 spectrophotometer equipped with a standard reflectance attachment for the ultraviolet and visible regions of the spectrum. The preparation of the chromatoplates for reflectance measurements and the packing of removed spots in cells suitable for quantitative work in the ultraviolet region have been described under General Procedure. It was found that the spectra of the triazines could be used for identification purposes. Reflectance spectra of triazines commonly used for large-scale weed control are recorded in Figure 25 and compared with the transmission spectra of the triazines dissolved in methanol.

The reflectance spectra in general have broader maxima because of increased light scattering and exhibit a more-or-less pronounced bathochromic shift. Using atrazine, the method was tested for its suitability for quantitative analysis. The spectra of atrazine taken at various concentrations from 1–40 μg per sample reveal two maxima suitable for analysis at 230 and 270 nm. A small bathochromic shift is usually observed with increasing concentration. However, a single wavelength could still be used for the construction of a calibration curve which covers the concentration range of interest. Linear plots were obtained for up to 50 μg of herbicide per sample by plotting the Kubelka-Munk function for diffuse reflectance $[(1 - R)^2/2R]$ against concentration. Empirical functions such as $(2 - \log\% R)$ plotted against the square root of concentration were also used successfully.

The precision of this technique was determined by analyzing six 10-μg samples of atrazine simultaneously. The standard deviation of the reflectance readings was found to be 0.50 when measured at 270 nm and 0.84 at 230 nm. The decrease in precision can be attributed to the

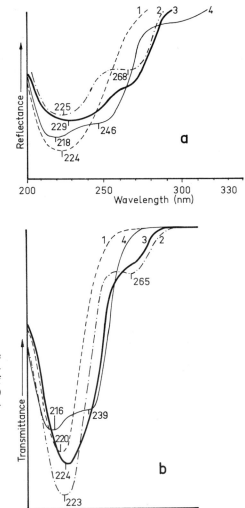

Figure 25. (a) Reflectance spectra on silica gel and (b) transmission spectra in methanol of (1) Prometon, (2) Propazin, (3) Prometryne, (4) Simazin in methanol.

decrease in radiation energy output at a lower wavelength; hence, more amplification is needed and as a result increased fluctuation of the meter needle is encountered. The corresponding accuracy of the method was found to be about ±3% for a 10-μg sample. Samples stored in a desiccator for several days showed no significant changes in measured per cent reflectance. The sensitivity of the technique ranges between 1 and 3 μg (at a 50% accuracy level) for all triazines investigated.

An *s*-triazine (Prometryne) has been used as a test substance to investigate parameters for the determination of substances from thin-layer plates by ultraviolet reflectance spectroscopy.[52] Chlorinated pesticides (such as aldrin, dieldrin, endrin, lindane, heptachlor, methoxychlor, toxaphene, and DDT and some of its derivatives) were determined by a group of scientists[40] with the use of a fiber optics device for reflectance measurements (see Instrumentation). The same experimental setup was also applied to some phosphorus pesticides. The separations were carried out on chromatoplates coated with florisil in the case of phosphorus pesticides and with silver nitrate-impregnated alumina for chlorinated pesticides.

Miscellaneous Compounds

A number of systems have been investigated using the Zeiss Chromatogram-Spectrophotometer (see Instrumentation). Reflectance spectra of caffeine[75] and phenacetin,[76] and the strychnic alkaloids, strychnine and brucine,[34] were obtained directly from the chromatoplates. The spectra of five opium alkaloids were obtained in an investigation of drug samples, and, with the use of appropriate absorption maxima, their quantitative determination was carried out.[77] Band positions of individual phenol ethers and phenyl propanes were studied[23,78] with the intention of characterizing chemical classes of drugs. It was possible to separate chromatographically mixtures of oils obtained from certain plants and to identify the zones selectively by spectral reflectance. Similar investigations served to identify phtalides in essential oils.[79] Other applications have included investigation of aromatic hydroxy, aldehyde derivatives[76] (vanillin, anisaldehyde and asarylaldehyde, for example) and in the investigation of the pyrethrins in pyrethrum and peony flowers.[80] Obviously the range of potential applications is tremendous, and the present success of *in situ* reflectance techniques will result in a significant increase in such work in the future.

Reflectance Spectroscopy of Inorganic Systems

A comprehensive review (32 references) of the application of diffuse reflectance spectroscopy to inorganic chemistry has been published by Clark.[81] The application of the technique to the structural analysis of metal complexes was particularly emphasized by this author, who has published several papers in this field. The first inorganic application of spectral reflectance to the problem of evaluating paper chromatograms was made by Vaeck.[82,83] A critical comparison of the reflectance and transmission techniques for the analysis of copper spots on paper chromatograms was carried out by Ingle and Minshall,[84] who found that the paper appears optically more uniform in reflected light. A precision of ±0.43% R was reported for four replicate analyses of copper rubeanate on paper. In view of these results, it was decided to investigate the applicability of this technique to inorganic systems (trace metals in particular) separated on thin-layer plates.

Rubeanic Acid Complexes

Complexes of rubeanic acid, a widely used chelating agent for nickel, cobalt, and copper trace analysis, were investigated in the adsorbed state on media commonly used in chromatography under various temperature, pH, and humidity conditions.[85]

After being coated, the 20 × 5-cm plates were heated at 110°C (1 hour for silica gel and alumina, 15 minutes for cellulose) and then were stored in a dry cabinet over silica gel adsorbent. The metal chloride solutions were applied with a 10-μl Hamilton microsyringe, dried for 5 minutes at 110°C, cooled to room temperature, and then chromatographed in a preconditioned (12-hour) chromatography chamber. The solvent used for TLC on Silica Gel G was 0.5% concentrated hydrochloric acid in acetone on Cellulose MN 300: methylethyl ketone–conc. HCl–H_2O (15:3:2), and on Aluminum Oxide G: *n*-butanol–12N HCl (75:25 v/v). After separation, the plates were dried in air or at 110°C for 5 minutes and the spots were made visible by spraying or dipping with 0.1% rubeanic acid in ethanol. The cells and the technique used in preparing the separated material for examination have been described earlier; the plate adsorbent and occasionally barium sulfate served as the reference standard. The 20–30-mg samples removed from the plates for analysis of the spots were weighed to ±0.1 mg and ground in a small agate mortar for two periods of 1 minute each to ensure homogeneity and a more uniform particle size. Samples that were not analyzed immediately were stored in a desiccator over silica gel.

The reflectance spectra of the rubeanic acid chelates adsorbed on Silica Gel G and recorded with a Spectronic 505 spectrophotometer are shown in Figure 26; the spots appear blue-purple for nickel, orange-yellow for cobalt and olive-green for copper. The reflectance spectra have absorption peaks somewhat broader than those of the corresponding transmission spectra in aqueous solution and show a shift in absorption maxima to higher wavelengths. An investigation of the influence of pH on complex formation revealed that for quantitative work best results are obtained at pH 7–8; this was achieved by subjecting the plates to ammonia vapor for 10 minutes before the complexing step to neutralize the small amount of hydrochloric acid present from the separation of the metals. Better results for cellulose layers were obtained by first spraying or dipping the plates after separation in ethanolic rubeanic acid solution, drying at 110°C for 5 minutes, and then dipping in a 5% ammonia solution and redrying at 110°C for 5–10 minutes. To determine the best treatment for the chromatoplates after applying the complexing agent, the plates were heated for different periods at temperatures commonly used in chromatographic work (up to 2 hours at 110°C). The cobalt, nickel and copper complexes are very stable; the rubeanic acid background, however, disappears almost completely after heating for 5 minutes at 110°C.

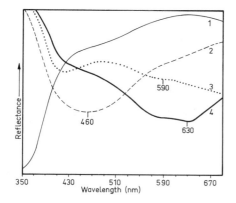

Figure 26. Reflectance spectra of (1) rubeanic acid and the complexes of (2) cobalt, (3) copper, and (4) nickel adsorbed on Silica Gel G.

On all adsorbents the intensity of the complex is enhanced by heating. This was greater for alumina and silica gel than for cellulose; the increase was also greater for cobalt and nickel chelates. After a 30-minute heating period at 110°C, the per cent increase in intensity of the complexes of Co, Ni, and Cu amounted to about 8, 4.3, and 2 on Aluminum Oxide G, to 5, 4.4, and 2 on Silica Gel G, and to 2, 1.5, and 1 on Cellulose MN 300, respectively. It is probable that the surface water of the adsorbent is removed on heating, leaving adsorption sites free for the metal complex and resulting in stronger complex-adsorbent interaction. An initial increase in intensity after heating for 30 minutes at 60°C or 5 minutes at 110°C suggests that most of the water has been removed; a small further increase in intensity occurs after heating at 110°C for 2½ hours but further heating produces little change. The process is reversible; a decrease in the intensity of heated samples was observed after storage of the samples in a humid atmosphere. The experiments show that heating of the chromatoplates at 110°C for 5 minutes is satisfactory; analysis time and adsorption intensity are most favorable, and the reagent background is sufficiently reduced to avoid any interference. Samples were stored in a desiccator over silica gel to avoid fluctuations, and reflectance readings of individual samples kept there varied by only 1–2% R

Table XI
Probable Relative Error in the Measurement of the
Concentration of Nickel, Cobalt and Copper Separated
on Cellulose and Stained by the Dipping Technique

	Nickel	*Cobalt*	*Copper*
Range (% R)[a]	78.0–79.0	80.1–81.0	84.8–85.6
Mean (% R)	78.4	85.1	85.1
Standard deviation (% R)	0.44	0.43	0.39
Equivalent change in measured concentration (μg)	0.06	0.06	0.07
Probable % relative error	3.7	3.7	4.4

[a]For 12 replicate samples of 1.6 μg cation per spot.

over several weeks. The detection limit with the spectrophotometer using 20-mg samples from the chromatoplates was 0.05 μg for nickel and 0.1 μg for cobalt. The visual sensitivity was 0.03 μg per spot for nickel and copper, and 0.05 μg for cobalt if the initial spot size was small (0.5-cm diameter) and no excessive tailing occurred. Reflectance-concentration plots give relatively smooth curves over the concentration range 0.05–20 μg per spot, but at higher concentrations the curves flatten to such a degree that very poor accuracy results.

To study the adherence of the systems to the Kubelka-Munk law, the Kubelka-Munk functions ($[1 - R]^2/2R$) were plotted against concentration. A linear curve was obtained for up to 10 μg of cobalt and nickel and over the entire concentration range for copper. The reproducibility of the method ranged from 0.55 to 0.77% R standard deviation for the spraying technique.

For cellulose layers, which are mechanically very stable, dipping rather than spraying gives better control and is more convenient. Reproducibility data for nickel, cobalt and copper chromatographed on cellulose and treated by the dipping technique are presented in Table XI. The improvement in reproducibility is particularly significant for cobalt;

Table XII
Probable Relative Error in the Measurement
of the Concentration of Nickel as a Function of Concentration

	Concentration of Ni (μg/spot)							
	0.1	*0.5*	*1.0*	*2.0*	*4.0*	*6.0*	*10*	*20*
Standard deviation	0.50	0.50	0.50	0.50	0.50	0.50	0.50	0.50
Equivalent change in measured concentration of nickel (μg per spot)	0.02	0.04	0.05	0.07	0.10	0.14	0.22	1.0
Probable % error	20	8.0	5.0	3.5	2.5	2.3	2.2	5.0

data obtained for cellulose layers using the spraying technique are similar to results for silica gel and alumina. The reproducibility for cobalt separated on cellulose on different days and treated by the dipping technique (four trials) was ±0.70% R average standard deviation; this is a decided improvement on similar trials using the spraying technique (standard deviation 1.37% R). Although the best reproducibility and accuracy are achieved by simultaneous processing of standards and samples, a single calibration curve can be used with satisfactory results; it is to be expected that the accuracy will vary with concentration despite the good reproducibility of reflectance readings. For nickel (Table XII), the accuracy decreases at low concentrations to 20% relative error for 0.1 μg per spot. The best accuracy was observed for 10 μg per spot.

Pyridine-2-aldehyde-2-quinolylhydrazone (PAQH) Complexes

The new chelating reagent PAQH developed by Ryan et al.[86] has been extensively investigated in connection with reflectance spectroscopy and thin-layer chromatography.[87–89] A method for trace analysis of nickel, copper, cobalt, and also iron has been worked out. The procedure used is almost identical to the one described for rubeanic acid. The PAQH reagent solution is 0.03% w/v in ethanol (0.01N in HCl for stabilization).[87] With the use of this chelating agent, control of pH was found to be even more important. After an extensive study of pH conditions, it was found that rendering the spray reagent 0.01M in sodium hydroxide shortly before use resulted in highest spot intensities for cobalt.

With nickel, PAQH reacts as a tridentate reagent to form either square planar (coordination number four) or octahedral (coordination number six) complexes with metals; both 1:1 and 2:1 (reagent to metal) complexes would be expected for nickel. Figure 27 shows the reflectance spectra for nickel on silica gel after spraying with solutions varying from 0.025N to 1.0N in sodium hydroxide. A red complex with a maximum at 520 nm is predominant at low basicity but conversion to a brown species (maximum 480–490 nm) occurs with increasing sodium hydroxide concentration; maximum sensitivity is obtained with 1.0N sodium hydroxide spray solution when nearly quantitative formation of the brown species has occurred. The brown complex is the 2:1 species normally encountered in solution. The red species observed at low basicity on silica gel is presumably the 1:1 planar complex; the 1:1 species is readily observed on silica gel but not in solution and the pronounced influence of adsorbent on equilibrium conditions is evident. The formation of the two complex species for copper, depending on pH, was also observed. In both cases, spraying with a 1.0N sodium hydroxide solution is recommended.

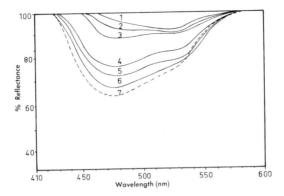

Figure 27. Reflectance spectra of nickel–pyridine-2-aldehyde-2-quinolyl-hydrazone (PAQH) complex adsorbed on silica gel and sprayed with NaOH solutions: (1) 0.025N; (2) 0.05N; (3) 0.10N; (4) 0.25N; (5) 0.50N; (6) 0.75N; (7) 1.0N NaOH.

The results of a temperature study with the nickel chelate are illustrated in Figure 28, which shows spectra obtained from various treatments after spraying. Immediate heating of the plate results in a considerable loss in intensity (curve 1). If the plate is allowed to stand for 1 hour, there is an increase in intensity of at least 5% (curve 2), since the reaction is not quantitative immediately after spraying. Curve 2 also shows that a significant portion of the nickel seems to be present in the red complex form after standing 1 hour. However, if the sample is now heated at 110°C for 5 minutes, the intensity increases and the red complex disappears to a large extent (curve 3). The increase in peak height at 480 nm occurs at the expense of the red modification which is converted to the brown species. Further heating results in only a minor increase of the peak, and the red complex disappears completely (curve

Figure 28. Reflectance spectra of nickel–PAQH complex on silica gel. (1) heated at 110°C for 5 minutes immediately after spraying; (2) air-dried for 1 hour; (3) as 2 and then heated for 5 minutes at 110°C; (4) as 2 and then heated for 30 minutes at 110°C.

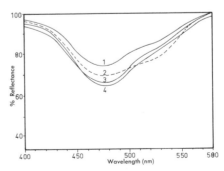

4); a small bathochromic shift is also observed upon prolonged heating. On cellulose, the samples are air-dried for 1 hour. Heating of the cellulose plates results in a dark yellow background staining that is probably due to attack of the cellulose by sodium hydroxide. As a result of temperature studies, heating at 110°C for 5 minutes after 1 hour of air-drying is recommended for nickel and copper. For cobalt, immediate heating at 110°C for 5 minutes is suggested.

Table XIII
Absorption Maxima (nm) of PAQH Complexes

	Aqueous solution	*Silica gel*	*Cellulose*
Co	500 (pH 7–8)	508 (0.01N NaOH)	536 (0.01N NaOH)
Ni	480 (pH 9)	490 (1.0N NaOH)	520 (1.0N NaOH)
Cu	475 (pH 9)	485 (1.0N NaOH)	505 (1.0N NaOH)

Both the pH and temperature studies are good examples of the use of reflectance spectroscopy in the investigation of adsorption properties of systems on chromatographic adsorbents. The sensitivity of this method was found to be about 0.01 μg per spot for all three cations at a 50% accuracy level. Linear calibration curves [F(R$_\infty$) vs. conc.] for concentrations up to 1.5 μg per spot were obtained. Absorption maxima used for analytical purposes are listed in Table XIII. The reproducibility of the method is similar to that of the rubeanic acid method, with a slight improvement on cellulose plates in connection with the dipping technique.

Iron, zinc, manganese, cadmium, and lead ions react with PAQH to form colored products but do not interfere in the determination of cobalt, nickel, and copper. Iron in commercial silica gel can be removed by chromatographing the plates with the solvent; iron impurities moving with the solvent front are then cut off and the plate is used for analysis. Cadmium, lead, and iron in the sample move with the solvent front. Zinc and cadmium are chromatographically separated from nickel, cobalt and copper and, in addition, even tenfold excesses of these metal complexes fade almost completely upon heating at 110°C on silica gel.

A combination of the two proposed methods has been used for the determination of trace metals in cereal.[88] Nickel and copper were determined as the rubeanic acid complex and cobalt as the PAQH complex. A standard ashing procedure was used. Results for the analysis of some oat samples are presented in Table XIV. Addition of about the same and twice the amount of the respective metals to the samples gave Co, Cu, and Ni recoveries of 88–115%, 103–105%, and 104–106%, respectively.

Table XIV

Analysis of Oats*

Amount of metal found (p.p.m.)	Sample No.				Average and standard deviation (p.p.m.)	Relative standard deviation (%)
	1	2	3	4		
Cobalt	0.03	0.02	0.02	0.03	0.03 ± 0.01	± 20
Copper	3.45	3.68	3.50	3.27	3.48 ± 0.17	± 4.9
Nickel	0.96	1.05	0.90	0.99	0.98 ± 0.06	± 6.4

*The value for each sample is the mean obtained from four spots run simultaneously.

In another study, PAQH was used as a semiselective scavenger and the metal chelates extracted in chloroform were chromatographically separated. This was followed by a reflectance spectroscopic investigation.[89] Several advantages over the methods previously proposed lie in this approach to metal trace analysis. The extracted chelates can be applied as concentrated solution directly to the chromatogram without prior sample preparation; the sensitivity is increased and adsorbent impurities do not interfere. In addition, faster and clearer separation of the metal chelates in comparison to separation of free metal ions can usually be achieved, because solvents having less polarity can be used for the separation process on highly polar adsorbents such as alumina and silica gel. Since the chelates are dyes, no spraying reagent is needed and variables such as background staining and irregular color development can be eliminated. Extraction procedures have been described by Ryan *et al.*[90] The complexes are formed in a solution adjusted by an ammonia–ammonium chloride buffer to about pH 10 and extracted with chloroform. To ensure complete recovery of cobalt, a second extraction with amyl alcohol is carried out.

The separation of iron, nickel, copper, and cobalt is of major interest because previous work has shown that their PAQH complexes are highly suitable for analytical purposes. The best separation is achieved on alumina layers with chloroform as solvent. Rf-Values of Fe^{3+}, Fe^{2+}, Ni^{2+}, Cu^{2+} and Co^{2+} complexes on Aluminum Oxide G were 0.82, 0.35, 0.07, 0.05, and 0.00, respectively. Other metal complexes had Rf-values in the range of 0.03 to 0.06 on alumina plates and slightly higher on alumina sheets. Their separation from the copper, the iron (III), and sometimes the cobalt complex was possible only by resorting to two-dimensional chromatography using 2% methanol in chloroform for the second dimension. The same order of separation was observed on alumina plates and alumina sheets but the Rf-values themselves, particularly for iron (III) and copper differed considerably. The separation on alumina sheets actually was found to be somewhat more efficient. A light yellow spot resulting from an excess of reagent extracted along with the complexes usually appeared between the copper and nickel spots, completely separated from the other components. The running time for the complete separation of the iron (III), nickel, copper, cobalt, and reagent spot ranged between 20 and 40 minutes.

The stability of these chelates at higher temperatures was also investigated by spectral reflectance. Complete decomposition of the adsorbed metal chelates was observed at the temperatures and times indicated in Table XV. The decomposition appeared as a progressive fading of the

Table XV

Complete Decomposition of PAQH-Chelates Adsorbed on Alumina

Metal	Decomposition temperature (°C)	Time
Fe^{3+}	180	1.5
Ni^{2+}	180	2
Cu^{2+}	180	2
Co^{2+}	200	4

spots until they could no longer be distinguished from the background. The color did not reappear after cooling. Interesting relationships were observed among Rf-values, decomposition temperatures, and position of the absorption maxima.[89]

In the analytical procedure, up to tenfold excesses of interfering metal can be tolerated. The detection limits are 0.01 μg per spot for iron, nickel, and copper, and 0.007 μg per spot for cobalt. Drying of the chromatoplates at 110°C for 5 minutes immediately after separation is recommended. For quantitative work, the reproducibility is considerably improved because of the absence of spraying procedures.[91] The total iron content of a solution can be determined by oxidizing all the iron (II) to the iron (III) state with H_2O_2 in acetic acid medium (pH ~ 5). On the other hand an able method was developed to determine Fe^{2+} and Fe^{3+} simultaneously,[91] since both form stable and intensely colored chelates with PAQH. Their Rf-values are indeed so different (0.05 and 0.82) that if no interfering ions are present, they can be separated within a few minutes. Identification of the metals can be made on the basis of color and Rf-values. The same group of metal chelates has recently been successfully investigated by ultraviolet reflectance spectroscopy.[91]

Dithizone and Oxine Complexes

Another investigation was carried out on a group of dithizone and oxine complexes[49] for the purpose of developing a qualitative analysis scheme, based on a combination of spectra and Rf-values, analogous to the one worked out for amino acids.[47]

After spotting of the cations (nitrates in aqueous solution), the plates were dried with compressed air and then developed in one dimension by the ascending technique with the use of 25% (v/v) hydrochloric acid (12N) in 1-butanol. The plates were then dried at 75°C for 30 minutes

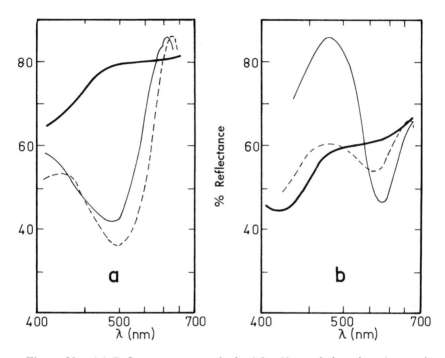

Figure 29. (a) Reflectance spectra obtained for 10 μg of chromium (——), lead (-----), and silver (——) cations adsorbed on cellulose after chromatoplates have been sprayed with dithizone–oxine reagent. (b) Reflectance spectra obtained for 10 μg of chromium (——), lead (——), and silver (-----) cations adsorbed on cellulose after chromatoplates have been sprayed with dithizone–oxine reagent and subsequently exposed to ammonia fumes.

and sprayed with a mixture consisting of equal volumes of 0.05% w/v dithizone in carbon tetrachloride and 1% w/v 8-hydroxyquinoline in carbon tetrachloride. The plates were air-dried for 10 minutes. The reflectance spectra of the samples were recorded with a Beckman DK-2 spectrophotometer. After the first set of spectra had been obtained, the reference and sample cells were exposed to ammonia vapor for at least 2 minutes in a chamber containing 15M ammonia and a second set of reflectance spectra was recorded. Some reflectance spectra obtained before and after treatment with ammonia are shown in Figure 29. Table XVI lists Rf-values and spectral data for all the cations investigated.

Table XVI
Rf-Values and Spectral Data for Cations Adsorbed on MN-Cellulose

Cation	Rf-value MN-300	Paper	After spraying with dithizone-oxine reagent Absorption maximum (nm)	Sensitivity (μg)	After spraying with dithizone-oxine reagent followed by ammonia treatment Absorption maximum (nm)	Sensitivity (μg)
Aluminum	0.04	0.04	—	—	380	2.3
Bismuth	0.56	0.60	505	2.2	515	2.2
Cadmium	0.90	0.83	498	1.6	519	1.6
Chromium	0.07	—	—	—	414	6.5
Cobalt	0.41	0.39	512	0.5	564	0.5
Copper	0.51	0.51	502	0.6	398	0.6
Iron	0.93	−.92	380	2.7	597	0.9
Lead	0.30	—	498	0.5	556	2.2
Manganese	0.16	—	510	2.2	507	2.6
Mercury	0.88	0.86	492	0.5	—	—
Nickel	0.09	0.04	503	1.2	514	0.6
Silver	0.00	0.00	492	2.0	574	0.6
Tin	0.80	—	510	0.9	—	—
Zinc	0.87	0.79	513	0.7	526	0.7

Miscellaneous Techniques

On the basis of the same principles a method was developed for the quantitative determination of copper, nickel and zinc.[93] Copper and nickel were determined without interference in the presence of 11 other cations by employing neocuproine and dimethylglyoxime, respectively, as chromogenic reagents. In the case of zinc, 3,3-dimethylnaphthidine was used with interferences occurring from tin, cadmium and iron. Accuracies of 2.1% and 2.8% were reported for nickel and copper and 5.6% for zinc.

Diffuse reflectance spectroscopy has also been used recently for the identification of various chromium (III) complexes on thin-layer chromatography sheets.[94] The application of this technique to the analysis of the photolysis products of $Cr(en_2)ox^+$ has been described.

The importance of the *in situ* reflectance technique as a tool for the inorganic as well as the inorganic-analytical chemist in investigations of complex metal chelate systems will be more and more realized in the future. Much data difficult or impossible to obtain working with solutions can be acquired on complex formation mechanisms. The increased knowledge about adsorption phenomena gained through this technique will enable chromatographers in the future to move away from an empirical approach.

APPENDIX

Derivation of the Kubelka-Munk Function

When a plane parallel layer of thickness d is irradiated diffusely and monochromatically with a beam of intensity I_o, the radiation flow in the positive x-direction can be represented by I and the radiation flow in the negative x-direction (caused by scattering) can be represented by J. An infinitesimally thin layer—dx—parallel to the surface is penetrated by the radiation in all possible directions with respect to the normal. The average path of the radiation, therefore, is not dx but

$$d\varphi_I = dx \int_0^{\pi 12} \frac{\delta I \ d\varphi}{I\delta\varphi\cos\varphi} \equiv udx \text{ or } d\varphi_J = dx \int_0^{\pi 12} \frac{\delta J d\varphi}{J\delta\varphi\cos\varphi} \equiv vdx \qquad (a)$$

where $\dfrac{\delta I}{\delta\varphi}$ and $\dfrac{\delta J}{\delta\varphi}$ stand for the angular distribution of the radiation.

Assuming conditions for ideal diffuse radiation,

$$\frac{\delta I}{\delta\varphi} = I \sin 2 \ \alpha \text{ and } \frac{\delta J}{\delta\varphi} = J \sin 2 \ \varphi \qquad (b)$$

where $u = v = 2$. This factor is included in s (scattering coefficient) and k (absorption coefficient). The component $kIdx$ of I is adsorbed in the layer dx while the component $sIdx$ is scattered backward. The radiation J in the negative x-direction contributes radiation $sJdx$ by scattering in the positive x-direction. The change in intensity of I in the layer dx, therefore, is composed of the following elements: $dI = -(k + s) \ Idx + sJdx$. By analogy, the decrease in intensity of J is

$$dJ = +(k + s) \ Jdx - sIdx \qquad (c)$$

These are the basic differential equations which describe the absorption and scattering processes. The indefinite integrals are:

$$I = A(1 - \beta)e\sigma x + B(1 + \beta)e^{-\sigma x} \qquad (d)$$

$$J = A(1 + \beta)e\sigma x + B(1 - \beta)e^{-\sigma x} \qquad (e)$$

with

$$\sigma = \sqrt{K(K + 2S)} \qquad (f)$$

and

$$\beta \equiv \frac{\sigma}{K + 2S} = \sqrt{K/(K + 2S)} \qquad (g)$$

The constants A and B are determined by the limiting conditions. If one integrates for the entire thickness, d, of the layer the conditions

for $$X = O : I = I_o$$
for $$X = d : I = I_{(x=d)}; J = O$$

are valid and one obtains

$$A = - \frac{(1 - \beta)e^{-\sigma d}}{(I + \beta)^2 e^{\sigma d} - (I - \beta)^2 e^{-\sigma d}} I_o \qquad (h)$$

$$B = \frac{(1 + \beta)e^{\sigma d}}{(1 + \beta)^2 e^{\sigma d} - (1 - \beta)^2 e^{-\sigma d}} I_o \qquad (i)$$

The transmission of the layer is therefore given by

$$T = \frac{I(x = d)}{I_o} = \frac{4\beta}{(1 + \beta)^2 e^{\sigma d} - (1 - \beta)^2 e^{-\sigma d}}$$
$$= \frac{2\beta}{(1 + \beta)^2 \sin h\sigma d + 2\beta \cos h\sigma d} \qquad (k)$$

the diffuse reflectance by

$$R = \frac{I(x = o)}{I_o} = \frac{(1 - \beta)^2 (e^{\sigma d} - e^{-\sigma d})}{(1 + \beta)^2 e^{\sigma d} - (1 - \beta)^2 e^{-\sigma d}}$$
$$= \frac{(1 - \beta)^2 \sin h\sigma d}{(1 + \beta)^2 \sin h\sigma d + 2\beta \cos h\sigma d} \qquad (l)$$

For $s = 0$ (nonscattering layer) and $\beta = I$, Equation k becomes Bouguer-Lambert's Law $T = e^{-kd}$, and R' becomes zero.

For infinite layer thickness, d approaches 0 and one obtains R'_∞

$$R'_\infty = \frac{1 - \beta}{1 + \beta} = \frac{S + K - \sqrt{K(K + 2S)}}{S} \qquad (m)$$

These conditions are achieved experimentally with 1-mm layers of fine powders and R'_∞ can therefore be measured. Equation m can be transformed to a more convenient form

$$\frac{(1 - R'_\infty)^2}{2R'_\infty} = \frac{k}{s} \qquad (n)$$

REFERENCES

1. Wendlandt, W. M., and H. G. Hecht. *Reflectance Spectroscopy* (New York: Interscience, 1966).
2. *Proceedings of the American Chemical Society Symposium on Reflectance Spectroscopy, September 1967, Chicago, Ill.* Edited by W. M. Wendlandt (New York: Plenum Press, 1967).
3. Winslow, E. H., and H. A. Liebhafsky. Anal. Chem. **21**, 1338 (1949).

4. Yamaguchi, K., S. Fujii, T. Tabata, and S. Katon. J. Pharm. Soc. Japan **74**, 1322 (1954).
5. Yamaguchi, K., S. Fukushima, and M. Ito. J. Pharm. Soc. Japan **74**, 556 (1955).
6. Fischer, R. B., and F. Vratny. Anal. Chim. Acta **13**, 588 (1955).
7. Pruckner, F., M. von der Schulenburg, and G. Schwuttke. Naturwiss. **38**, 45 (1951).
8. Schwuttke, G. Z. Angew. Phys. **5**, 303 (1953).
9. Lermond, C. A., and L. B. Rogers. Anal. Chem. **27**, 340 (1955).
10. Kubelka, P., and F. Munk. Z. Tech. Physik. **12**, 593 (1931).
11. Kubelka, P. J. Opt. Soc. Am. **38**, 448 (1948).
12. Kortüm, G. Angew. Chem. Intern. Ed. Engl. **2**, 333 (1963).
13. Kortüm, G. Spectrochim. Acta Suppl. **1957**, 534.
14. Kortüm, G., and F. Vogel. Z. Physik. Chem. **18**, 230 (1958).
15. Kortüm, G. Trans. Faraday Soc. **58**, 1624 (1962).
16. Kortüm, G., and J. Vogel. Z. Physik. Chem. **18**, 110 (1958).
17. Schreyer, G. Z. Physik. Chem. **18**, 123 (1958).
18. Van den Akker, J. A. Tappi. **1949**, 498.
19. Judd, D. B., and G. Wyszecki. *Color in Business and Industry,* 2nd ed. (New York: John Wiley and Sons, Inc., 1963).
20. Zeitlin, H., and A. Niimoto. Anal. Chem. **31**, 1167 (1959).
21. Goldman, J., and R. R. Goodall. J. Chromatog. **32**, 24 (1968).
22. Frei, R. W., and M. M. Frodyma. Anal. Chim. Acta **32**, 501 (1965).
23. Jork, H. Z. Anal. Chem. **221**, 17 (1966).
24. Lieu, V. T., and M. M. Frodyma. Talanta **13**, 1319 (1966).
25. Klaus, R. J. Chromatog. **16**, 311 (1964).
26. Klaus, R. Pharm. Ztg. Ver. Apotheker-Ztg. **112**, 480 (1967).
27. Frei, R. W., D. E. Ryan, and V. T. Lieu. Can. J. Chem. **44**, 1945 (1966).
28. Ringbom, A. Z. Anal. Chem. **115**, 332 (1939).
29. Ayres, G. H. Anal. Chem. **21**, 652 (1949).
30. Lermond, C. A., and L. B. Rogers. Anal. Chem. **27**, 340 (1955).
31. Gänshirt, H., in *Dünnschicht Chromatographie.* Ed. by E. Stahl (Berlin: Springer-Verlag, 1967), p 142.
32. Pamphlet 50-657/K-e, Zeiss, Oberkochen, Germany.
33. Jork, H. Z. Anal. Chem. **236**, 310 (1968).
34. Jork, H. Cosmo Pharma. **1**, 33 (1967).
35. Stahl, E., and H. Jork. Zeiss Inform. **16**, (#68) 52 (1968).
36. Struck, H., H. Karg, and H. Jork. J. Chromatog. **36**, 74 (1968).
37. Jork, H. J. Chromatog. **33**, 297 (1968).
38. Jork, H. Cosmo Pharma. **4**, 12 (1968).
39. De Galan, L., J. van Leeuwen, K. Camstra. Anal. Chim. Acta **35**, 395 (1966).
40. Beroza, M., K. R. Hill, and K. H. Norris. Anal. Chem. **40**, 1611 (1968).
41. Frodyma, M. M., V. T. Lieu, and R. W. Frei. J. Chromatog. **13**, 520 (1965).
42. Frodyma, M. M., and V. T. Lieu. Anal. Chem. **39**, 814 (1967).

43. Frei, R. W., and M. M. Frodyma. Anal. Biochem. **9**, 310 (1964).
44. Lieu, V. T., M. M. Frodyma, L. S. Higashi, and L. H. Kunimoto. Anal. Biochem. **19**, 454 (1967).
45. Frei, R. W., N. S. Nomura, and M. M. Frodyma. Mikrochim. Acta **1967**, 1099.
46. Frei, R. W., and N. S. Nomura. Mikrochim. Acta **1968**, 565.
47. Frei, R. W., I. T. Fukui, V. T. Lieu, and M. M. Frodyma. Chimia (Aarau) **20**, 23 (1966).
48. Frodyma, M. M., R. W. Frei, and D. J. Williams. J. Chromatog. **13**, 61 (1964).
49. Frei, R. W. Unpublished data.
50. Lieu, V. T., R. W. Frei, M. M. Frodyma, and I. T. Fukui. Anal. Chim. Acta **33**, 639 (1965).
51. Klaus, R. J. Chromatog. **34**, 539 (1968).
52. Huber, W. J. Chromatog. **33**, 378 (1968).
53. Frei, R. W., H. Zeitlin, and M. M. Frodyma. Chem. Rundschau (Solothurn) **19**, 411 (1966).
54. Mottier, M. Mitt. Gebiete Lebensm. Hyg. **47**, 372 (1956).
55. Frodyma, M. M., and R. W. Frei. J. Chem. Educ. **45**, 522 (1969).
56. Frei, R. W., and H. Zeitlin. Anal. Chim. Acta **32**, 32 (1965).
57. Zeitlin, H., R. W. Frei, and M. McCarter. J. Catalysis **4**, 77 (1965).
58. Frei, R. W., and M. M. Frodyma. Chem. Rundschau (Solothurn) **19**, 26 (1966).
59. Pataki, G. Chromatographia **1**, 492 (1968).
60. Moffat, E. D., and R. I. Lytle. Anal. Chem. **31**, 926 (1959).
61. Brenner, M., and A. Niederwieser. Experientia **16**, 378 (1960).
62. Bull, H. B., J. W. Hahn, and V. R. Baptist. J. Am. Chem. Soc. **71**, 550 (1949).
63. Frodyma, M. M., and R. W. Frei. J. Chromatog. **15**, 501 (1964).
64. El-Khadem, S., Z. M. El-Shafei, and M. M. A./Abdel Rahman. Anal. Chem. **35**, 1766 (1963).
65. Frodyma, M. M., and R. W. Frei. J. Chromatog. **17**, 131 (1965).
66. Thaller, F. J. M.S. Thesis, University of Hawaii (1965).
67. Frei, R. W., F. J. Thaller, and M. M. Frodyma. Unpublished work.
68. Vomhof, D. W., and T. C. Tucker. J. Chromatog. **17**, 300 (1965).
69. McCready, R. N., and E. A. McComb. Anal. Chem. **26**, 1645 (1954).
70. Pataki, G. Unpublished data.
71. Pataki, G. *Techniques of Thin-Layer Chromatography in Amino Acid and Peptide Chemistry* (Ann Arbor, Michigan: Ann Arbor Science Publishers, 1968).
72. Frei, R. W. Unpublished data.
73. Randerath, K. *Thin-Layer Chromatography* 2nd ed. (New York: Academic Press, 1966), p 223.
74. Gänshirt, H., and A. Malzacher. Naturwiss. **47**, 279 (1960).
75. Jork, H. *Chromatography Symposium IV, Conference Proceedings*, **1966**, p 193.
76. Jork, H. IVth International Symposium of Chromatography and Electrophoresis, Brussels, Sept. 1966. Lecture.

77. Stahl, E., and H. Jork. Arzneimittel-Forsch. (in press, 1969).
78. Stahl, E., and H. Jork. Arch. Pharm. **299,** 670 (1966).
79. Stahl, E., and H. Bohrman. Unpublished data.
80. Pfeifle, J. Thesis, University of the Saarland, Germany (1966).
81. Clark, R. T. H. J. Chem. Educ. **41,** 488 (1964).
82. Vaeck, S. V. Nature **172,** 213 (1953).
83. Vaeck, S. V. Anal. Chim. Acta **10,** 48 (1954).
84. Ingle, R. B., and E. Minshall. J. Chromatog. **8,** 369 (1962).
85. Frei, R. W., and D. E. Ryan. Anal. Chim. Acta **37,** 187 (1967).
86. Heit, M. L., and D. E. Ryan. Anal. Chim. Acta **32,** 448 (1965).
87. Frei, R. W., R. Liiva, and D. E. Ryan. Can. J. Chem. **46,** 167 (1968).
88. Frei, R. W. J. Chromatog. **34,** 563 (1968).
89. Frei, R. W., D. E. Ryan, and C. A. Stockton. Anal. Chim. Acta **42,** 159 (1968).
90. Singhal, S. P., and D. E. Ryan. Anal. Chim. Acta **37,** 91 (1967).
91. Frei, R. W. Unpublished data.
92. Zaye, D. F., R. W. Frei, and M. M. Frodyma. Anal. Chim. Acta **39,** 13 (1967).
93. Frodyma, M. M., D. F. Zaye, and V. T. Lieu. Anal. Chim. Acta **40,** 451 (1968).
94. Kirk, A. D., K. C. Moss, and J. G. Valentin. J. Chromatog. **36,** 332 (1968).
95. Niederwieser, A. Chromatographia **2,** 23 (1969); and **2,** 362 (1969).
96. Frei, R. W., H. Zürcher, and G. Pataki. J. Chromatog. **43,** 551 (1969).

Chapter 2

GC-TLC: Two-Dimensional Chromatography Using Gas Chromatography as One Dimension

by J. Janák

Although chromatography is one of the most powerful methods for separating complex mixtures of substances of different chemical structures, zone overlapping takes place very often.

In planar chromatographic techniques, such as paper chromatography (PC), thin-layer chromatography (TLC), or electrophoresis (E), the two-dimensional technique is used in order to improve the separation. After chromatography of a substance mixture with one solvent in one direction of the layer and evaporation of the solvent, a second run is effected with another solvent in a perpendicular direction. During the experiment, one type of layer and two kinds of solvent of convenient chemical composition are used to obtain the best possible separation.

In column chromatographic techniques such as gas chromatography (GC), liquid (column) chromatography (LC), or ion-exchange chromatography, use is made of two or more stationary phases that selectively retain the different components of a mixture. Chromatography is performed in either of the following ways:

(1) The whole mixture is chromatographed in two or more parallel columns packed with different ad sorbents and percolated with a suitable solvent or gas.

(2) The mixture is separated to simpler fractions which are subsequently introduced onto another column for further separation.

Both methods give results which are similar to those of the two-dimensional chromatography "in plain."

Recently, many combinations of "planar" and column techniques have been used in order to obtain complete separation of all possible components of complex mixtures.[1-15] Most often a mixture is subjected to preliminary separation by TLC, and then the preseparated fractions of the mixture are completely separated by GC. A more intricate method[2] has been described in which GC on one stationary phase is used with subsequent separation of the gas chromatographic fractions by TLC, followed in turn by separation of the eluted thin-layer chromatographic fractions by GC on some other GC stationary phase.

The combination of TLC (or PC) with GC offers certain advantages over two-dimensional TLC (or PC). In gas chromatography, the vapor pressure (volatility) of compounds contributes remarkably to separation, as a factor which can by no means contribute to the separation on the layer. For example, a nonpolar stationary phase in GC will separate substances to the first approximation according to the increasing number of C-atoms in their molecules or according to their molecular weights. In column chromatography, however, the polar adsorbent used at room temperature shows a much higher polarity than any known polar stationary phase used in GC. Therefore, the separation depends first of all upon the type of functional groups and/or their steric shielding, while their molecular weight plays a less important role than in GC.

This chapter will discuss in detail the technique[2, 16-30] in which GC is used as the first dimension of chromatography. As with other techniques combining known methods to reach a qualitatively new level, the technique described here has some idea-precursors. In the paper by Casu and Cavalloti[16] a strip moving under the outlet of the gas chromatograph enabled the detection of gas chromatographic fractions as colored spots. One of our earliest papers on the topic[2] reversed an arrangement that Mangold and Kammereck[1] had employed, that of GC before TLC. In addition, Nigam *et al.*[17] referred to a thin-layer chromatographic separation of terpenoid compounds from one gas chromatographic peak trapped on a thin-layer plate. It is evident that the principle of two-dimensional chromatography using GC as the first dimension had been worked out in early 1963.[18]*

---

*Because any new technique finds its origin in progressive trends of thought, experimental art, and/or technology, it is likely to be reported simultaneously by more than one laboratory. Unfortunately, not all papers on the topic are such as they claim to be, a fact which we can prove with relative ease by thoroughly inspecting the circulating data.

In our arrangement, the gas chromatographic effluent is applied directly on the starting line of a dry thin-layer or a chromatographic paper. The sampling can be carried out either in consecutive steps,[2, 17] one for each eluted fraction of GC, or continuously.[16, 19] In the case of an uninterrupted sampling procedure the thin-layer can be moved at a linear[21] or programmed[22] (*e.g.,* logarithmic) rate. TLC is performed after trapping of the gas chromatographic effluent along the starting line of the layer.

This new type of two-dimensional chromatography exploits to the maximum both extreme separation processes: (1) separation according to dispersion forces (determined mainly by the number of C atoms and/or molecular weight) by gas chromatography along the time axis that coincides with the starting line of the thin-layer or paper; and (2) separation according to orientation forces (determined mainly by the type and number of functional groups) by thin-layer chromatography (or paper chromatography) in the direction of solvent flow.

It is evident that it is possible to extract the twice-separated substances from the thin-layer (or chromatographic paper) and, if necessary, to chromatograph the extracted microgram quantities again by means of GC on another stationary phase. Other methods of identification, *e.g.,* spectroscopic methods (particularly mass spectrometry and UV spectroscopy), microscopy, crystallography, or colorimetry can be used in connection with the procedure.

THEORY

In order to prepare a thin-layer chromatogram, a sample of the mixture to be separated is applied at one point of the starting line, producing a spot of a certain diameter. During the chromatographic process diffusion takes place, producing spot broadening.

Consecutive Chromatography

When different chromatographic methods are used one after another, it is necessary to consider the effects of two or more diffusion processes upon zone broadening. If fractions of a gas chromatographic effluent are trapped along the starting line of a thin-layer or paper, the neighboring components will be satisfactorily resolved[31] provided

$$\Delta t_{Rx} = 4\sigma \tag{1}$$

where $\Delta t_{Rx} = t_{Rx_1} - t_{Rx_2}$ is the difference between the retention times of the peaks of components 1 and 2, and σ is the variance of the peaks, assumed to represent a Gaussian distribution.

During the subsequent TLC the two zones 1 and 2, shown in Figure 1, can overlap again as a result of the second diffusion process. In an

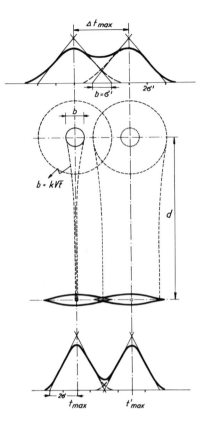

Figure 1. Band broadening of gas chromatographic zones on a thin layer. For explanations of symbols see text. [Reproduced from J. Janák. J. Chromatog. **15**, 15 (1964), by permission of Elsevier Publishing Co., Amsterdam, The Netherlands.]

extreme case, under unsuitable conditions, this overlapping can nullify the gas chromatographic resolution. If two different spots are clearly detectable after TLC, the relation between zone width b on the thin-layer and σ in the gas chromatogram must be given by $b \leqq 2\sigma$.

Zone width b can be expressed in terms of the number of theoretical plates, n, as commonly used in chromatography

$$n = 16 \ (d/b)^2 \qquad (2)$$

where d is the distance of the zone from the starting line on the thin-layer plate.

The number of theoretical plates, n, can be expressed as the height equivalent to a theoretical plate H, i.e., $n = d/H$. The zone distance d can be written in terms of Rf and length L of the solvent-wetted layer, i.e., $d = RfL$, so that

$$b = 4\sqrt{d^2/n} = 4\sqrt{Hd} = 4\sqrt{HRfL} \qquad (3)$$

Hence, b increases linearly with d (see also Reference 33), since $d^2 \sim t$, with t signifying the time of thin-layer chromatography, and $b^2 \sim t$.

Spot-spreading with respect to time t proceeds in a parabolic course, as has been found both for paper[34] and thin-layer chromatography on bound[32] or loose[21] layers of silica gel.

Driving Velocity of the Thin-Layer

The position of the gas chromatographic "peak" on the starting line is given by $t_R v$, where v is velocity at which the plate is driven under the outlet orifice of the gas chromatograph. In accordance with condition (1) for satisfactory separation of two substances, one can write

$$b \leq 2\sigma \leq \frac{1}{2} \cdot \Delta t_R v \qquad (4)$$

Combining Equations 3 and 4 gives, for v,

$$v \geq \frac{8}{\Delta t_R} \sqrt{HRfL}$$

The driving velocity necessary to satisfy this condition will be the lower, the larger is t_R, and/or the lower is zone width b, defined by the square root of the product of chromatographic quantities H, Rf and L.

Upon artificially suppressing lateral diffusion of the zone by dissecting the layer into a system of narrow discrete strips of width a, the relation for the minimum driving velocity of the plate can be written in the form

$$v_{min} = \frac{a}{b} \cdot \frac{8}{\Delta t_R} \sqrt{HRfL} = \frac{Ha}{\Delta t_R} \qquad (5)$$

and any influence of chromatographic parameters like Rf, L, and H is fully eliminated.

Programmed Shifting of the Thin-Layer

The retention times, t_R, for homologous substances are related to the separation factor[35] for the homologous $-CH_2$-increment by

$$q = RT \ln \frac{t_{R_2}}{t_{R_1}} = RT \ln \frac{K_2}{K_1}$$

where K is the partition coefficient of homologs 1 and 2. K and likewise t increase exponentially with an increasing number of increments, *i.e.*, C-number. If the recording is made in a logarithmic scale of t, then the zones in the chromatogram corresponding to compounds differing by a $-CH_2$-group will be spaced at regular distances. The spacings are additive for members of a homologous series.

Positions of the individual components in the chromatogram can be established for $y_1 = \log t_i$ and $y_{i-1} = \log t_{i-1}$, the straight-line equations for the standard *n*-paraffin series, and the homologous series to

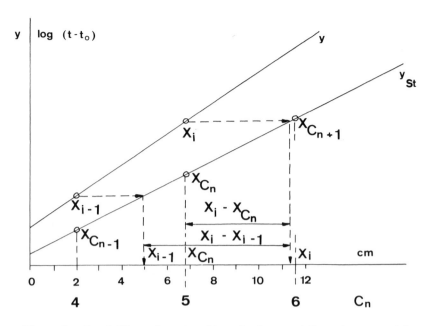

Figure 2. Graph illustration of position of substance i (in cm) measured from the edge of thin layer, in relation to a chosen homologous series. For explanations of symbols see text. [Reproduced from J. Janák, I. Klimeš, K. Hána. J. Chromatog. **18**, 270 (1965), by permission of Elsevier Publishing Co., Amsterdam, The Netherlands.]

which component i belongs. This follows from the definition of the Kováts index;[36] the procedure is illustrated graphically in Figure 2.

$$x_i - x_{i-1} = (x_{Cn} - x_{Cn-1}) \frac{\log t_i - \log t_{i-1}}{\log t_{Cn} - \log t_{Cn-1}}$$

and

$$x_{Cn} - x_i = (x_{Cn} - x_{Cn-1}) \frac{\log t_{Cn} - \log t_i}{\log t_{Cn} - \log t_{Cn-1}}$$

At a logarithmic shifting of the layer,[22] $\log t$ is directly given by linear section l of the starting line on the layer. If we correlate some of the zones in the chromatogram to the retention indices of n-paraffins, we can directly mark the values that will correspond to the component or increment of the series for the Kováts retention indices on the starting line of the layer.

$$I_{\text{subst}} = 100 \frac{l_i - l_{Cn}}{l_{Cn} - l_{Cn-1}} + 100 \, Cn$$

$$I_{CH_2} = 100 \frac{l_i - l_{i-1}}{l_{Cn} - l_{Cn-1}}$$

Similarly, proceeding from the supposition[37] that boiling points of nonpolar substances are determined by dispersion forces—and by using a nonpolar stationary phase—we can calculate the boiling point of component i in the chromatogram over a sufficiently wide range of boiling points:

$$(BP)_i = (BP)_x + \left\{ (BP)_y - (BP)_x \right\} \frac{l_x - l_i}{l_x - l_y}$$

Test of Theory

Using a silica gel–benzene system and aromatic hydrocarbons (*e.g.,* biphenyl, acenaphthene, fluorene, and phenanthrene) as model compounds,[21] we found the following mean values: $L = 19.0$ cm, $t = 525$ sec, Rf = 0.94, $\Delta t_R = 1.3$ min.

For the pair biphenyl–acenaphthene the minimum driving velocity of the layer under the gas chromatograph outlet was

$$v_{\min} = \frac{8}{1.3} \sqrt{0.000259 \cdot 18} = 1.33 \text{ cm/min}$$

Using strips of a $= 0.30$ cm, the minimum velocity is

$$v_{\min} = 1.33 \frac{0.30}{0.34} = 0.475 \text{ cm/min}$$

Considering the experimental results in Figure 3 we can see that at a driving velocity of 0.22 cm/min (Figure 3a) the pairs biphenyl–acenaphthene and acenaphthene–fluorene overlap ($b > 2\sigma$), whereas at a velocity of 0.63 cm/min (Figure 3b) all zones can be identified ($b = 2\sigma$). Finally, at a driving velocity of 1.49 cm/min (Figure 3e) no overlap is recorded where $b \ll 2\sigma$.

On the other hand, the zones of fluorene and phenanthrene (Figure 3a) are well separated even at the layer driving velocity of 0.22 cm/min, because $\Delta t_R = 3.7$ min and, for this pair of hydrocarbons,

$$v_{\min} = \frac{8}{3.7} \cdot \frac{0.30}{0.84} \cdot 0.216 = 0.163 \text{ cm/min}$$

Finally, the example in Figure 3c shows that zone broadening on a layer where lateral diffusion has not been suppressed gives poorer resolution at a driving velocity of 0.63 cm/min than the use of notched plates at the same velocity, because again $b > 2\sigma$ (Figure 3b). If 0.10-cm notches are used, the resolution of all zones is perfect (Figure 3d), because $b \ll 2\sigma$.

Position of Zones on the Layer and Structural Correlations

The potentialities of identifying the individual substances on the thin-layer by their position in the chromatogram and of making structural correlations by two-dimensional GC-TLC are well-documented by, for example, analysis of a complex mixture of C_{14}–C_{22} fatty acids.[27]

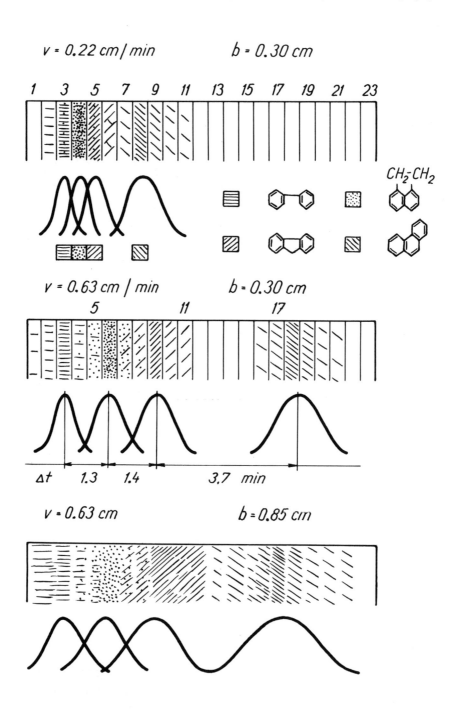

Gas chromatography on a nonpolar stationary phase (Apiezon L, first dimension, separation based on dispersion forces) results in a good separation of fatty acid methyl esters by their C-numbers, while the number of double and triple bonds has only a minor influence on their retention. The upper gas chromatogram in Figure 4 shows a practical result. The nonselective grouping of acid esters according to their C-numbers is obvious. For the sake of comparison, another gas chromatogram (bottom, Figure 4) has been carried out on Reoplex 400, a polypropyleneglycol adipate polyester acting as a strong acceptor of the double bond π-electrons. Regrouping of fatty acids occurs here, and although the well-known distinction between saturated and unsaturated acids is now possible, the regrouping leads to overlaps. Thus the complex pattern of the upper chromatogram of Figure 4 has not been simplified. This can be explained by the fact that vapor pressure will always

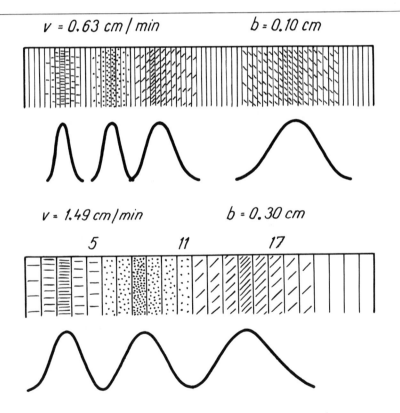

Figure 3 (at left and above).   Examples of band broadening of different shifting velocities of the layer and different side diffusion hindrances. For explanations of symbols see text. [Reproduced from J. Janák.   J. Chromatog. **15**, 15 (1964), by permission of Elsevier Publishing Co., Amsterdam, The Netherlands.]

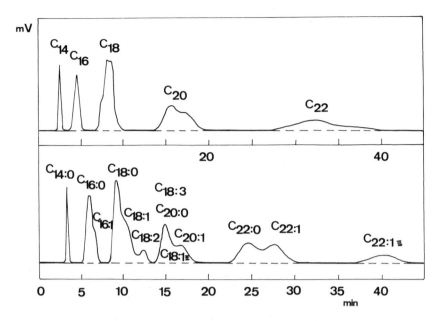

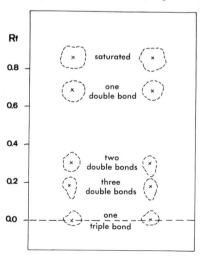

Figure 4. Gas chromatograms of a mixture of C_{14}–C_{22} fatty acid methyl esters. Above: Apiezon L at 220°C; below: Reoplex 400 at 200°C. $\equiv$ means triple bond. [Reproduced from N. Ruseva-Atanasova, J. Janák. J. Chromatog. **21**, 207 (1966), by permission of Elsevier Publishing Co., Amsterdam, The Netherlands.]

play a role in gas chromatography in addition to the selective separation achieved with the latter phase.

Thin-layer chromatography on silica gel impregnated with silver nitrate (second dimension, separation by orientation forces leading to com-

Figure 5. Thin-layer chromatogram of a mixture of C_{14}–C_{22} fatty acid methyl esters. Silica gel coated by $AgNO_3$ (1:2.6, w/w); petrol ether–diethyl ether (7:3, v/v).

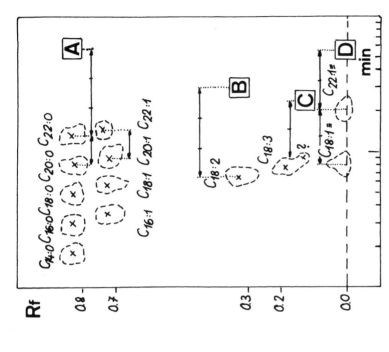

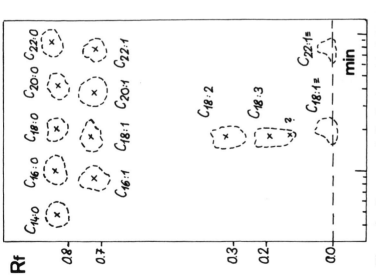

Figure 6. Programmed distribution of individual C_{14}–C_{22} fatty acid methyl esters in the two-dimensional chromatograms. First dimension (GLC): Left, Apiezon L at 220°C; right, Reoplex · 00 at 200°C. Second dimension (TLC): Silica gel coated by AgNO₃ (1:2.6, w/w); petrol ether–diethyl ether (7:3, v/v). For explanations of symbols see text. [Reproduced from N. Ruseva-Atanasova, J. Janák. J. Chromatog. 21, 207 (1966), by permission of Elsevier Publishing Co., Amsterdam, The Netherlands.]

plex formation) separates fatty acid esters according to their degree of unsaturation, and the number of C-atoms in the acid ester molecule has only minor influence on Rf-values (Figure 5). In accordance with this statement, there can be found only five spots with Rf-values representative of saturated fatty acids—acids with one, two, and three double bonds—and one spot of a higher unsaturated fatty acid. There is no indication of separation according to C-number.

In the two-dimensional chromatograms in Figure 6 all the components of the mixture are again well separated, having complied with both of the above principles. A small zone of an impurity is detectable in the mixture examined. The position of the spot in the upper chromatogram in Figure 4 is clearly one of a C_{18} fatty acid, and, as its Rf-value implies, of an acid containing more than three double bonds. The correlation shown in Figure 7 was prepared from the relative positions of saturated and unsaturated C_{18} acids, as obtained in the two-dimensional chromatogram to the right in Figure 6. It confirms that the impurity is a C_{18} fatty acid and unambiguously establishes the presence of four double bonds in the molecule.

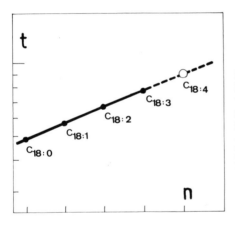

Figure 7. Identification of an unknown fatty acid methyl ester from band positions of known members of the structural similar series. For explanations of symbols see text. [Reproduced from N. Ruseva-Atanasova, J. Janák. J. Chromatog. **21**, 207 (1966), by permission of Elsevier Publishing Co., Amsterdam, The Netherlands.]

The scope and simplicity of the method render it well suited for identification of compounds of most diverse structures. This can be demonstrated as follows: symbols A to D in the right chromatogram in Figure 6 indicate positions at which hypothetical fatty acids of a particular structure can be expected. The positions of areas marked by these symbols are determined by measuring the distance corresponding to the sum of increments for an arbitrary member of a homologous series in an arbitrary structure. Therefore, the saturated C_{28} methyl ester should be situated in area A, whereas area B should contain the C_{24} acid ester with two double bonds; the C_{22} acid ester with four double bonds should be in

C, and D should be representative of a C_{26} methyl ester with one triple bond, and so on. Compounds having structures as stated above, therefore, can be expected to appear at the indicated positions on the thin-layer chromatogram.

INSTRUMENTATION AND METHODS

First Dimension: Gas Chromatography

Any commercial or homemade gas chromatograph that offers the possibility of transferring GC fractions from the column outlet onto the layer without condensation or destruction can be used. A heated glass

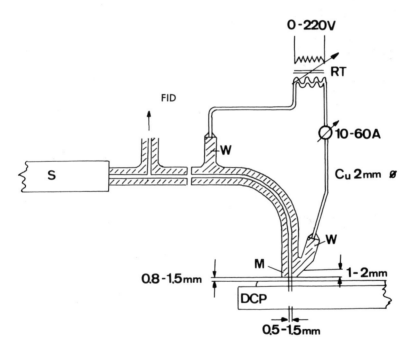

Figure 8. Diagram of a heated joint for application of gas chromatographic effluent to the thin-layer: 10A (to the right on diagram) corresponds to about 150°C. For explanations of symbols see text. [Reproduced from R. Kaiser. Z. Anal. Chem. **205**, 284 (1964), by permission of Zeitschrift für analytische Chemie.]

or metal junction, which should be as short as possible is employed. Glass is heated with an electrical heating coil; metal can be heated by direct low-voltage heating of the outlet joint. In both cases, the temperature can be controlled to advantage by using an autotransformer. It is preferable to divert a small portion of the GC effluent (about 5–10%)

into a suitable detector, thus simultaneously producing a gas chromatogram. Flame ionization detection is most frequently used for this purpose, because its sensitivity is high enough to permit reduction of
the necessary volume of effluent down to about 1%. One of the simplest
versions of such an assembly is diagrammed in Figure 8, and an actual
apparatus is shown in Figure 9.

Figure 9. Apparatus for GC-TLC analysis. (Reproduced from I. Flament, M. Winter, F. Gautschi, B. Willhalm, M. Stoll. 4th Intern. Symp.
Chromatog. Electrophoresis, Brussels, Sept. 1966, by permission.)

The amount of sample to be injected into the gas chromatograph must
be adequate to meet the requirements of the total sample quantity to
be transferred onto the layer. It is necessary to point out that during
TLC the quantity of sample per unit area of the layer will decrease
because of diffusion and separation of the initial mixture into two or
more zones. The calculation of the amount of sample to be injected is
thus controlled by the detection sensitivity on the layer or by any other
procedure adopted to perform this task. Thus, if the lower sensitivity
limit for unit area of a phenanthrene spot is 10 μg phenanthrene, for
example (detection with a tetracyanoethylene spray on a loose thin-layer
of silica gel), and if the initial mixture contains about 5% of this compound, it is necessary to apply at least 0.8–0.9 mg of the original mixture
to trap the phenanthrene fraction from GC along a 1.5-cm section of the
starting line.

For further details on gas chromatographic separation procedures, consult one of the recent technical handbooks (see, for example, Reference 38).

Application of GC Effluent on the Starting Line of the Thin-Layer

The trapping of GC fractions proceeds surprisingly well and loss of material is comparable to or smaller than losses experienced with the trapping techniques commonly used in preparative gas chromatography. As far as chromatographic paper is concerned, higher losses are encountered here than with a thin-layer of adsorbent.

The outlet orifice diameter must be kept within about 1–2 mm for carrier gas flow rates of up to 1 ml/sec. The jet should not be positioned at a distance farther than 2 mm from the layer, or nearer than 1 mm to it and about 10 mm from its bottom edge. No disturbance of a loose thin-layer, either on the part of the carrier gas or the solvent will take place under these conditions, and the loss of volatile material will be higher than 20% only in exceptional cases. The spot area on the starting line is usually comparable to that of a spot applied in the usual way in TLC or PC (less than 3-mm diameter).

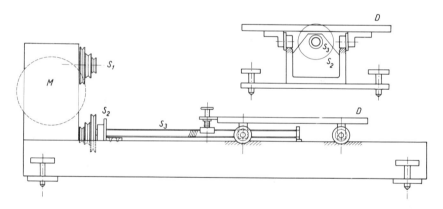

Figure 10. Equipment for shifting thin-layer plates. For explanations of symbols see text. [Reproduced from J. Janák. J. Chromatog. **15**, 15 (1964), by permission of Elsevier Publishing Co., Amsterdam, The Netherlands.]

If chromatographic paper with little or no adsorption capacity for the trapped substances is used, cooling of the starting-line area of the paper is recommended. This can be done by means of a hollow supporting table (*e.g.,* Figure 10) cooled by circulating cooling liquid or, as described elsewhere, by blowing nitrogen over it (about 60 liters per hour fed through a coiled tube placed in liquid air or nitrogen). The stream of cooled nitrogen is directed at the rear side of the moving layer support, opposite the outlet orifice. The latter method often leads to losses by strong cooling of trapped material, resulting in the formation of aerosol particles.

Shifting of the Layer

Thin-layer plates or sheets of chromatographic paper are placed on desk D of a small flat carriage, shown in Figure 10. The carriage is driven by motor M via endless screw S3. The motor revolutions can be geared down by means of gears S1 and S2 to run the carriage at variable speeds. The linear driving velocity should be adjustable over a range of 2–75 mm/min.

Many other feasible and useful designs exist, *e.g.,* direct coupling of the carriage and GC recorder.[16] The recorder chart is moved by transmitting the driving force via a gearbox and transmission shaft to a pinion which drives a rack mounted on the layer-supporting carriage. This arrangement permits one to synchronize the speed of the layer with that of the recorder chart. Synchronization should be better than 1%.

Programmed driving of the carriage (layer), if required, can be achieved in one of the two following manners:

(1) Continuous shifting at a logarithmic driving program results in linear spacing of the members of a homologous series along the starting line on the layer, *i.e.,* by Kováts retention indices.[22, 26]

(2) Discontinuous stepwise changes in the position of the layer according to a set program or to received pulses[24] make possible the application of any GC fraction at some other point on the plate.

The electrical schematic for a logarithmic driving program is shown in Figure 11. This device consists of a Wheatstone bridge, logarithmic potentiometer P1, electron tube impendence transformer, amplifier Z, and motor M (see Figure 10), moving the carriage which is coupled with the potentiometer slide. The synchronous motor drives the slides of the logarithmic potentiometer P1, thus producing on the cathodes of the EF-80 tube a voltage derived from the bridge voltage. The voltage difference is conveyed to amplifier Z, feeding the two-phase induction motor (type RD 09). The sliding contact of the Wheatstone bridge moves so that the voltage difference at the input slide of the amplifier approaches zero. If the carriage is in a position corresponding to the shift of the sliding contact of P1, the amplifier receives zero input voltage and the carriage stops. The modulus of the logarithmic movement can be varied with potentiometers P2, P3 and P4. The carriage can be set to its starting position with the potentiometer; movement of the carriage satisfactorily follows a logarithmic course.

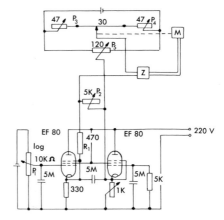

Figure 11. Electrical scheme of device for logarithmic shifting. [Reproduced from J. Janák, I. Klimeš, K. Hána. J. Chromatog. **18**, 270 (1965), by permission of Elsevier Publishing Co., Amsterdam, The Netherlands.]

For the stepwise mode of operation, the recorder can be provided with a microswitch. The respective circuit is to be arranged so that an electrical pulse will be sent to motor M at any movement of the recorder pen (Figure 12). In this way, the layer can be quickly transported over a distance of about 10–15 mm. The recorder switch contact RS actuates the coil of a relay and switch *a* closes in position I, thus energizing the second coil, B; this in turn closes switches b1 and b3 and opens b2. At a movement determined by a 0.1M resistor, the switch-on time elapses, switches b1 and b3 open, and b2 closes so that the mechanism is pre-

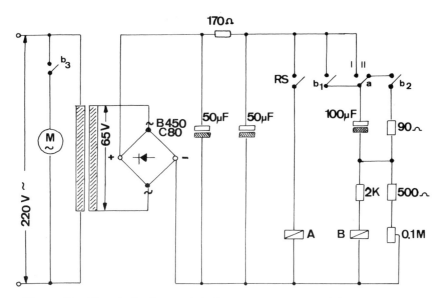

Figure 12. Electrical scheme of device for step-by-step shifting. For explanations of symbols see text. [Reproduced from R. Kaiser. Z. Anal. Chem. **205**, 284 (1964), by permission of Zeitschrift für Analytische Chemie.]

pared for a new recorder pulse. Small fractions whose peaks do not bring the pen high enough to close the circuit are collected as a single spot between two subsequent pulse-producing peaks.

Closely similar results can be obtained if gas chromatography is performed at a linear temperature program and the layer is shifted at a linear driving velocity. In this case the spacings between the homologs are not exactly additive, particularly near the origin or end of the chromatogram, as follows from the theory of programmed temperature GC (see Reference 39). Figure 13 gives an actual "gas chromatogram"

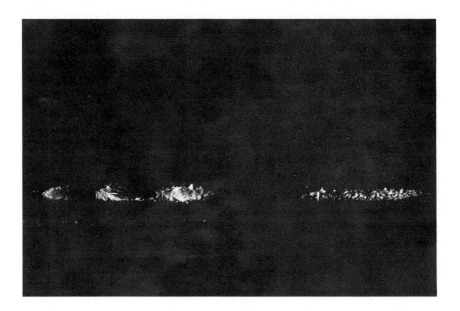

Figure 13. Visible sublimated zones of gas chromatographic fraction of, from left to right: biphenyl, acenaphthene, fluorene and carbazole (GC isotherm, linear shifting of a glass plate, lateral illumination, plate angle about 30°). [Reproduced from J. Janák. J. Chromatog. **16,** 494 (1964), by permission of Elsevier Publishing Co., Amsterdam, The Netherlands.]

of readily subliming aromatic hydrocarbons transferred onto a glass plate.

Second Dimension: Thin-Layer Chromatography

Any commercial or homemade TLC accessory can be used. A description of the techniques and methods of TLC is beyond the scope of this survey. Detailed information on this subject can be obtained by consulting any of the more recent textbooks (see, for example, References 40 and 41).

New Adsorbents

The only problem to be accentuated is that of selecting the stationary phase. This problem is a crucial one in gas chromatography and the underlying theory and methods have been thoroughly investigated. The number of stationary phases available is extensive and many of them have been designed for specialized separations. Some of them, though, are also applicable in thin-layer chromatography.

For example, molecular sieves[2] (series A and X) are synthetic hydrosilicates of a lattice structure which become a highly porous material with pore diameters of molecular dimensions when they are dehydrated at 400°C. They act as abstractors of small, linear, and/or polar molecules such as water, alcohols, *n*-paraffins, etc.

The only applicable solvents are hydrocarbons with a molecular diameter larger than the pore diameter of the molecular sieve (isooctane, Decalin, etc.). As the diffusion rate and mass transfer from the solvent to the pores assume considerable values, it is necessary to work at the smallest possible "percolation" rates to obtain reasonable results.

Substituted montmorillonites[42] (Bentone) are hydrated magnesium silicates with a typical elastic layer bound to the basic lattice. The hydroxyls at their surface have been displaced by alkyl ammonium salts having sufficiently long alkyl chains (C_{10}–C_{16}). The interphase between two inorganic layers is formed by two layers of alkyl groups spaced very regularly and oriented toward each other within the lattice. This causes solvation effects such as swelling, which may influence the thin-layer chromatography. Separations can be expected mainly according to differences in the entropy term of the free energy change. The material is a very fine powder and mixing it with some inert porous solid such as Celite or Chromosorb W is recommended.

Porous polyhydrocarbons (Porapak) are copolymers of styrene and ethylvinylbenzene cross-linked with divinylbenzene. The white, hard beads can be produced with controlled particle size. They have a very high internal porosity and specific area ($500 \ m^2/g$). The material is an interesting, nonpolar, solid stationary phase, insoluble in nonpolar solvents (CCl_4) but well penetrated also by polar solvents like water–methanol mixtures. Separations of polar from nonpolar substances can be expected with this material.[43, 44]

Borosilicates surface-modified with different groups (Durapak) are produced from porous glass beads (Porasil) through a chemical process; they are available with controlled pore diameters. The surface has the character of "brush-like," oriented, highly polar cyanoethoxy groups. High surface homogeneity of the organic substituents and stability of the inorganic lattice (the main difference between them and substituted

montmorillonites) cause the resolution of substances and their chromatographic behavior (Rf) to be independent, over wide limits, of solvent
stream velocity. Such materials, of course, should be expected to show
some chemical lability (hydrolysis).[45]

New, interesting TLC separations have been suggested and/or
achieved with these types of material. One example from our own
practice is reported below (Table I).

Further Treatment of the Thin-Layer

Common methods of spot visualization can be used. They have been
exhaustively surveyed in the principal textbooks or reviews.[40, 46] If the
separated components are to be investigated by some other chromatographic or spectroscopic or still other method, elution of the chromatographic zone from the respective part of adsorbent (as determined by
t_R for the gas chromatogram or Rf for the thin-layer chromatogram)
is the preferred procedure. Loose layers can be collected by suction of
the thin-layer material into a glass capillary (Figure 14).

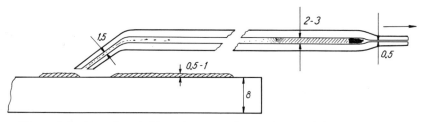

Figure 14. Transfer capillary for extracting TLC material for further examination (dimensions in mm). [Reproduced from J. Janák. J. Chromatog. **15**, 15
(1964), by permission of Elsevier Publishing Co., Amsterdam, The Netherlands.]

The suction is to be performed starting at the center of the expected
zone on the layer and proceeding spirally outward to its hypothetic cir-
cumference. The small adsorbent column contained in the capillary is
then extracted with a suitable solvent. All of the substance is usually
contained in the first two drops emerging from the capillary column,
and these can serve as a stock solution for further examination. With
bound layers, it is preferable to cut out the critical part of the layer and
to elute it again with the smallest possible volume of solvent.

Most of the known color reactions used in thin-layer chromatography
are not applicable or become comparatively difficult to effect with the
new adsorbents described in the previous paragraph; the adsorbents are
not stable and/or they give a highly colored background. With such
cases, the following technique has been found convenient in our practice.

A sheet of chromatographic paper or a bound thin-layer of silica gel treated with the required reagents is placed on a metal or glass plate which can be cooled by a circulating coolant or simply by dry CO_2 applied from the rear. The pretreated layer is then juxtaposed to the sample-containing thin-layer which is placed on a heating block or is otherwise heated from the rear side. The separated compounds will sublime or be distilled from the adsorbent and condense on the reagent-containing layer, thus revealing its position on the thin-layer. Heat can also be applied only locally. This method can be used halfway so that only a smaller portion of the material from the thin-layer will be transferred and the main portion will remain on the plate for further examination.

It has been shown elsewhere that crystallographic examination is possible in some cases, followed by colorimetry in submicrocells of silica gel.[47] This method can be demonstrated, particularly in such cases where sublimation of the substance will occur. Figure 15, left, shows a carbazol crystal of *ca.* 10^{-8} g obtained by sublimation from the GC "peak." Its crystalline habitus is a typical one. It was dissolved in a small drop of benzene and this solution was transferred by capillary forces into a single grain of silica gel shown in Figure 15. After evaporating the benzene, the whole quantity of carbazol was now contained in a cell of about 10^{-3} mm³ in volume. It is evident that if a small drop of any reagent giving a color test of common sensitivity is imbibed in the silica gel grain, a deep staining will result. This occurs even when the experiment is carried out with nano- to picogram amounts of sample. The black grain (the coloration is in fact deep blue) in Figure 5, right, represents a colored product of this single crystal of carbazole and tetracyanoethylene. This technique has now been developed into a quantitative tool[48] and seems to be of prospective value for inorganic as well as for organic substances.

APPLICATIONS

The method can be applied to advantage in all cases where chemically distinct materials are to be separated from very complex mixtures. It follows from the character of gas chromatography that it can be used only for fairly volatile compounds. On the other hand, the character of thin-layer chromatography requires that the separated compounds be only somewhat volatile; otherwise, loss of material cannot be avoided. Further, the fact that TLC is first of all a qualitative method makes combined GC-TLC a qualitative tool (for identification), whereas accurate quantitative results usually require the use of GC subsequent to

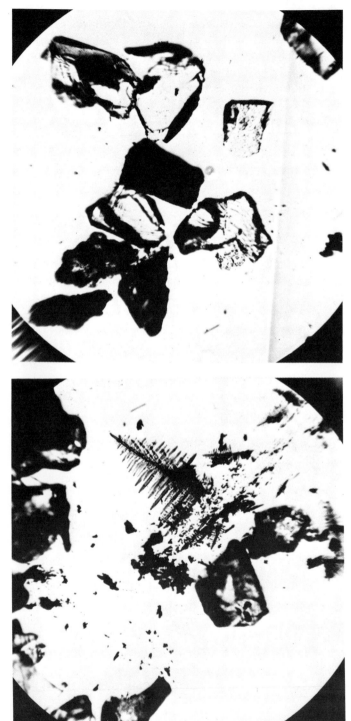

Figure 15. Left: Microscopic picture of a carbazole crystal (approx. weight 10^{-8} g) transferred among silica gel grains (approx. diameter 0.15 mm). Right: Presentation of color intensity of the blue carbazole–tetracyanoethylene π-complex in black and white (approx. 20 · 10^{-9} g of carbazole. [Reproduced from J. Janák. J. Chromatog. 16, 494 (1964), by permission of Elsevier Publishing Co., Amsterdam, The Netherlands.]

TLC. The accuracy of quantitative work with combination GC-TLC is inferior to the reversed TLC-GC procedure.

Coal Tar Chemistry

The original version of two-dimensional GC-TLC was applied mainly in this analytical field.[19, 21] The tar, constituting an unusually rich mixture of compounds widely varying in their chemical natures cannot be separated to its individual constituents by using a single separation method. Potential scope of the method in this field can be judged from inspection of Table I, which lists gas chromatographic relative retention

Table I

Gas and Thin-Layer Chromatographic Behavior of Some Tar Compounds

			TLC	
		GLC	*Silica gel benzene/hexane (1:1)*	*Porapak Q ethanol*
Substance	*B.P. °C*	*r_{1,2}*	*Rf*	*Rf*
Fluorene	298	0.59	0.93	0.27
Phenanthrene	337	1.0	0.92	0.26
Anthracene	341	1.0	0.92	0.16
Acridine	344	1.1	0.01	0.80
Carbazole	353	1.2	0.55	0.62
2-Hydroxyfluorene	352	1.0	0.20	0.66
1-Methylphenanthrene	399	1.4	0.92	0.23
Fluoranthrene	384	2.0	0.92	0.05
Pyrene	394	2.6	0.90	0.16

data $r_{1,2}$ and thin-layer chromatographic Rf-values of typical tar constituents, as compiled from related literature.[21, 44] Figure 16 illustrates the distribution of 14 model compounds in a two-dimensional GC-TLC chromatogram. Similar promising results also were obtained by Kaiser[24, 25] for the separation of monobasic phenols. By using two-dimensional chromatography (GC-TLC) together with additional color reactions, he was able to isolate more than 40 phenols from the xylenol fraction.

Steroids

Gas chromatography of steroids requires temperatures as high as 200–240°C, at which the choice of stationary phase becomes rather restricted. The combination of GC and TLC enables use of gas chromatographic columns of mediocre separation efficiency for compounds containing various functional groups. Curtius and Müller[30] documented the applicability of this method by separating 12 steroids (Figure 17).

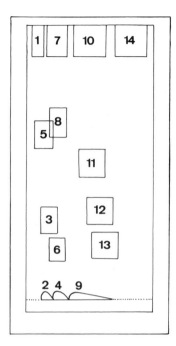

Figure 16. Position of zones in a two-dimensional chromatogram of coal tar substances. First dimension: GLC, silicone elastomer E-301 at 220°C; second dimension: TLC, silica gel and benzene. (1) naphthalene (B.P. 238°C); (2) quinoline (237°); (3) 4-hydroxyhydrindene (247°); (4) 3-methyl–isoquinoline (251°); (5) indole (255°); (6) 5-hydroxyhydrindene (255°); (7) biphenyl (255°); (8) 3-methylindole (266°); (9) 2,4-dimethylquinoline (273°); (10) acenaphthene (277°); (11) 2-hydroxybiphenyl (286°); (12) 1-naphthol (288°); (13) 2-naphthol (296°); (14) fluorene (298°). [Reproduced from J. Janák. J. Gas Chromatog. 1, 20 (1964), by permission of Journal of Gas Chromatography.]

Lipids

Although gas chromatography of fatty acids has been thoroughly investigated and gives excellent results, the combination of GC and TLC offers certain advantages in the identification of unusual types of fatty acids and of biological material in general. The results obtained by Ruseva-Atanasova and Janák[27] (see Figures 6 and 7) show that the method is favorable for the investigation of miscellaneous lipids, as well as for the detection of differences in the composition of specimens stemming from various biological materials or exposed to various conditions in the organism.

Other Applications

The described type of two-dimensional chromatography has been developed by Parker, Wright, and Hine[49] into a workable tool in forensic toxicology. Very complex mixtures of unknown substances with quite different structures often occurring in this type of analysis can be effectively simplified by GC-TLC, as Curry[50] stated most recently.

Flament *et al.*[26] used GC-TLC for the identification of constituents of coffee flavor. They used programmed driving layers in the Kováts index scale for interpreting their chromatograms. The striking resolution of components that can be achieved is shown in Figure 18.

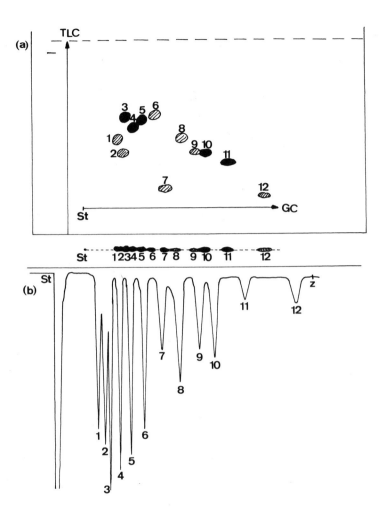

Figure 17. GC-TLC of trisilyl ethers of steroids. (a) GC-TLC. First dimension: GLC, XE-60 at 210°C; second dimension: TLC, Silica Gel G, chloroform–ethanol (9:1, v/v). (b) gas chromatogram. St = start; z = end. (1) allopregnanediol; (2) pregnanediol; (3) androsterone; (4) etiocholanolone; (5) dehydroepiandrosterone; (6) pregnanolene; (7) pregnanetriol; (8) 11-ketoandrosterone; (9) 11-ketoetiocholanolone; (10) 11-hydroxyandrosterone; (11) 11-hydroxyetiocholanolone; (12) pregnanetriolone. [Reproduced from H. C. Curtius and M. Müller. J. Chromatog. **32**, 222 (1968), by permission of Elsevier Publishing Co., Amsterdam, The Netherlands.]

They were able to identify 60 colored spots in their chromatograms. Some of the GC peaks were separated to five or more components by TLC (*e.g.,* I = 900; 1555, etc.).

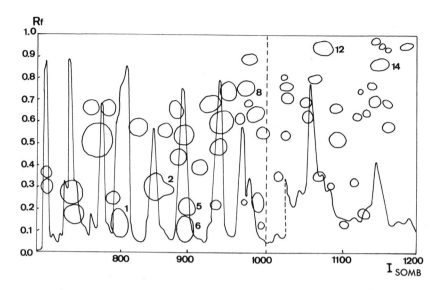

Figure 18. GC-TLC of coffee extract with respect to components having Kováts retention indices 700–1200. First dimension: GLC, silicone oil (May & Baker for GC, SOMB) linear programmed temperature from 40°C; second dimension: TLC, Silica Gel G, benzene–diethyl ether (5:1, v/v). (Reproduced from I. Flement, M. Winter, F. Gautschi, B. Wilhalm, and M. Stoll. 4th Intern. Symp. Chromatog. Electrophorese, Brussels, Sept. 12, 1966, by permission.)

It is remarkable that this technique can also be used for the separation of rather volatile compounds. Nigam *et al.*[20] used GC-TLC for distinguishing essential oils of different proveniences. Resolution by TLC of a single GC peak characteristic of the quality and origin of Japan mint oil is shown in Figures 19 and 20. In this way Nano *et al.*[51] distinguished several isomers of thujyl alcohol.

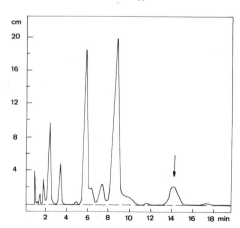

Figure 19. Gas chromatogram of a Japan mint oil (Reoplex 400 at 150°C). [Reproduced from I. C. Nigam, M. Sahasrabudhe, and L. Levi. Can. J. Chem. **41,** 1535 (1963), by permission of Canadian Journal of Chemistry.]

Kaiser[24] achieved a complete separation of amines also, by the GC-TLC combination in such mixtures where use of either method alone gave only an incomplete resolution.

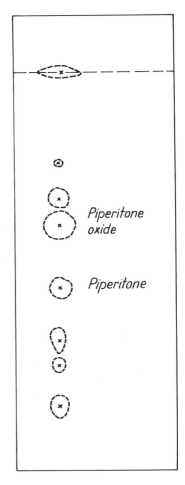

Figure 20. Thin-layer chromatographic identification of piperitone and its oxide in a single GC peak (see Figure 19). Silica Gel G, hexane–diethyl ether (10:1, v/v). [Reproduced from I. C. Nigam, M. Sahasrabudhe, and L. Levi. Can. J. Chem. **41**, 1535 (1963), by permission of Canadian Journal of Chemistry.]

The GC-TLC technique has been used recently for the separation of highly volatile compounds such as aldehydes and ketones[28] and alcohols.[29] The effluent from the gas chromatograph was trapped along the starting line of a thin-layer pretreated with reagents (2,4-dinitrophenylhydrazine, *p*-nitrophenylhydrazine, and 2,4-dinitrophenylsemicarbazide for carbonyl compounds, and 3,5-dinitrobenzoyl chloride or *o*-nitrophenyl isocyanate for hydroxyl compounds). The components from GC reacted at the starting line to form derivatives amenable to TLC separation. At the same time, their volatility was considerably reduced.

Prospective Applications

There is no doubt that the technique described here can be of value in solving a number of other problems that deal with the analysis of technical products, pharmaceuticals, pesticides, and natural products, in air pollution studies, toxicology, occupational medicine, etc.

REFERENCES

1. Mangold, H. K., and R. Kammereck. Chem. Ind. (London) **1961**, 27, 1032.
2. Janák, J. Nature **195**, 696 (1962).
3. Capella, P., and E. Fedele. Riv. Ital. Sostanze Grasse **40**, 660 (1963).
4. Collins, W. P., and I. F. Sommerville. Nature **203**, 836 (1964).
5. Morris, L. J. Lab. Pract. **13**, 284 (1964).
6. Holloway, P. W., and S. J. Wakil. J. Biol. Chem. **239**, 2489 (1964).
7. Horning, E. C., and W. J. A. Vandenheuvel, in *New Biochemical Separations.* Ed. by A. T. James and L. J. Morris (Princeton, N. J.: Van Nostrand, 1964), p 25.
8. Wotiz, H. H., and S. C. Chattoray. Anal. Chem. **36**, 1466 (1964).
9. Shapiro, I. L., and D. Kritchevsky. J. Chromatog. **18**, 599 (1965).
10. Luisi, M., G. Gambrassi, V. Marescotti, C. Savi, and F. Polvani. J. Chromatog. **18**, 278 (1965).
11. Iwasa, J., S. Naruto, and Y. Utsui. J. Pharm. Soc. Japan **86**, 369 (1966).
12. Avancini, D., G. Pedroni, and F. deFrancesco. Riv. Ital. Sostanze Grasse **48**, 450 (1966).
13. Davidson, A. W. J. Assoc. Offic. Anal. Chem. **49**, 468 (1966).
14. Ray, B. R., and M. Wilcox. J. Chromatog. **30**, 428 (1967).
15. Markovetz, A. J., and M. J. Klug. J. Chromatog. **36**, 341 (1968).
16. Casu, B., and L. Cavalloti. Anal. Chem. **34**, 1514 (1962).
17. Nigam, I. C., M. Sahasrabudhe, T. W. M. Davis, J. C. Bartlet, and L. Levi. Perfumery Essent. Oil Record **53**, 614 (1962).
18. Janák, J., in *Gas-Chromatographie May 1963.* Ed. by H. G. Struppe and H. P. Angelé (Berlin: Akademie-Verlag, 1964), No. 6, p 81.
19. Janák, J. J. Gas Chromatog. **1**, 20 (1963).
20. Nigam, I. C., M. Sahasrabudhe, and L. Levi: Can. J. Chem. **41**, 1535 (1963).
21. Janák, J. J. Chromatog. **15**, 15 (1964).
22. Janák, J., I. Klimeš, and K. Hána. J. Chromatog. **18**, 470 (1965).
23. Nigam, I. C., and L. Levi. J. Pharm. Sci. **53**, 1008 (1964).
24. Kaiser, R. Z. Anal. Chem. **205**, 284 (1964).
25. Kaiser, R. *Chromatographie in der Gasphase: Band IV, Quantitative Auswertung* (Mannheim: Bibliograph. Institut, 1965), p 222.
26. Flament, I., M. Winter, F. Gautschi, B. Willhalm, and M. Stoll. IVth International Symposium of Chromatography and Electrophoresis, Brussels, Sept. 1966.

27. Ruseva-Atanasova, N., and J. Janák. J. Chromatog. **21**, 207 (1966).
28. Tumlinson, J. H., J. P. Minyard, P. A. Hedin, and A. C. Thompson. J. Chromatog. **29**, 80 (1967).
29. Minyard, J. P., J. H. Tumlinson, A. C. Thompson, and P. A. Hedin. J. Chromatog. **29**, 88 (1967).
30. Curtius, H. C., and M. Müller. J. Chromatog. **32**, 222 (1968).
31. Strickler, M., and E. Kováts. J. Chromatog. **8**, 289 (1962).
32. Brenner, M., A. Niederwieser, G. Pataki, and R. Weber, in *Dünnschicht-Chromatographie*. Ed. by E. Stahl (Berlin: Springer-Verlag, 1962), p 100.
33. Giddings, J. C., G. H. Steward, and A. L. Ruoff. J. Chromatog. **3**, 239 (1960).
34. Ruoff, A. L., and J. C. Giddings. J. Chromatog. **3**, 438 (1960).
35. James, A. T., and A. J. P. Martin. J. Appl. Chem. **6**, 105 (1956).
36. Kováts, E. Z. Anal. Chem. **181**, 351 (1961).
37. Desty, D. H., and E. H. P. Whyman. Anal. Chem. **29**, 320 (1957).
38. Ettre, L. S., and A. Zlatkis. *The Practice of Gas Chromatography* (New York: Interscience, 1967).
39. Harris, W. E., and H. W. Habgood. *Programmed Temperature Gas Chromatography* (New York: John Wiley, 1966).
40. Stahl, E. *Dünnschicht-Chromatographie,* 2nd ed. (Berlin: Springer-Verlag, 1965).
41. Bobbitt, J. M. *Thin-Layer Chromatography* (New York: Reinhold Publ., 1963).
42. Ritter, F. J., G. M. Meyer, and F. Geiss. J. Chromatog. **19**, 304 (1965).
43. Janák, J. Chem. Ind. (London) **1967**, 1137.
44. Janák, J., and V. Kubecová. J. Chromatog. **33**, 132 (1968).
45. Janák, J. J. Chromatog. (1970).
46. Macek, K., I. M. Hais, J. Kopecký, and J. Gasparič. *Bibliography of Paper and Thin-Layer Chromatography 1961–1965 and Survey of Applications* (Amsterdam: Elsevier, 1968).
47. Janák, J. J. Chromatog. **16**, 494 (1964).
48. Klimeš, I., and J. Janák. Microchem. J. **13**, 534 (1968).
49. Parker, K. D., J. A. Wright, and C. H. Hine. J. Forensic Sci. Soc. **7**, 162 (1967).
50. Curry, A. S. In *Gas Chromatography in Biology and Medicine.* Ed. by R. Porter (London: Churchill, 1969), p 132.
51. Nano, G. M., P. Sancin, and A. Martelli. J. Gas Chromatog. **3**, 85 (1965).

Chapter 3

Azeotropic Mixtures as Chromatographic Solvents in TLC

by E. Röder

In TLC, reproducibility depends on numerous parameters;[1] included among them the grade of activity of TLC plates plays a considerable part.[2–5] Further, the grade of saturation is important.[6–9] Saturation can be improved and the appearance of edge effects avoided by lining the chromatographic chamber with filter paper. It is also possible to successfully work out standard conditions for other parameters, not mentioned here, by which the constancy of the Rf-values is improved. The problem with respect to the solvent in this connection is still considered to be not satisfactorily solved.

Using a pure one-component solvent for chromatography, the composition of liquid phase and gas phase remains constant—apart from the presence of air. Unfortunately, however, the application of one-component solvents is very restricted. It is only in mixtures of solvents that the polarity and therefore the elution effect can be varied and adapted to requirements of the substance to be analyzed by chromatography. Most solvent mixtures are composed of liquids with different boiling points. The composition of these solvent mixtures changes during repeated use, due to the difference in the evaporation rates of the components. The fact that the elution effect of the solvent will also be changed hereby is disadvantageous for the constancy of the Rf-values.

In spite of these defects, these solvents are widely employed. To avoid too strong a change of the mixture due to evaporation, it is usually necessary to discard the chamber-filling after three chromatography processings; otherwise the Rf-values obtained are inexact. Besides this, the procedure becomes uneconomical. In order to avoid these difficulties, the use of homogenous azeotropic solvent mixtures is suggested.

THE USE OF AZEOTROPIC MIXTURES

The main advantage of an azeotropic mixture is that it behaves like a pure solvent with respect to temperature and pressure ranges.[10, 11, 12] Since it is known that numerous combinations of the usual solvents are azeotropic mixtures, a variation for the polarity is possible. This is shown in Figure 1 by two typical systems: methanol–acetone and ethanol–water.[13] Using such a mixture as solvent for TLC, good reproducible Rf-values can be expected when chromatography is performed under the standard conditions mentioned above.

Based on the numerous solvents described in literature, about 100 azeotropic mixtures which promised a good separating effect were chosen and examined. The mixtures were prepared by the blending of their components in the proportions mentioned in literature and by subsequent distilling in order to remove any possible impurities. Only that fraction which showed the boiling point of the azeotropic mixture was used for tests. Estrogens, gestagens, alkaloids, sulfonamides, psychopharmaceutics, narcotics, and local anesthetics were separated by the 21 azeotropic mixtures that proved to be suitable.

In Table I these mixtures are shown with their respective compositions, boiling points, and dielectric constants, the latter serving as a measure of their polarity. In general, neutral silica gel plates were used. For the separation of basic substances the adsorbent was alkalized with sodium carbonate, because suitable basic azeotropic mixtures are not known. The thin-layer plates were prepared with silica gel of different origins by the addition of a fluorescent indicator which is sensitive to UV light at a wavelength of 254 nm. To produce alkalized plates the silica gel was not mixed with water but with 0.1N sodium carbonate solution, which was applied with an applicator to the 200 × 200-mm plates. The layer thickness was 0.25 or 0.3 mm. After activation at 105°C the plates were stored at 23± 2°C at a relative air humidity of 40–60%, and were used for chromatography under the same conditions.

It has to be pointed out that only one chamber-filling was used. When the level of the fluid reached about the 75-ml mark, the chamber was refilled with the same solvent up to the 100-ml mark and was further used for chromatography. To simplify the procedure, a special

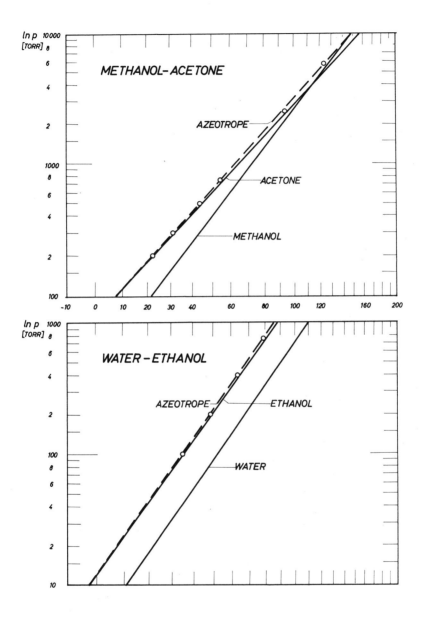

Figure 1. Cox vapor pressure charts of two typical positive azeotropes. Where the curve of azeotrope crosses the curve of a component the azeotrope disappears (see top system). Such a restriction is not detectable in the water–ethanol system at higher vapor pressures.

Table I

Boiling Points and Dielectric Constants
of Some Azeotropic Mixtures

No.	Solvent	% w/w	760 Torr Bp °C	25° DC ±0.05
I	Ethyl acetate	46.0		
	Cyclohexane	54.0	71.6	3.95
II	Isopropanol	16.3		
	Diisopropyl ether	83.7	66.2	5.75
III	Methyl acetate	83.0		
	Cyclohexane	17.0	54.9	5.80
IV	Ethanol	8.0		
	Chloroform	92.0	59.4	6.05
V	Ethanol	16.0		
	Carbon tetrachloride	84.0	65.0	6.30
VI	Ethanol	30.4		
	Benzene	10.8		
	Cyclohexane	58.8	65.05	6.56
VII	Ethanol	31.7		
	Benzene	68.3	68.0	7.50
VIII	Methanol	17.8		
	Methyl acetate	48.6		
	Cyclohexane	33.6	50.8	8.35
IX	Ethanol	48.0		
	Heptane	52.0	72.0	9.50
X	Methanol	12.6		
	Chloroform	87.4	53.4	9.80
XI	Methanol	7.3		
	Dichloromethane	92.7	37.8	10.50
XII	Methanol	17.7		
	Methyl acetate	82.3	53.9	10.75
XIII	2-Butanone	73.0		
	Heptane	27.0	77.0	12.30
XIV	Methanol	16.0		
	Acetone	43.5		
	Cyclohexane	40.5	51.1	13.25
XV	Methanol	39.1		
	Benzene	60.9	57.5	13.40
XVI	Methanol	21.6		
	Methyl acetate	27.0		
	Chloroform	51.4	56.4	13.65
XVII	Acetone	67.5		
	Cyclohexane	32.5	53.0	13.75
XVIII	Ethanol	10.4		
	Acetone	24.3		
	Chloroform	65.3	63.2	13.90
XIX	Ethanol	68.0		
	Toluene	32.0	76.5	17.25

Table I (continued)

No.	Solvent	% w/w	760 Torr Bp °C	25° DC ±0.05
XX	2-Butanone	83.0		
	Chloroform	17.0	79.9	17.30
XXI	Acetone	87.4		
	Carbon tetrachloride	12.6	56.0	19.30
XXII	Methanol	23.0		
	Acetone	30.0		
	Chloroform	47.0	57.5	19.80
XXIII	Methanol	12.0		
	Acetone	88.0	55.5	22.05
XXIV	Water	4.0		
	Ethanol	96.0	78.2	25.40

chamber has been developed[23]* which secures a constant level of the solvent in conjunction with a storage reservoir so that frequent refilling is unnecessary. Besides the UV light of 254 nm, the usual color reagents serve for detection.

The Rf-values given in Tables II–IX indicate the average values of at least five separate analyses of each substance, and the mean error of a single determination has also been calculated. The average error[22] is about 5 hRf-values (hRf = Rf × 100).

Table II

Separation of Estrogens and Gestagens[14, 15]

No.	Estrogen 1,2 Gestagen 3–10	hRf-Values Solvent no. I	IX
1	Ethynylestradiol	51	40
2	Mestranol	61	55
3	Progesterone	35	53
4	Chlormadinone acetate	30	45
5	Megestrol acetate	33	48
6	Norethisterone acetate	40	48
7	Ethynodiol acetate	64	60
8	Lynestrenol	67	59
9	Norgestrel	43	49
10	Medroxyprogesterone acetate	33	51

Silica Gel G (Merck), neutral, layer thickness: 0.3 mm; length of run: 15 cm. Detection: (a) phosphoric acid 85%–methanol (1:1); (b) antimony trichloride–acetic acid (1:1).

*Manufacturers of the chromatographic chamber and cover plate with tube: Desaga GmbH, Heidelberg, Germany. The storage reservoir with contact valve was produced in the workshop of the Department of Pharmacy, University of Mainz, Mainz, Germany.

Table III

Separation of Alkaloids[16]*

No.	Alkaloid	hRf-Values		
		Solvent no. XV	XVI	XXII
1	Brucine	8	3	7
2	Quinine	38	24	39
3	Quinidine	39	26	32
4	Codeine	16	8	14
5	Narcotine	84	79	77
6	Papaverine	77	74	66
7	Pilocarpine	36	26	31
8	Scopolamine	43	34	38
9	Strychnine	15	4	9
10	Veratrine	32	10	15

*Reproduced from Reference 16 by permission of Arch. Pharm.
Silica Gel GF$_{254}$ (Merck), neutral, layer thickness: 0.3 mm; length of run: 15 cm.
Detection: (a) ultraviolet light (254 nm); (b) Dragendorff reagent.

Table IV

Separation of Sulfonamides[16]*

No.	Sulfonamide	hRf-Values in solvent no.		
		III	XVI	XXII
1	Sulfanilamide	45	8	62
2	Sulfanilylthiocarbamide	47	10	55
3	Sulfanilylacetamide	33	11	54
4	Sulfanilylcarbamide	14	10	10
5	Sulfathiazole	20	8	53
6	Sulfamerazine	36	24	56
7	Sulfisomidine	13	8	46
8	Sulfadimethoxine	51	38	67
9	Sulfamethyldiazine	33	30	59
10	Sulfamethoxydiazine	38	31	61
11	Sulfamethoxypyridazine	36	30	61
12	Sulfaphenazole	48	33	63
13	Sulfadimethyloxazole	42	12	56
14	Sulfisoxazole	45	22	56
15	Sulfaguanidine	8	3	42
16	Phthalylsulfathiazole	18	11	13

*Reproduced from Reference 16 by permission of Arch. Pharm.
Silica Gel GF$_{254}$ (Merck), neutral, layer thickness: 0.3 mm; length of run: 15 cm.
Detection: (a) ultraviolet light (254 nm); (b) Ehrlich reagent.

Table V

Separation of Diazepins[17]*

No.	Diazepin	hRf-Values in solvent no.				
		XXIII	XXIV	II	VIII	XII
1	Chlorodiazepoxide	48	48	29	57	46
2	Diazepam	59	55	59	69	59
3	Oxazepam	46	37	29	48	48
4	Nitrazepam	61	55	54	59	58

*Reproduced from Reference 17 by permission of Z. Anal. Chem.
Silica Gel GF$_{254}$ (Merck), basic, layer thickness: 0.3 mm; length of run: 15 cm.
Detection: (a) ultraviolet light (254 nm) (b) Dragendorff reagent.

Table VI

Separation of Ergot Alkaloids[17]*

No.	Ergot alkaloid	hRf-Values in solvent no.			
		XI	IV	XX	XVII
1	Agroclavine	60	48	26	41
2	Dihydroergocornine	54	46	31	46
3	Dihydroergocristine	60	49	31	46
4	Dihydroergotamine	52	39	11	30
5	Elymoclavine	34	16	3	8
6	Ergine	49	45	23	41
7	Ergocornine	66	61	43	53
8	Ergocristine	69	61	43	53
9	Ergocristinine	80	72	62	66
10	Ergocryptine	66	61	44	55
11	Ergometrine	30	16	2	10
12	Ergometrinine	41	37	22	35
13	Ergosine	54	44	18	31
14	Ergotamine	56	44	16	31
15	Ergotaminine	77	67	51	58
16	Peniclavine	33	53	4	10

*Reproduced from Reference 17 by permission of Z. Anal. Chem.
Silica Gel GF$_{254}$ (Merck), basic, layer thickness: 0.3 mm; length of run: 13 cm.
Detection: (a) ultraviolet light (254 nm), (b) van Urk reagent.

Table VII

Separation of Some Local Anesthetics[19]*

No.	Local anesthetic	hRf-Values in solvent no.				
		XVII	II	XIV	VI	XIII
1	Benzocaine	56	80	41	43	58
2	Cornecaine	14	7	20	9	7
3	Procaine	40	27	27	19	22
4	Hydroxyprocaine	56	40	33	35	29
5	Oxybuprocaine	59	35	36	48	26
6	Tetracaine	28	20	30	19	15
7	Cinchocaine	51	22	43	44	20
8	Mepivacaine	41	28	45	47	22
9	Leucinocaine	58	28	45	47	22
10	Stadacain	64	41	45	47	22

*Reproduced from Reference 19 by permission of Pharm. Acta Helv.
Silica Gel G/UV$_{254}$ (Macherey, Nagel & Co.), basic, layer thickness: 0.3 mm; length of run: 15 cm
Detection: (a) ultraviolet light (254 nm); (b) Dragendorff reagent.

Table VIIIa

Separation of Psychopharmaceutics[18, 20]

No.	Phenothiazine	hRf-Values in solvent no.				
		XXIII	XIV	II	VIII	XII
1	Alimemazine	40	30	35	65	34
2	Butaperazine	15	14	0	36	13
3	Chlorpromazine	28	21	17	50	23
4	Dixyrazine	29	32	0	47	26
5	Fluphenazine	24	29	0	41	23
6	Levomepromazine	47	33	28	65	40
7	Periciacinum	45	36	9	39	40
8	Perphenazine	20	23	0	39	21
9	Profenamine	57	44	67	80	54
10	Promazine	10	12	7	31	11
11	Promethazine	26	21	16	47	20
12	Trifluoperazine	17	17	0	40	16
13	Trifluopromazine	35	25	21	56	28
14	Thioproperazine	12	9	0	18	9
15	Thioridazine	35	19	15	45	26

Silica Gel G/UV$_{254}$ (Macherey, Nagel & Co.), basic; layer thickness: 0.25 mm; length of run: 15 cm.
Detection: (a) ultraviolet light (254 nm); (b) Dragendorff reagent.

Table VIIIb

No.	Psycholeptic 1–13 without diazepines and phenothiazines psychoanaleptic 14–36	hRf-Values in solvent no.				
		XXIII	V	VII	XIX	VIII
1	Meprobamate	68	70	72	71	33
2	Hydroxyzine-hydrochloride	45	40	48	53	49
3	Prothipendyl-hydrochloride	16	37	32	24	29
4	Chlorprothixene	30	62	58	53	61
5	Clopenthixol-dihydrochloride	19	31	40	40	34
6	Flupenthixol	25	37	43	37	39
7	Haloperidol	50	74	61	52	56
8	Trifluperidol	53	63	64	57	59
9	Floropipamide	21	57	27	24	24
10	Moperonum-hydrochloride	44	39	55	49	52
11	Benperidol	51	54	67	62	59
12	Fluanisone	59	67	82	66	77
13	Oxypertine	58	56	78	67	69
14	Imipramine	24	54	43	29	41
15	Amitriptyline	25	60	49	34	46
16	Opipramol	16	28	29	24	26
17	Desipramine	10	16	17	10	13
18	Nortriptyline	10	24	23	12	18
19	Melitracene	45	53	50	41	54
20	Trimipramine	40	80	65	50	64
21	Phenelzine-dihydrogen sulfate	60	66	69	68	69
22	Nialamide	21	19	30	35	21
23	Tranylcypromine-sulfate	57	41	50	41	47
24	Amphetamine	37	18	19	19	19
25	Methamphetamine	12	14	16	10	12
26	7-Ethyltheophylline-amphetamine	31	33	37	31	35
27	Prolintane-hydrochloride	37	61	51	48	58
28	Phenmetrazine-hydrochloride	16	24	34	29	26
29	Methylphenidate-hydro-chloride	31	51	54	50	52
30	Fencamfaminum	37	49	62	41	57
31	Pentetrazole	18	42	0	0	20
32	Etamivanum	48	44	63	57	58
33	Pyritinol	16	11	27	36	20
34	Meclofenoxate-hydrochloride	28	54	10	20	51
35	Pemoline	38	15	41	52	29
36	Pipradol-hydrochloride	47	64	68	60	58

Silica Gel G/UV$_{254}$ (Macherey, Nagel & Co.), basic, layer thickness: 0.25 mm; length of run: 15 cm.
Detection: (a) ultraviolet light (254 nm); (b) Dragendorff reagent.

Due to the different affinities of the solvent components to the adsorbent, a concentration of the polar solvent on the silica gel of the plates must be reckoned with, and a concomitant change of solvent mixture composition can be expected. To determine the extent of the change in the examples, a number of azeotropic mixtures which were used as solvents were consequently examined. After having chromatographed the fifth and tenth plates (layer thickness 0.3 mm), a sample was taken from the chamber and examined by gas chromatography. The results of the quantitative analysis are shown on Figure 2.[23] It is evident that for a solvent which contains a polar component of low concentration

Table IX

Separation of Narcotics[21]*

No.	Narcotic	X	XV	XXI	VII	XI
		\multicolumn{5}{c}{hRf-Values in solvent no.}
1	Cocaine	68	68	51	62	64
2	Dextromoramide	90	78	61	74	72
3	Diphenoxylate	94	86	71	84	79
4	Fentanyl	90	80	64	76	77
5	Hydrocodone	56	31	6	15	31
6	Hydromorphone	41	21	7	14	20
7	Ketobemidone	42	40	10	27	33
8	Levorphanol	34	25	6	18	19
9	Methadone	66	69	48	62	48
10	Morphine	34	25	7	15	12
11	Normethadone	81	68	31	55	60
12	Oxycodone	78	70	49	64	76
13	Pethidine	71	68	22	54	59

*Reproduced from Reference 21 by permission of Deut. Apotheker-Ztg.
Silica Gel GF$_{254}$ (Merck), layer thickness: 0.3 mm, basic, length of run: 15 cm.
Detection: (a) ultraviolet light (254 nm); (b) Dragendorff reagent.

only, as in case of solvents IV, V, X, XI, and XVIII, an exhaustion of methanol or ethanol occurs. Azeotropic solvents of this kind cannot be used for repeated chromatography. In such cases, the chamber-filling should be replaced after at least the tenth chromatographic run. With increasing concentration of the polar component, *e.g.,* solvent XXIII, the effect of exhaustion will be weakened. Such a solvent can be used as often as required.

The use of homogenous azeotropic mixtures for TLC leads to comparatively exact Rf-values. Moreover, due to the possibility of applying solvents as often as required, this method is particularly economical.

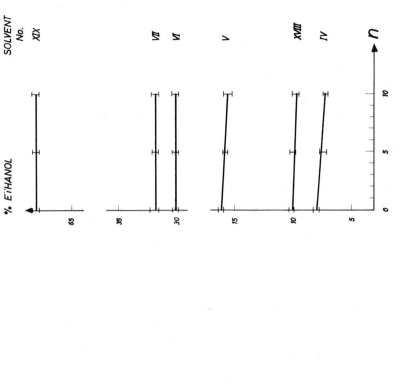

Figure 2. Change of solvent composition of azeotropes (starting condition) during repeated use for TLC. n = number of thin-layer chromatograms performed.

103

REFERENCES

1. Brenner, M., A. Niederwieser, G. Pataki, and A. R. Fahmy. Experientia **18**, 101 (1962).
2. Geiss, F. Z. Anal. Chem. **213**, 331 (1965).
3. Geiss, F., and A. Klose. Z. Anal. Chem. **213**, 321 (1965).
4. Geiss, F., H. Schlitt, F. Ritter, and W. M. Weimar. J. Chromatog. **12**, 469 (1963).
5. Keleman, J., and G. Pataki. Z. Anal. Chem. **195**, 81 (1963).
6. Stahl, E. Arch. Pharm. (Berlin) **292**, 411 (1959).
7. Honegger, C. G. Helv. Chim. Acta **46**, 1730 (1963).
8. Demole, E. J. Chromatog. **1**, 30 (1958).
9. Stahl, E. (Ed.) *Dünnschicht-Chromatographie* (Berlin, Göttingen, Heidelberg: Springer-Verlag 1967).
10. Kortüm, G., and H. Buchholz-Meisenheimer. *Die Theorie der Destillation und Extraktion von Flüssigkeiten* (Berlin, Göttingen, Heidelberg: Springer-Verlag, 1952).
11. Krell, E. *Handbuch der Laboratoriumsdestillation* (Berlin: VEB Gustav Fischer-Verlag, 1958).
12. Nutting, H. S., and L. H. Horsley. Anal. Chem. **19**, 602 (1947).
13. Cox, E. R. Ind. Eng. Chem. **15**, 592 (1923).
14. Röder, E. Deut. Apotheker-Ztg. **107**, 1007 (1967).
15. Röder, E. Unpublished data.
16. Röder, E., E. Mutschler, and H. Rochelmeyer. Arch. Pharm. **301**, 627 (1968).
17. Röder, E., E. Mutschler, and H. Rochelmeyer. Z. Anal. Chem. **244**, 45, 46 (1968).
18. Röder, E., E. Mutschler, and H. Rochelmeyer. Pharmazie **24**, 238 (1969).
19. Röder, E., E. Mutschler, and H. Rochelmeyer. Pharm. Acta Helv. **44**, 644 (1969).
20. Röder, E., E. Mutschler, and H. Rochelmeyer. J. Chromatog. **42**, 131 (1969).
21. Röder, E., E. Mutschler, and H. Rochelmeyer. Deut. Apotheker-Ztg. **109**, 1219 (1969).
22. Küster, F. W., A. Thiel, and K. Fischbeck. *Logarithmische Rechentafeln* (Berlin: W. de Gruyter-Verlag, 1962).
23. Röder, E., and E. Mutschler. Arch. Pharm. **303** (in press, 1970).

Chapter 4

The Chemistry, Physical Properties, and Chromatography of Lipids Containing Ether Bonds

by F. Snyder

Naturally occurring glycerol or diol lipids containing ether bonds can be classified as alkyl (I or II) or alk-1-enyl* (III or IV) types.[1]

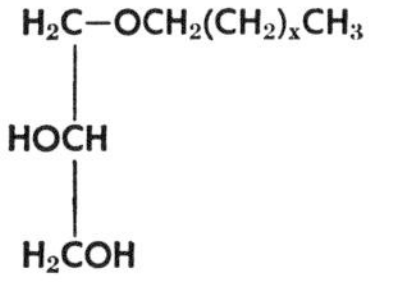

$$H_2C-OCH_2(CH_2)_xCH_3$$
$$|$$
$$HOCH$$
$$|$$
$$H_2COH$$

I

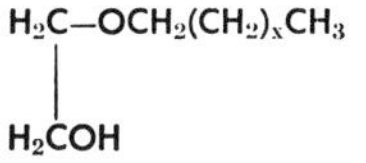

$$H_2C-OCH_2(CH_2)_xCH_3$$
$$|$$
$$H_2COH$$

II

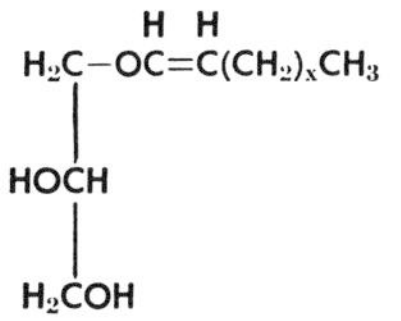

$$\overset{H\ \ H}{H_2C-OC=C(CH_2)_xCH_3}$$
$$|$$
$$HOCH$$
$$|$$
$$H_2COH$$

III

$$\overset{H\ \ H}{H_2C-OC=C(CH_2)_xCH_3}$$
$$|$$
$$H_2COH$$

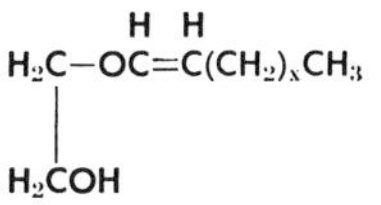

IV

This study was supported in part by the U. S. Atomic Energy Commission and American Cancer Society Grant No. P-470.
*Glyceryl ethers as used in this review refer to alkyl and alk-1-enyl types unless otherwise designated. *Alkyl* and *alk-1-enyl* refer to the α,β carbon linkage; the other carbon-to-carbon linkages may or may not be unsaturated.

The alk-1-enyl types are often referred to as plasmalogens, vinyl ethers, or enol ethers; *phosphatidal* has been used to distinguish alk-1-enyl phosphoglycerides from the more common acyl type, referred to as *phosphatidyl*.[2] Free alkyl glyceryl ethers (I) have been detected in nature, but acyl groups generally occupy position 2 of the glycerol types (I and III) and additional alkyl ether moieties can also be attached at this position. Position 3 can contain acyl, phosphate, or phosphoryl-base moieties. Phosphonic acid groups[3] in position 3 and methoxy groups[4] at the number 2 carbon of the ether chain have also been isolated (Formula I). The alk-1-enyl lipids occurring in nature are all *cis*. In general, neutral lipids contain mostly alkyl-type ethers, and phospholipids mostly the alk-1-enyl type.[1, 5, 6] All ether lipids known except the 1,2-dialkyl types[7] contain the ether linkage only in the 1-position, as defined in Hirschmann's system of nomenclature.[8] The diacyl glyceryl ethers, like triglycerides, exhibit polymorphism.[9] A recent review is available on the biochemistry of glyceryl ethers in nature.[1]

The diol lipids isolated in nature usually contain acyl or alkyl substituents,[10] but a phosphorylated type[11] has also been found. Recently, a group of diol compounds depicted by Formula V was reported in the

$$CH_2(CH_2)_xCH_3$$
$$|$$
$$HOCH$$
$$|$$
$$H_2COH$$

V

$$\overset{O}{\overset{\|}{RCO}}-\overset{CH_2(CH_2)_xCH_3}{\overset{|}{CH}}$$
$$|$$
$$O=C-OCH_2R$$

VI

$$\overset{O}{\overset{\|}{RCO}}-\overset{CH_2(CH_2)_xCH_3}{\overset{|}{CH}}$$
$$\overset{O}{\overset{|}{\underset{\|}{H_2C-OCR}}}$$

VII

$$CH_2(CH_2)_xCH_3$$
$$|$$
$$HCOH$$
$$|$$
$$HCOH$$
$$|$$
$$CH_3$$

VIII

$$\overset{OH\ OH}{CH_3(CH_2)_xC-C(CH_2)_xCOOH}$$
$$\underset{H\ \ H}{}$$

IX

lipids of sebaceous glands.[12, 13] These diols together with α-hydroxy fatty acids can occur as wax esters of the type shown in Formulas VI and VII.[13] Although they do not contain ether bonds, they can be mistaken for glyceryl ethers in biological samples when identification is based solely on thin-layer chromatographic analyses of the unesterified forms. Other diol lipids (Formula VIII)[10] and dihydroxy fatty acids (Formula

IX) also exhibit many chromatographic and chemical properties similar to those of the glyceryl ethers, but partition chromatography[13, 14] and adsorption-TLC of their isopropylidene derivatives[15] can resolve such components.

The two types of ether lipids (I or III and II or IV) and certain derivatives can be resolved from their corresponding acyl analogs by adsorption-TLC. Subfractionation of these compounds can be made according to molecular weight, degree of unsaturation, or isomeric form by gas-liquid chromatography (GLC), or by thin-layer chromatography (TLC) on adsorbent layers impregnated with metal ions.[16] Mangold and Baumann[17] have discussed some of the techniques used in GLC of these compounds.

Several reviews have dealt with the analysis of glyceryl ethers[17-20] and aldehydes[21] derived from alk-1-enyl types. This review limits itself to procedures that have been developed for the simultaneous analysis of alkyl and alk-1-enyl ethers in lipids and to information about their physical properties. The main emphasis is on techniques that our laboratory has developed for glycerolipids and, to some extent, for diol lipids containing ether bonds. Pertinent methods for analyses of derived products are also included.

METABOLISM AND SIGNIFICANCE OF ETHER LIPIDS IN BIOLOGICAL SYSTEMS

In spite of the widespread occurrence of ether lipids,[1] a biochemical pathway for the formation of the ether linkage has only recently been discovered. The formation of alkyl ethers can occur via microsomal enzymes using dihydroxyacetone-3-phosphate and fatty alcohols as substrates.[22, 23] Enzyme systems have been described for the biocleavage of alkyl[24, 25] and alk-1-enyl ethers[26-28] of glycerol, deacylation of alkyl glyceryl ethers,[29] acylation of alkyl[30] and alk-1-enyl ethers[31] of glycerol, and phosphoryl-base transfers[32] with alk-1-enyl glyceryl ethers as substrates. The interconversions of alkyl and alk-1-enyl types or of their derivatives are still poorly understood, but it appears that alkyl ethers can be desaturated to form alk-1-enyl ethers.[33] Detailed structural studies of ether-linked lipids have provided important information on possible metabolic relationships.[34, 35] Knowledge of the biosynthesis and catabolism of diol lipids is essentially lacking, although much is known about their occurrence and chemistry.[10]

The abnormally high levels of glyceryl ethers—primarily the alkyl type—in a wide variety of neoplastic cells of man[36] and animals,[37] the high content of ether lipids in nerve tissue and muscle,[1, 38] the presence of ether lipids in plasma membranes and organelles,[1] and the many reported biological activities of glyceryl ethers[1] have increased interest in their role in mammalian cells. The development and improvement of analytical procedures for glyceryl ethers have now made the detailed exploration of ether-linked lipids in complex biological material a relatively straightforward task.

PHYSICAL PROPERTIES AND CHEMISTRY OF ETHER LIPIDS

Discussion of published work on melting points,[9, 10, 14, 16, 39–44] on critical solution temperatures,[14, 42] and on optical rotations,[45–49] and a general survey of methods used in the establishment of ether structures

Table I

Melting Points and Critical Solution Temperatures
of Some Alkyl Glyceryl Ethers

		Critical solution temperatures	
*Alkyl ether moiety**	*Melting points*	*Nitromethane*	*Acetonitrile*
10:0, 1	34.5–36.0[a]	—	—
10:0, 2	30.4–31.5[a]	—	—
12:0, 1	47.2–48.0[a]	—	—
12:0, 2	45.0–46.5[a]	—	—
14:0, 1	55.4–56.1[a] 37[c]	61.5[c]	32.5[c]
14:0, 2	54.9–55.4[a]	—	—
16:0, 1	59.9–60.6[a] 57.0–57.5; 62.5–63.0[b] 47.5[c]	70.5[c]	43.5
16:0, 2	62.5–63.3[a] 62.5–63.0[b]	—	—
18:0, 1	65.0–65.7[a] 67–68;70–71[b] 58[c]	77.5[c]	53[c]
18:0, 2	68.5–69.0[a] 70.0–71.0[b]	—	—
18:1(9c), 1	17.6–18.5[a]	—	—
18:1(9c), 2	13–14[a]	—	—
18:2(9c,12c), 1	−4.5−−4.0[a]	—	—
18:2(9c,12c), 2	−0.8–0[a]	—	—
20:0, 1	64.5[c]	84[c]	61[c]
22:0, 1	71.5[c]	90.5[c]	68.5[c]
24:0, 1	76.5[c]	95.5[c]	76[c]

[a]From Reference 16. [b]From Reference 9. [c]From Reference 42.
*See Reference 16 for complete description of shorthand nomenclature [chain length:double bonds (c = *cis* and location); number after comma indicates 1 or 2 isomers].

in lipids[16, 17, 40, 41] can be found in other articles. To provide a concise summary of melting points and critical solution temperatures for a broad series of glyceryl ethers of interest to the biochemist, Table I is included here. Variation in values for certain of the physical constants shown can be attributed to polymorphic forms.[9]

The chemical syntheses and properties of ether-linked lipids[19, 50] and the preparation of labeled glyceryl ethers have also been reviewed.[51] Bergelson[10] has surveyed the general organic procedures for preparing diol lipids, and specific papers on the synthesis of alkyl[14] and alk-1-enyl[52, 53] ethers of glycol are also available. So I will restrict myself to a brief discussion of the application of infrared (IR) and nuclear magnetic resonance (NMR) to the analysis of ether-linked lipids, and to a survey of the chemical and enzymatic reactions that are generally prerequisite procedures for structural and chromatographic analysis of lipid ethers. An application of some of these procedures is illustrated in a paper on the structural proof of glyceryl ethers found in neoplasms.[54] Although not discussed in this review, mass spectrometry is a powerful tool for ascertaining the structure of these compounds; it has seen only limited use in this field.[4, 55, 56]

Infrared

Ether bonds and alk-1-enyl linkages in lipids are easily distinguished by infrared spectroscopy. Typical spectra can be found in a variety of papers on this subject.[4, 9, 16, 44, 54, 57–64] Piantadosi and co-workers[65] and Wood and Snyder[16] have published spectra on the cyclic acetal form of alk-1-enyl ethers. Infrared spectra of thioether lipids[59] and ether-linked diol lipids[53] are also available. Oswald *et al.*[9] have described shifts in the spectra of polymorphic forms of certain glyceryl ether derivatives.

The absorption band that identifies the ether linkage occurs at approximately 9 microns (Figure 1); slight shifts[16] in the location of this band have been detected in glycerolipids that contain the aliphatic ether linkage in the 1-position (8.93 microns) or in the 2-position (9.15 microns). A prominent absorption band at 6.1 microns is characteristic for the alk-1-enyl hydrocarbon moiety in lipids containing ether bonds. Other features of the IR spectra of ether lipids are exceedingly useful in establishing the presence of additional functional groups such as methoxy substituents,[4] double bonds[16] along the ether-linked hydrocarbon chain, and substituents attached to the other positions of the glycerol or diol molecules.

Nuclear Magnetic Resonance

Nuclear magnetic resonance spectra of alkyl glyceryl ethers and certain derivatives have recently been illustrated and discussed.[4, 16, 54, 66] The

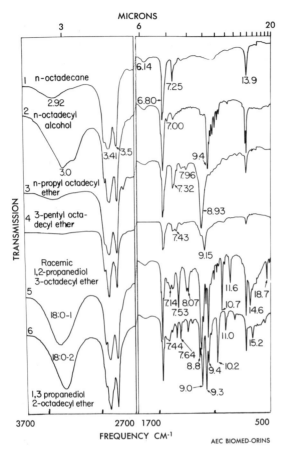

Figure 1. Infrared spectra of 18:1–1 and 18:0–2 isomeric glyceryl ethers and their derivatives. [R. Wood and F. Snyder. *Lipids* 2, 161 (1967). Reproduced by permission of *Lipids*.]

early work by Carter *et al.*[57] gave NMR spectra of diacetate derivatives of the 1- and 2-isomers of batyl alcohol and the corresponding monoglycerides. NMR spectra for alk-1-enyl ethers have also been published for phospholipids[55, 60-62] and neutral lipids.[49] Isomeric forms of saturated, monoenoic, and dienoic glyceryl ethers[16] are also recognizable from NMR spectra (Figure 2). Such studies have demonstrated that NMR spectra are particularly useful in distinguishing the isomeric position of the ether-linked aliphatic moiety on glycerol. Baumann *et al.*[53] have described NMR spectra of the diol lipids containing ether bonds; this powerful technique has also been applied to the differentiation of S-ethers and O-ethers.[59]

Chemical and Enzymatic Degradative Reactions

Many of the reactions described for the alkyl and alk-1-enyl glycero-lipids are also useful in the analysis of glycolipids that contain ether bonds.[67] Furthermore, all of the reactions involving O-alkyl ethers are applicable to S-alkyl ethers.[59]

TMS

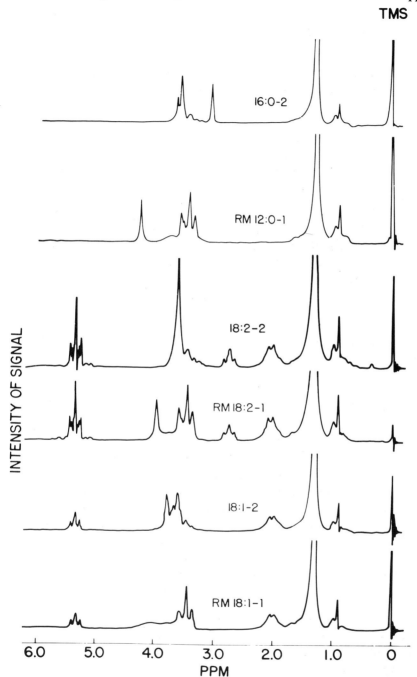

Figure 2. Proton resonance spectra of saturated, mono-, and diunsaturated isomeric glyceryl ethers obtained at 60 mc. [R. Wood and F. Snyder. *Lipids* **2,** 161 (1967). Reproduced by permission of *Lipids*.]

Cleavage of Ether Bonds

Alkyl Ether Bonds

Alkyl ethers can be cleaved only under vigorous conditions such as with hydriodic acid at high temperatures.

$$
\begin{array}{l}
H_2C-OCH_2R \\
\quad | \\
HOCH \qquad + HI \longrightarrow RCH_2I + glycerol \\
\quad | \\
H_2COH
\end{array}
$$

Guyer *et al.*[68] have used GLC for measuring the alkyl iodides liberated by HI. However, HI can also attack on either side of double bonds, forming isomeric products, and therefore it is not recommended for structural studies of unsaturated glyceryl ethers.[69] Enzymes can cleave alkyl glyceryl ethers,[24, 25] but such preparations have not yet been sufficiently purified for use in studies of structure.

Alk-1-enyl Ether Bonds

Acids readily cleave alk-1-enyl ethers to form glycerol and long-chain fatty aldehydes; the composition of the latter can be analyzed directly by GLC.[21, 70]

$$
\begin{array}{l}
\qquad\;\; H\;\; H \\
H_2C-OC=CCH_2R \\
\quad | \qquad\qquad\qquad\qquad\qquad\; O \\
\quad | \qquad\qquad\;\; [H^+] \qquad\qquad\; \| \\
HOCH \qquad \longrightarrow \qquad RC + glycerol \\
\quad | \qquad\qquad\qquad\qquad\qquad\; H \\
H_2COH
\end{array}
$$

The acid hydrolysis is generally carried out with the use of fumes or sprays directly on thin-layer chromatograms in conjunction with a "separation-reaction-separation" technique.[71] These procedures have also been applied directly to alk-1-enyl phosphoglycerides.[72–75] Owens[72] used a spray reagent containing $HgCl_2$ for the hydrolysis of alk-1-enyl chains.

Although the hydrolysis carried out on silica gel layers yields aldehydes representing the composition of the hydrocarbon moieties in ether linkage, it is not quantitative.[76] Quantitative release of aldehydes from alk-1-enyl glyceryl ethers is virtually complete ($\simeq 95\%$) if the silica gel containing the alk-1-enyl lipids is shaken with concentrated HCl in diethyl ether.[76]

Enzymes from liver[26, 28] and brain[27] have also been used to hydrolyze alk-1-enyl ether phosphoglycerides. Such preparations are too impure to apply in the structural analysis of ether lipids.

Removal of Acyl, Phosphate, and Related Substituents

Lithium Aluminum Hydride Reduction

Lithium aluminum hydride quantitatively removes acyl and phosphoryl-base groups from lipids containing alkyl- and alk-1-enyl ethers.[38, 77] The reaction is rapid and it has no adverse effect on alk-1-enyl linkages, a common problem with other methods of hydrolysis. The procedure has been adapted for quantitative measurements of both types of ethers by TLC photodensitometry.[38]

The reduction is carried out in dry diethyl ether for 30 minutes, and then the reaction mixture is treated with water. No reduction of carbon-to-carbon double bonds occurs with the $LiAlH_4$ reagent.

Saponification

Boiling in alcoholic KOH or NaOH adequately removes acyl moieties from glycerol or diol lipids containing ether bonds.

Thompson[3] has used an alkaline hydrolysis for the selective removal of other lipid contaminants from phosphonolipids. Selective hydrolysis procedures have been described in detail.[78–81] Bevan et al.[82] have suggested a mechanism for acyl migration that occurs during dephosphorylation of diacyl phosphatides. During saponification the phosphate at position 3 can form a cyclic compound through an interaction with the free hydroxyl group at the 2-position.[57, 83]

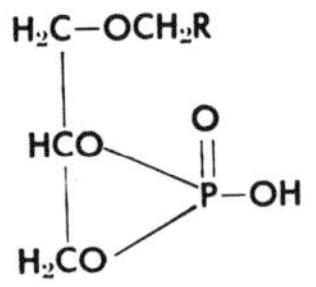

$$
\begin{array}{c}
H_2C-OCH_2R \\
| \\
HCO \diagdown \quad O \\
\quad\quad\, \diagup P-OH \\
| \quad\quad \diagup \\
H_2CO
\end{array}
$$

Basic hydrolysis of alk-1-enyl lipids yields numerous components of unknown structures.[84] Since these disadvantages are not inherent with LiAlH$_4$ reduction, saponification is seldom used in the analysis of lipids that contain ether bonds.

Deacylation with Grignard Reagent (RMgBr)

The reagent of choice is CH_3CH_2MgBr when one removes acyl moieties from glycerolipids in the initial steps of the stereospecific analysis of glycerides[85] and glycerides containing ether bonds.[34]

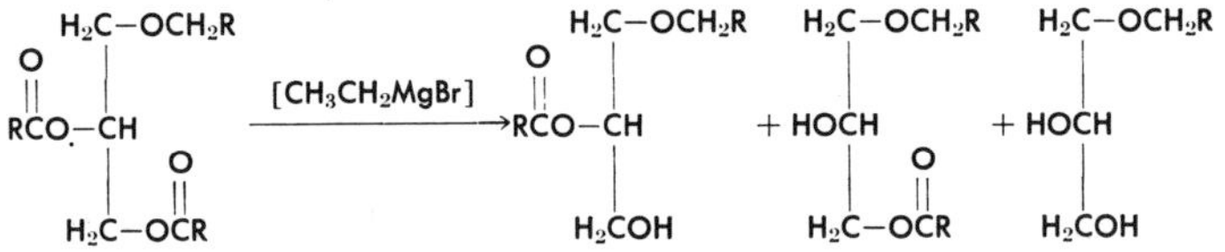

$$
\begin{array}{c}
\quad\quad H_2C-OCH_2R \\
O \quad\quad | \\
|| \quad\quad\quad\quad\quad\quad\quad [CH_3CH_2MgBr] \\
RCO-CH \quad\quad \xrightarrow{\hspace{2cm}} \\
\quad\quad\quad | \quad\; O \\
\quad\quad\quad H_2C-OCR
\end{array}
\quad
\begin{array}{c}
H_2C-OCH_2R \\
O \quad | \\
|| \quad\quad \\
RCO-CH \\
\quad\quad | \\
\quad\quad H_2COH
\end{array}
\;+\;
\begin{array}{c}
H_2C-OCH_2R \\
| \\
HOCH \\
\quad | \quad O \\
\quad H_2C-OCR
\end{array}
\;+\;
\begin{array}{c}
H_2C-OCH_2R \\
| \\
HOCH \\
| \\
H_2COH
\end{array}
$$

The advantage of a Grignard reagent in stereospecific analysis is that deacylation to the 1-alkyl-2-acyl type is achieved with a minimum of acyl migration and in a random manner.

Lipolysis

Pancreatic Lipase.   Purified lipase specifically hydrolyzes acyl moieties from the 1- and 3-positions of acyl-substituted glycerols.[86, 87] Lipolytic contaminants in commercial preparations can also cause hydrolysis of acyl moieties at the 2-position of glycerol;[88] however, lipase or its contaminants do not affect alkyl[29] or alk-1-enyl[61, 62] moieties. The acyl group at position 1 of phosphoglycerides can be hydrolyzed[89] by electrophoretically pure lipase, whereas unpurified preparations will also remove the acyl moiety from the 2-position of phosphoglycerides.[89, 90] No reports have been published on the specificity of pancreatic lipases for diol lipids. The action of lipase on diacyl glyceryl ethers[29] is depicted in the following scheme:

(a) *1-O-Alkyl linkage*

$$
\begin{array}{ccccc}
\underset{\underset{RCO-CH}{\overset{O}{\parallel}}}{\overset{H_2C-OCH_2R}{\big|}} & \xrightarrow[\text{lipase}]{\text{pancreatic}} & \underset{\underset{RCO-CH}{\overset{O}{\parallel}}}{\overset{H_2C-OCH_2R}{\big|}} & \xrightarrow[\text{(acyl migration)}]{H^+} & \underset{HOCH}{\overset{H_2C-OCH_2R}{\big|}} & \xrightarrow[\text{lipase}]{\text{pancreatic}} & \underset{HOCH}{\overset{H_2C-OCH_2R}{\big|}} \\
\overset{O}{\underset{H_2C-OCR}{\big|}} & & \underset{H_2COH}{\big|} & & \overset{O}{\underset{H_2C-OCR}{\big|}} & & \underset{H_2COH}{\big|}
\end{array}
$$

(b) *2-O-Alkyl linkage*

$$
\begin{array}{ccccc}
\overset{\overset{O}{\parallel}}{H_2C-OCR} & & \overset{\overset{O}{\parallel}}{H_2C-OCR} & & H_2COH \\
HC-OCH_2R & \xrightarrow[\text{lipase}]{\text{pancreatic}} & HC-OCH_2R & \xrightarrow[\text{lipase}]{\text{pancreatic}} & HC-OCH_2R \\
\underset{H_2C-OCR}{\overset{O}{\parallel}} & & H_2COH & & H_2COH
\end{array}
$$

These reactions have proved useful in structural analysis of glyceryl ether lipids. Lipase can also serve to prepare 1,2- and 1,3-alkyl acyl derivatives of glycerol for use as standards and substrates in biochemical studies.[29]

Phospholipases. Specificities of the phospholipases for linkages in ether-containing phosphoglycerides are illustrated in the following scheme:

$$
\begin{array}{ll}
& H_2C-OCH_2R' \quad \text{(R' represents alkyl or} \\
& \overset{O}{\underset{RCO-CH}{\overset{\parallel}{|}}} \quad\quad \text{alk-1-enyl moieties)} \\
\text{Phospholipase A} & \quad\quad\quad\quad \overset{O}{\parallel} \\
\text{(EC 3.1.1.4)} & \quad\quad\quad H_2C-OPO_2\text{base} \\
\text{Phospholipase C} & \quad\quad\quad\quad\quad\quad \text{Phospholipase D} \\
\text{(EC 3.1.4.3)} & \quad\quad\quad\quad OH \quad\quad\quad \text{(EC 3.1.4.4)}
\end{array}
$$

Van Deenen and de Haas[91] have written an excellent review on the phospholipases. Little is known about the influence of alkyl versus alk-1-enyl ether moieties on the specificities or the rates of reactions for the phospholipases. On the other hand, numerous papers have appeared[92-97] on the relative reactivities of alk-1-enyl versus acyl substituents in such compounds. Phospholipases generally have been found to be sluggish when ether linkages are present in the glycerolipids, but this depends on the source of the enzyme. In fact, Lands and Hart[96] reported that phospholipase D from cabbage is inert with ether-linked substrates, while Hack and Ferrans[98] and Slotboom[61, 62] found that it could slowly attack alk-1-enyl phosphoglycerides; yet phospholipase D from *B. cereus* is extremely active under similar conditions.[34, 99] Reactions of phospholipases utilizing diol P-lipids as substrates are poorly understood.[10]

Determination of the Double Bond Location

Reductive Ozonolysis

The aliphatic ether moieties of naturally occurring glyceryl ethers are almost exclusively saturated or monoenoic,[1] and this has simplified the task of determining the location of double bonds in such molecules. Reductive ozonolysis of the intact monoenoic glyceryl ethers in conjunction with gas-liquid chromatography has been used to determine the precise location of the double bonds;[35, 100] the ozonolysis and reduction (Adams catalyst) procedures used are similar to those developed for determining the location of double bonds in fatty acids.[101] Long-chain fatty aldehydes (from the terminal end of the aliphatic chain) and glyceryl ether aldehydes are produced from monoenoic glyceryl ethers.

$$
\begin{array}{lcl}
\mathrm{H_2C-O(CH_2)_xC\overset{H}{=}\overset{H}{C}(CH_2)_7CH_3} & & \mathrm{H_2C-O(CH_2)_xCHO} \\
| & & | \\
\mathrm{HOCH} \quad\quad +\,O_3 \xrightarrow{\quad H_2O\quad} & & \mathrm{HOCH} \quad\quad +\,CH_3(CH_2)_7CHO \\
| & & | \\
\mathrm{H_2COH} & & \mathrm{H_2COH}
\end{array}
$$

Gas-liquid chromatography of the glyceryl ether aldehyde fragments is performed on their isopropylidene derivatives, prepared usually before ozonolysis; the fatty aldehyde fragments can be analyzed intact by GLC. Ramachandran et al.[100] have used reductive ozonolysis of alkyl iodides derived from glyceryl ethers subsequent to hydriodic acid cleavage of the ether linkage to determine the location of double bonds.

The number of double bonds in alk-1-enyl ethers can be measured only after acid hydrolysis of the aldehydogenic moieties. Although this approach has not yet been reported, the acids or alcohols derived from aldehydes could be subjected to ozonolysis in a conventional manner. The location of double bonds in unsaturated glycolipids has not been described.

Permanganate–Periodate Oxidation

Hanahan et al.[102] have used permanganate–periodate oxidation to establish the position of the double bond in selachyl alcohol derived from fish oil. The products, monocarboxylic acids and dicarboxylic acids containing an ether bond, were analyzed as their methyl esters by gas-liquid chromatography.

$$\begin{array}{c}\overset{\text{H H}}{\text{H}_2\text{C}-\text{O(CH}_2)_x\text{C}=\text{C(CH}_2)_7\text{CH}_3}\\|\\\text{HOCH}\\|\\\text{H}_2\text{COH}\end{array} + \text{KMnO}_4 + \text{KIO}_4 \longrightarrow \text{CH}_3(\text{CH}_2)_7\text{COOH} + \begin{array}{c}\text{H}_2\text{C}-\text{O(CH}_2)_x\text{COOH}\\|\\\text{COOH}\end{array} + \text{HCOOH}$$

The method described by Hanahan's group is based on a procedure originally described by von Rudloff.[103]

Chromic Acid Oxidation

Chromic acid has also been used in conjunction with gas-liquid chromatographic analysis to determine the location of double bonds in glyceryl ethers isolated from liver oils of elasmobranch fishes.[104]

$$\begin{array}{c}\overset{\text{H H}}{\text{H}_2\text{C}-\text{O(CH}_2)_x\text{C}=\text{C(CH}_2)_7\text{CH}_3}\\|\\\text{HOCH}\\|\\\text{H}_2\text{COH}\end{array} + \text{H}_2\text{CrO}_4 \longrightarrow \begin{array}{c}\text{H}_2\text{C}-\text{O(CH}_2)_x\text{COOH}\\|\\\text{HOCH}\\|\\\text{H}_2\text{COH}\end{array} + \text{CH}_3(\text{CH}_2)_7\text{COOH}$$

The monocarboxylic acids produced were analyzed as their methyl esters. The glyceryl ether fragment, containing a terminal carboxyl group, was measured as the dimethoxy derivative (see next section); the carboxyl group was methylated.

Periodate Oxidation

Oxidation by periodate has been combined with the analysis of alkyl glyceryl ethers in spectrophotometry[105] and gas-liquid chromatography.[17] The products of this reaction are formaldehyde and an alkoxy acetaldehyde.

$$\begin{array}{c}\text{H}_2\text{C}-\text{OCH}_2\text{R}\\|\\\text{HOCH}\\|\\\text{H}_2\text{COH}\end{array} + \text{HIO}_4 \longrightarrow \begin{array}{c}\text{H}_2\text{C}-\text{OCH}_2\text{R}\\|\\\text{HC}=\text{O}\end{array} + \text{H}_2\text{C}=\text{O}$$

Colorimetric measurements are based on the reaction of chromotropic acid with the formaldehyde. The alkoxy acetaldehyde can be directly analyzed by GLC. The acidic conditions of this reaction preclude its use with alk-1-enyl glyceryl ethers. Obviously, glycol derivatives do not participate in this reaction, but the procedure has been useful in preparing diol lipids from glycerolipids.[11,53] However, Baumann and co-workers[106] have demonstrated that cleavage of long-chain 1,2- and 2,3-diols and alkyl and alk-1-enyl glyceryl ethers to aldehydes can be accomplished with sodium metaperiodate[106] in pyridine.

Reactions for Stereospecific Analysis

Brockerhoff and co-workers[85,107] and Lands *et al.*[108] have described approaches to the stereospecific analysis of triglycerides. Stereospecific analyses depend first on the preparation of diglycerides either by lipase[107,108] or Grignard reactions.[85] Next, the diglycerides are phosphorylated, either chemically[107] or enzymatically.[108] Finally, the fatty acids from the 2-position of the newly formed phosphatide are removed by phospholipase A.[107,108] The products of hydrolysis are examined by GLC at each stage of the reaction sequence; these analyses and calculations yield the stereospecific composition of the hydrocarbon chains originally attached to glycerol at the various positions.

Wood and Snyder[34] have described in detail a modified Brockerhoff scheme, based on the Grignard reagent, for the stereospecific analysis of glycerides, phosphoglycerides, and ether-containing glycerides in Ehrlich ascites cells. Previous descriptions of stereospecific analyses of glycerides did not include the aliphatic ether-linked moieties.

Preparation of Derivatives for Gas-Liquid Chromatography

Alkyl Ethers

Acetates

Blomstrand and Gürtler used GLC to analyze the diacetates of glyceryl ethers.[109] However, some unsaturated glyceryl ether acetates are not resolved by GLC, and all these acetates have long GLC retention times.

$$
\begin{array}{c}
H_2C-OCH_2R \\
| \\
HOCH \\
| \\
H_2COH
\end{array}
+ (CH_3CO)_2O \longrightarrow
\begin{array}{c}
H_2C-OCH_2R \\
\underset{\displaystyle O}{\overset{\displaystyle O}{\|}} \\
CH_3CO-CH \\
| \quad \overset{O}{\|} \\
H_2C-OCCH_3
\end{array}
$$

Others have used acetylation in conjunction with the analysis of molecular species of lecithin[110] and with high-temperature GLC analysis[34,111] of ethers of the diglyceride type isolated from phosphoglycerides.

$$
\begin{array}{c}
\overset{O}{\|} \\
RCO-CH \\
| \\
H_2COH
\end{array}
\begin{array}{c}
H_2C-OCH_2R \\
| \\
\\
\end{array}
+ (CH_3CO)_2O \longrightarrow
\begin{array}{c}
H_2C-OCH_2R \\
\overset{O}{\|} \quad | \\
RCO-CH \\
| \quad \overset{O}{\|} \\
H_2C-OCCH_3
\end{array}
$$

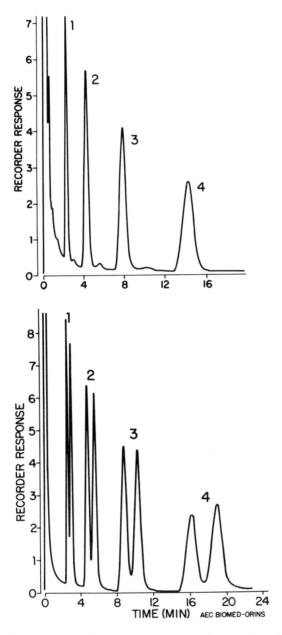

Figure 3. Chromatograms showing the resolution of purified synthetic 1- and 2-glyceryl ether TMS-derivatives (top) and TFA-derivatives (bottom). Resolutions were obtained with a 5-foot × ⅛-inch stainless steel column packed with 3% XE-60 on 80–100 mesh Gas-Chrom Q operating at an isothermal temperature of 200°C. The numbered peaks are: (1) 12:0; (2) 14:0; (3) 16:0; and (4) 18:0. The 2-isomers were eluted after the 1-isomers for the TFA-derivatives. [R. Wood and F. Snyder. *Lipids* 1, 62 (1966). Reproduced by permission of *Lipids*.]

Trifluoroacetates

Trifluoroacetate (TFA) groups on glyceryl ethers greatly increase their volatility and therefore are much better suited for GLC analysis of ether derivatives than the acetates described earlier. In addition, the 1- and 2-isomeric forms of glyceryl ether TFA-derivatives are easily resolved[112] (Figure 3). Wood and Snyder[112] have described the analysis of TFA-derivatives of standard mixtures of glyceryl ethers on polar and nonpolar columns.

$$
\begin{array}{ccc}
H_2C-OCH_2R & & H_2C-OCH_2R \\
| & & \overset{O}{\underset{\|}{|}} \\
HOCH \quad + (CF_3CO)_2O & \longrightarrow & CF_3CO-CH \\
| & & \overset{O}{\underset{\|}{|}} \\
H_2COH & & H_2C-OCCF_3 \\
\end{array}
$$

Diol lipids have also been resolved by GLC as TFA-derivatives.[67]

Isopropylidenes

The isopropylidene derivatives of glyceryl ethers are most convenient for routine GLC analysis of chain lengths and degree of unsaturation. Hanahan and co-workers[102] pioneered their use.

$$
\begin{array}{ccc}
H_2C-OCH_2R & \overset{O}{\underset{\|}{}} & H_2C-OCH_2R \\
| & & | \\
HOCH \quad + CH_3CCH_3 & \longrightarrow & HCO \diagdown \quad \diagup CH_3 \\
| & & \qquad C \\
H_2COH & & H_2CO \diagup \quad \diagdown CH_3 \\
\end{array}
$$

The addition of acetone in this reaction is catalyzed by $HClO_4$. Wood[113] has described a scaled-down modification of the procedure[102] for making the isopropylidenes. A typical chromatogram of isopropylidene derivatives from a natural source is illustrated in Figure 4.

Alkoxy Acetaldehydes

Alkoxy acetaldehydes are formed during the reaction of glyceryl ethers with periodate as described above. The oxidation of glycerol at room temperature with periodate was originally reported by Hardegger et al.[114] Mangold and Baumann[17] have described the application of this reaction to GLC analysis.

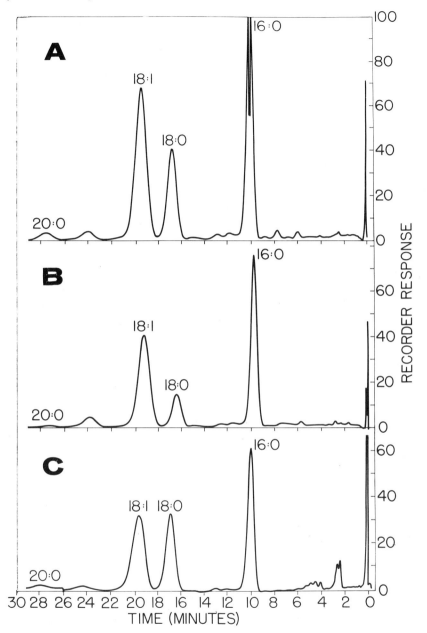

Figure 4. A typical chromatogram showing the resolution of the isopropylidene derivatives of alkyl glyceryl ethers by gas-liquid chromatography. The alkyl glyceryl ethers were isolated from (A) diacyl glyceryl ethers; (B) choline phosphatides; and (C) ethanolamine phosphatides found in a taper liver tumor. [F. Snyder. *Advan. Exptl. Med. Biol.* **4**, 609–621 (1969). Reproduced by permission of Plenum Publishing Corp.]

Trimethylsilyl Ethers

Wood and Snyder[112] prepared trimethylsilyl (TMS) ether derivatives of glyceryl ethers for subsequent GLC analysis (Figure 3).

$$\begin{matrix}
H_2C-OCH_2R & & & H_2C-OCH_2R \\
| & & & | \\
HOCH & + (CH_3)_3SiCl \longrightarrow & (CH_3)_3SiO-CH \\
| & & & | \\
H_2COH & & & H_2C-OSi(CH_3)_3
\end{matrix}$$

Unlike the TFA-derivatives, the 1- and 2-isomers of the TMS-derivatives of glyceryl ethers could not be resolved by GLC. In general, therefore, the TMS-derivatives of glyceryl ethers are not recommended for maximum resolution; the isopropylidene and TFA-derivatives possess more advantages for GLC analysis.

Alkyl Iodides

Guyer and co-workers[68] have described the analysis of alkyl iodides by GLC, and Ramachandran and co-workers[100] have published a recent modification. The preparation of alkyl iodides by HI cleavage of the ether bond has been discussed on page 112.

Dimethoxy Derivatives.   Hallgren and Larsson[104] analyzed glyceryl ethers by GLC of their dimethoxy derivatives. Unfortunately, this procedure is not quantitative since the derivative requires purification before GLC.

$$\begin{matrix}
H_2C-OCH_2R & & & H_2C-OCH_2R \\
| & & & | \\
HOCH & + BF_3 + CH_2N_2 - \longrightarrow & CH_3O-CH \\
| & & & | \\
H_2COH & & & H_2C-OCH_3
\end{matrix}$$

Alk-1-enyl Ethers

Intact Aldehydes

Many of the reactions described above for alkyl ethers are not suitable for the analysis of intact alk-1-enyl glyceryl ethers, since acidic conditions cleave the aldehydogenic moiety and can produce compounds of unknown structure[84] and cyclic acetals.[65] However, under suitable conditions acid hydrolysis can cleave the alk-1-enyl ether bond[71-76] so that the intact long-chain aldehydes may be resolved and identified by GLC.[21, 70] Free aldehydes appear to remain stable for many months when stored in carbon disulfide at −20°C.[70] Figure 5 displays a GLC tracing of intact fatty aldehydes liberated by acid hydrolysis of alk-1-enyl ethers isolated from glyceryl ether diesters, and choline and ethanolamine phosphatides from a taper liver tumor of mice.[20]

Dimethyl Acetals of Fatty Aldehydes

The dimethyl acetals of long-chain fatty aldehydes have been used most frequently for gas-liquid chromatography. These derivatives are prepared by refluxing the aldehydes or total lipids containing 0-alk-1-enyl groups with methanolic hydrogen chloride.[115] The reaction, thought to be quantitative,[21] proceeds as follows:

$$\underset{RC=O}{\overset{H}{}} + 2CH_3OH \xrightarrow{H^+} \underset{RC}{\overset{H}{}} \overset{OCH_3}{\underset{OCH_3}{}}$$

When the dimethyl acetal procedure is used to analyze alk-1-enyl glyceryl ethers, methyl esters of fatty acids are formed and chromatographed with the dimethyl acetals of the aldehydes. This is not a problem where simple mixtures of lipids are concerned, since polarity differences between methyl esters and dimethyl acetals are sufficient for resolution. However, errors in identification of these two derivatives increase with the increasing complexity of the lipid mixture. Papers dealing with this reaction and related procedures have been thoroughly reviewed by Gray.[21]

Miscellaneous Derivatives

Fatty aldehydes derived from alk-1-enyl glyceryl ethers can be reduced to fatty alcohols by $LiAlH_4$ and the alcohols are then converted to an acetate derivative for GLC analysis.[115] Oxidation of aldehydes to acids has also been used in the analysis of saturated aldehydes. However, oxidation procedures are limited because they also cause degradation of the unsaturated chains.[21, 115]

ANALYSIS OF ETHER LIPIDS BY TLC

Resolution of Classes: Neutral Lipids

Adsorption chromatography using thin-layers of silica gel can successfully resolve the various classes of alkyl and alk-1-enyl nonphospholipid ether-linked lipids (Table II). The ether-linked classes migrate at a higher Rf than the corresponding acyl analogs, and the alk-1-enyl-type ethers at a higher Rf than the alkyl-type ethers;[39, 116] similar migrations of the corresponding diol lipids containing ether bonds have been reported by Baumann and co-workers.[14, 53] This apparent decreased polarity of the alk-1-enyl ethers compared to alkyl ethers is probably re-

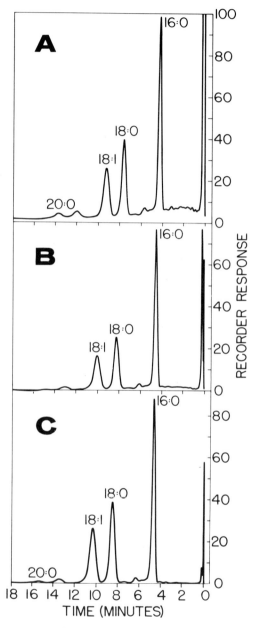

Figure 5. A typical chromatogram showing the resolution of intact fatty aldehydes by gas-liquid chromatography. The aldehydes were isolated from the alk-1-
enyl ethers of (A) diacyl glyceryl ethers; (B) choline phosphatides; and (C) ethanolamine phosphatides found in a taper liver tumor. [F. Snyder. *Advan. Exptl.
Med. Biol.* **4**, 609–621 (1969). Reproduced by permission of Plenum Publishing
Corp.] The aldehydes were measured by the method of Wood and Harlow.[70]

Table II

Thin-Layer Chromatography Solvents for the Resolution of Lipids
Containing Ether Bonds on Silica Gel G

Lipid groups	Solvent	References showing typical chromatograms
I. Trisubstituted glycerols (P-free), *e.g.,* triglycerides, diacyl glyceryl ethers (alkyl and alk-1-enyl)	Hexane–diethyl ether (95:5)	20, 39, 51, 116
II. Disubstituted glycerols (P-free), *e.g.,* diglycerides, monoacyl glyceryl ethers (alkyl and alk-1-enyl)	Chloroform–methanol–acetic acid (98:2:1) or hexane–diethyl ether–methanol–acetic acid (80:20:10:1 or 80:20:5:1)	29, 51, 111
III. "Free" glyceryl ethers, *e.g.,* batyl, chimyl or selachyl alcohols	Diethyl ether–acetic acid (100:0.5)	38, 51
IV. Phosphoglycerides (after preparation of N-dinitrophenyl O-methyl derivative)	Toluene–chloroform (2:8)	120; Chapter 5 in this volume

lated to differences in configuration caused by the *cis* bond in the α- and β-position of the aliphatic moiety.[38]

Glyceryl Ethers

Diacyl glyceryl ethers can be separated from triacylglycerols in relatively nonpolar solvents (Figure 6) such as hexane–diethyl ether (95:5 or 90:10, v/v) or hexane–benzene–diethyl ether–acetic acid (50:45:5:1, v/v). Other components that appear in the area of diacyl glyceryl ethers are long-chain fatty aldehydes, methyl esters of fatty acids, waxes, dialkyl-acyl glyceryl ethers, trialkyl glyceryl ethers, and even certain vitamins. Using a variety of solvents for chromatography or simply varying the polarity by alteration of the ratios of solvents can minimize the risk of confusing these compounds with the diacyl glyceryl ethers. For example, over a wide range of solvent proportions of hexane–diethyl ether–acetic acid, methyl esters of fatty acids and diacyl glyceryl ethers will migrate both ahead of triacylglycerols and below sterol esters; yet the position of the methyl esters of fatty acids relative to the diacylglycerols will be lower with the higher polarity solvent mixtures and higher with those of lower polarity (Figure 7).

Monoacyl glyceryl ethers and diacylglycerols can also be resolved in the hexane–diethyl ether solvents described for the trisubstituted glycerols. However, glacial acetic acid must also be¹ added to prevent the free fatty acids from interfering, and even then these solvents are not suitable for separating the four possibilities of 1,2- and 1,3-isomeric

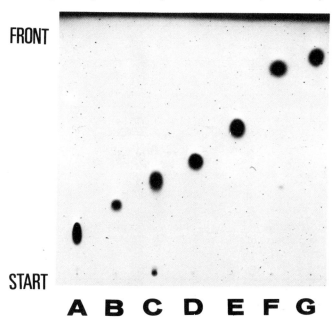

Figure 6. Resolution of "triglyceride-type" lipids containing ether bonds on Silica Gel G. The solvent used for TLC was hexane–diethyl ether (95:5, v/v). Identification of lipid classes depicted in chromatographic lanes: (A) triglycerides; (B) alkyl-diacyl glyceryl ethers; (C) alk-1-enyl diacyl glyceryl ethers; (D) dialkyl-acyl glyceryl ethers; (E) trialkyl glyceryl ethers; (F) wax esters; (G) cholesteryl esters. [F. Snyder. *Advan. Exptl. Med. Biol.* **4**, 609–621 (1969). Reproduced by permission of Plenum Publishing Corp.]

forms of these diglyceride types. Such difficult separations are improved in still more polar solvents.[29, 111] One such solvent we have found useful is chloroform–methanol–acetic acid (98:2:1, v/v) (Figure 8). With it, we have even been able to demonstrate small differences in Rf's of 1-alkyl-2-acyl and 1-acyl-2-alkyl glyceryl ethers. Although the difference in migration of these isomers is slight, it does reflect the excellent capabilities of adsorption-TLC in distinguishing the subtle differences in polarity of lipid molecules associated with slight differences in rearrangement of acyl and ether moieties.

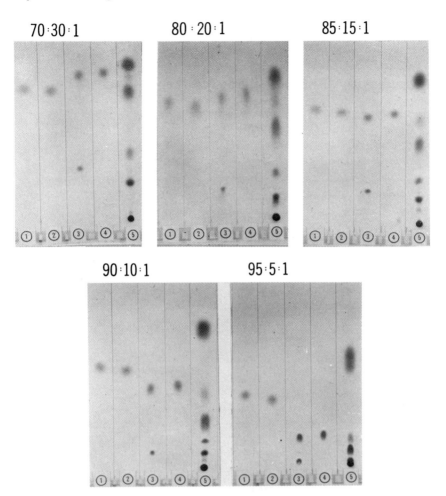

Figure 7. Thin-layer chromatograms of fatty acid methyl esters, diacyl glyceryl ethers, and total lipids from Ehrlich ascites cells (Silica Gel G used as adsorbent). Numbers above each chromatogram refer to solvent ratio v:v:v of hexane–diethyl ether–acetic acid. Lane 1, methyl stearate; Lane 2, methyl oleate; Lane 3, dipalmitoyl batyl alcohol (upper spot) and monopalmitoyl batyl alcohol (lower spot); Lane 4, distearoyl batyl alcohol; and Lane 5, total lipids from Ehrlich ascites cells. The polarity of the solvents decreases from top to bottom and from left to right. [F. Snyder, E. A. Cress, and N. Stephens. *Lipids* **1**, 381 (1966). Reproduced by permission of *Lipids*.]

Free (unesterified) alkyl and alk-1-enyl ethers of glycerol can be resolved from monoacylglycerols on silica gel (Figure 9) in a number of solvents[38,51] such as hexane–diethyl ether–methanol–acetic acid (80:20:5:1 or 80:20:10:1, v/v), chloroform–methanol (98:2, v/v), diethyl ether–water (100:0.5, v/v), or diethyl ether–acetic acid (100:

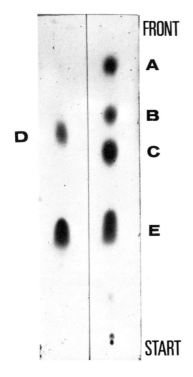

FRONT

A

B

D

C

E

START

Figure 8. Thin-layer chromatogram of (A) diacyl glyceryl ether and methyl oleate (used as carrier for lipase reaction); (B) 1-alkyl-3-acyl glyceryl ether; (C) 1-alkyl-2-acyl glyceryl ether; (D) 1-acyl-2-alkyl glyceryl ether; and (E) free fatty acids. The chromatogram was prepared on a Silica Gel G layer in solvent of chloroform–methanol–acetic acid (98:2:1, v/v).

0.5, v/v). Like the other acyl-substituted lipid classes of glyceryl ethers, alk-1-enyl ethers migrate ahead of the alkyl ethers. Best results for quantitation of the alkyl and alk-1-enyl glyceryl ethers by photodensitometry[38] are obtained in diethyl ether–acetic acid (100:0.5, v/v). The O- and S-ethers of glycerol are not separated unless they are chromatographed as their isopropylidene derivatives in a solvent of hexane–diethyl ether (90:10, v/v).[59] The isopropylidene derivatives of related diols[12, 13] can also be resolved from glyceryl ethers in this solvent.[15]

Diol Ethers

The glycerolipids trap[10, 117] diol lipids to the extent that the natural mixtures are not easily separated by adsorption TLC. Synthetic diol and glycerolipids containing ether bonds have been chromatographed by adsorption and reversed-phase partition TLC;[14, 53] chromatography based on partition instead of adsorption processes was capable of separating the classes of diol lipids from the corresponding classes of glycerolipids. Under certain conditions, countercurrent distribution can successfully resolve diacyl diols from triacylglycerols.[10] Gas-liquid chromatographic techniques have also been developed for the resolution of intact diol lipids from other lipid classes more plentiful in biological samples.[10, 67, 117]

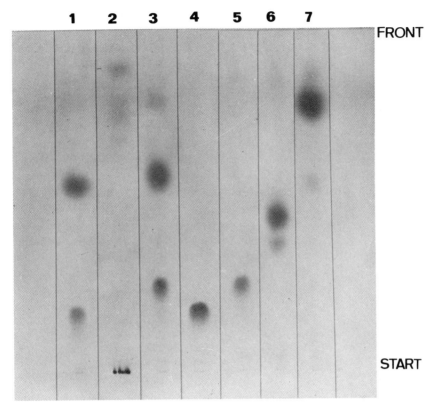

Figure 9. Products of LiAlH₄ hydrogenolysis of alkyl-acyl phosphatidic acid (Lane 1) and alk-1-enyl diacyl glyceryl ethers (Lane 3). The chromatoplate also contains alkyl-acyl phosphatidic acid (Lane 2), 1-glyceryl *cis* 9-octadecenyl ether (Lane 4), alk-1-enyl glyceryl ether (Lane 5) isolated by TLC after LiAlH₄ reduction, cyclic acetal (Lane 6) which was prepared from the alk-1-enyl glyceryl ether shown in Lane 5, and aldehydes (Lane 7) isolated after hydrolysis of alk-1-enyl glyceryl ethers. Silica Gel G was used as the adsorbent and the solvent was diethyl ether–30% aqueous ammonia (100:0.25, v/v). [R. Wood and F. Snyder. *Lipids* 3, 129 (1967). Reproduced by permission of *Lipids*.]

Resolution of Classes: Phospholipids

The alkyl, alk-1-enyl, and acyl phospholipids cannot be completely resolved from one another as intact molecules. Adequate subfractionation of these phosphorus-containing lipids requires selective removal of the phosphate, phosphoryl-base, or both the phosphate and acyl moieties before chromatography.

Phospholipase C, a key enzyme in the positional analysis of phospholipids, is used for cleaving the phosphoryl-base group attached to glycerol. The resulting diglyceride types can be analyzed by TLC (described earlier) and, after acetylation, by high-temperature GLC. Two-dimensional separation-reaction-separation TLC has also been applied[75] to the analysis of diglyceride acetates derived from the alkyl-acyl, alk-1-enyl-acyl, and diacyl forms of choline phosphatides. Generally, alk-1-enyl ethers must be cleaved by acid or hydrogenated before GLC analysis.

The removal of both phosphoryl-base and acyl moieties is accomplished by LiAlH$_4$ reduction.[38] The products, alkyl and alk-1-enyl glycerol or diol lipids, can be analyzed using TLC systems for free ether-linked glycerol and glycol compounds. Selective removal of the acyl group in position 2 of glycerolipids is possible with phospholipase A; however, the reactivity of ether-linked lipids as substrates for phospholipases is generally slow.

Attempts to fractionate the intact subclasses of phosphoglycerides by partition chromatography[118] and by argentation-TLC[119] have been successful in concentrating the alk-1-enyl ether-linked phosphoglycerides. However, so far, neither procedure has provided resolution as clear-cut as that obtained for the various subclasses of neutral lipids.

Renkonen[120] has described a new approach to the resolution of molecular species of phosphoglycerides as intact molecules (see Chapter 5 in this volume). The polar phosphoryl-base moiety is masked with a methyl and dinitrophenyl group. These derivatives are illustrated below for the alkyl and alk-1-enyl ethanolamine phosphoglycerides.

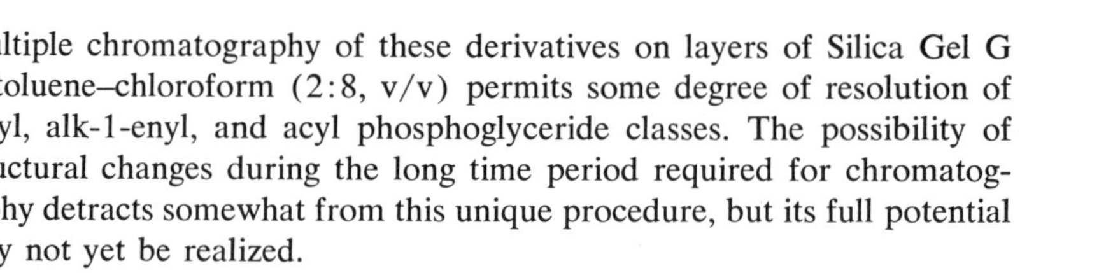

Multiple chromatography of these derivatives on layers of Silica Gel G in toluene–chloroform (2:8, v/v) permits some degree of resolution of alkyl, alk-1-enyl, and acyl phosphoglyceride classes. The possibility of structural changes during the long time period required for chromatography detracts somewhat from this unique procedure, but its full potential may not yet be realized.

Resolution of Subclasses by Metal Ions

Argentation-TLC permits the fractionation of lipids on the basis of number of double bonds[121] (see Volume I, Chapter 3, of this series[126]). An example of this type of fractionation is illustrated for glyceryl ethers[112] in Figure 10. Silver ions form π bond complexes with C-to-C double bonds; these complexes dissociate easily during extraction of the lipid fractions from the silicic acid. One silver ion is required per double bond. Morris[121] has discussed the nature of the π complex depicted below.

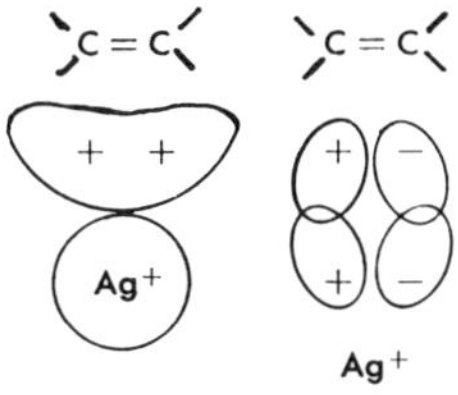

Other metal ions have also been useful in the subfractionation of lipid classes. Arsenite or borate ions can form complexes with compounds that have two adjacent free hydroxyl groups.[122] Wood and Snyder[16] used these ions to resolve 1- and 2-isomers of glyceryl ethers. The 2-isomers do not react, but the 1-isomers are thought to form the following complexes:

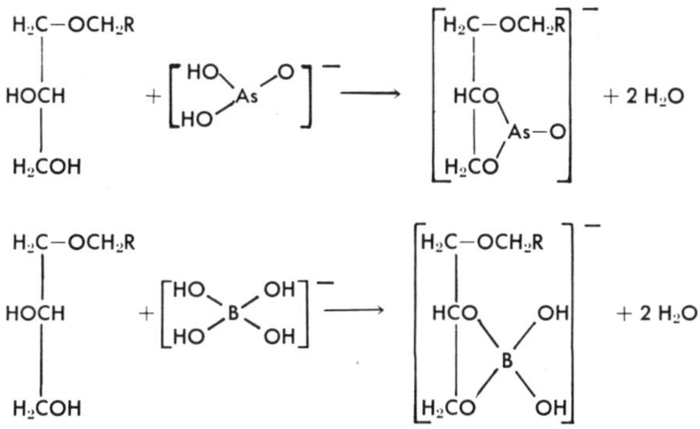

The difference in polarities between the metal complexes of the 1-isomers and the unreacted 2-isomers provides an excellent separation (Figure 11) on Silica Gel G in hexane–diethyl ether–methanol (80:20:5, v/v). The 1-isomer migrates faster than the 2-isomer on arsenite-impregnated plates, but slower than the 2-isomer on borate-impregnated plates. This behavior occurs because the borate complex (containing two free hydroxyl groups) is more polar than the arsenite complex and the 2-isomers of glyceryl ethers.[16]

Reversed-Phase Systems

Partition chromatography on adsorbent layers has also been used to separate homologs of the 0-alkylglycerols.[116] In general, this technique

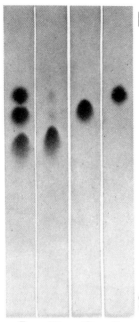

FRONT

Figure 10. Separation of a mixture of free glyceryl ethers according to degree of unsaturation on Silica Gel G layers impregnated with silver ions. Chromatography was performed twice in chloroform–ethanol (90: 10, v/v). The alkyl moieties of the glyceryl ethers are: (Lane A) mixture of 18:0, 18:1, and 18:2; (Lane B) 18:2; (Lane C) 18:1; and (Lane D) 18:0. [R. Wood and F. Snyder. *Lipids* **1**, 62 (1966). Reproduced by permission of *Lipids*.]

START

A B C D

is of little practical value unless gas-liquid chromatographs are not available. Problems are encountered with critical pairs that are not resolved, *e.g.*, linolenic + lauric acid or palmitoleic + linoleic + myristic acids. However, the major alkyl and alk-1-enyl chains in nature (16:0, 18:0, and 18:1) are easily resolved on siliconized paper and on thin-layers; tetrahydrofuran–water (60:40, v/v) is used as solvent.[116] Batyl alcohol has an Rf-value of 0.38 and selachyl alcohol a 0.45 Rf-value under these conditions.[116] Quantitation with reversed-phase systems is difficult, although the stationary phase can generally be removed at reduced pressures and relatively low temperatures. The lipids remain behind and can be quantitated by conventional procedures.

ANALYSIS OF ETHER LIPIDS BY GAS-LIQUID CHROMATOGRAPHY

High-Temperature Techniques for Resolution of Intact Ether Lipids

In lipid research, high-temperature gas-liquid chromatography of intact compounds or of fragments of high-molecular-weight compounds was initially applied to the analysis of triglycerides.[123] These procedures have now been adapted to the analysis of glyceryl ethers,[34] diglyceride acetates,[34, 110, 111] and diol lipids.[67] Phospholipids have also been analyzed at high temperatures by GLC,[124] but the method is not quantitative and

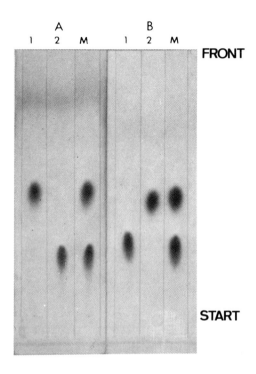

Figure 11. Separation of 18:1–1 (Lane 1) and 18:1–2 (Lane 2) isomeric glyceryl ethers on Silica Gel G adsorbent layers impregnated with sodium arsenite (A) and boric acid (B). [R. Wood and F. Snyder. *Lipids* **2**, 161 (1967). Reproduced by permission of *Lipids*.]

fragmentation of the phosphoglycerides occurs. The phosphoglycerides are, therefore, usually converted to neutral glycerides for high-temperature GLC. This is accomplished by using phospholipase C to remove the phosphoryl-base moieties; the diacyl-, alkyl-acyl-, or dialkyl glycerols produced are acetylated. The acetates are then analyzed[34, 110, 111] in a manner analogous to that used for triglyceride analysis. Figure 12 illustrates some typical tracings obtained by these procedures applied to triglycerides and diacyl glyceryl ethers. Bergelson and co-workers[117] were the first to carry out the GLC analysis of intact esterified diol molecules.

Resolution of Homologous Series of Ether Lipids According to Chain Length and Degree of Unsaturation

The GLC resolution of alkyl ether chains attached to glycerol or glycol requires masking of the free hydroxyl groups with TFA, TMS, methoxy, or acetate moieties. The measurement of diols was originally based largely on chromatographic behavior of hydrolyzed lipid samples,[10] but a number of ethers and esters of diols prepared synthetically have recently been analyzed by GLC as acetates, trifluoroacetates, and trimethylsilyl ethers on polar and nonpolar liquid phases.[67] Similar tech-

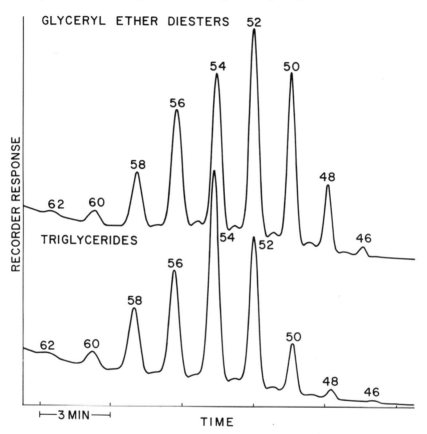

Figure 12.   Gas-liquid chromatograms obtained by analysis of intact triglycerides and diacyl glyceryl ethers from Ehrlich ascites cells. The carbon numbers represent the sum of the carbon atoms in the carbon chains. [R. Wood and F. Snyder.   *Arch. Biochem. Biophys.* **131,** 478 (1969). Reproduced by permission of Academic Press, Inc.]

niques have also been applied to the analysis of dihydroxy fatty acids.[125] Cleavage of the ether bond by HI has also been used to obtain compounds (alkyl iodides) suitable for GLC. Acetaldehyde and especially isopropylidene derivatives (Figure 4) can be used for GLC analysis of alkyl glyceryl ethers, but they cannot be employed for that of glycol ethers. Typical chromatograms of the TFA- and TMS-derivatives of alkyl glyceryl ethers are shown in Figure 3.

Because of the acidic conditions of the reactions, alk-1-enyl ethers are not amenable to the same derivative preparations used for alkyl ethers. However, lipids containing alk-1-enyl ether bonds can be hydrogenated with platinum as catalyst preceding GLC if only chain lengths need to be resolved. After hydrogenation, the same derivatives and GLC conditions as those employed for alkyl glyceryl ethers are used. It is generally much more satisfactory to cleave the alk-1-enyl ethers with acid, subsequently analyzing the aldehydes produced (Figure 4). Storage of the free aldehydes in carbon disulfide appears to prevent polymerization, oxidation, and other alterations that could affect their quantitative analysis.[70] Analysis of the fatty aldehydes derived from alk-1-enyl ether lipids provides information about chain lengths and degree of unsaturation; usually all major homologs of the ether-linked side chains found in nature can be resolved.[21, 70]

Table III summarizes the conditions used for gas-liquid chromatography of various derivatives acquired from lipids containing alkyl and alk-1-enyl ether bonds. As with most chromatographic procedures, maximum information about a molecule can be obtained only when other chemical procedures and other types of chromatography are used to their fullest extent.

Table III

Experimental Conditions for Gas-Liquid Chromatography
of Ether-Linked Lipids, Their Derivatives, and Related Compounds

Class of lipids (or derivatives)	*Liquid phase*	*Support*	*Temperature °C*	*Reference*
FREE GLYCERYL ETHERS				
Isopropylidenes	15% EGSS-X	Gas Chrom P (100–120 mesh)	170	113
	20% EGS	Gas Chrom E (80–100 mesh)	210	102
TFA	15% EGSS-X	Gas Chrom P (100–120 mesh)	170	112
TMS	5% Apiezon L	Chromosorb W (60–80 mesh)	250	112
Alkyl acetaldehydes	20% EGS	Gas Chrom P (80–100 mesh)	160	17
Alkyl iodides	10% EGS	Gas Chrom P (60–80 mesh)	200	68, 100
Dimethoxy	25% EGS	Kieselguhr (60–80 mesh)	243	104
Acetates	LHC IR-296 (polyester)	Celite (100–140 mesh)	218	109
DIACYL GLYCERYL ETHERS (including acetates)	1% OV-1	Gas Chrom Q (100–120 mesh)	Temperature programmed at 5°/minute; 200–335	34

Table III (continued)

Class of lipids (or derivatives)	Liquid phase	Support	Temperature °C	Reference
ALKYL ACYL GLYCEROLS	1% OV-1	Gas Chrom Q (100–120 mesh)	Temperature programmed at 5°/minute; 150–275	111
GLYCOL ETHERS				
TFA, TMS, and acetates	15% EGSS-X	Gas Chrom P (100–120 mesh)	Temperature programmed at 3°/minute; 125–190	67
TFA, TMS, and acetates	5% SE-30	Chromosorb W (60–80 mesh)	Temperature programmed at 3°/minute; 150–235	67
GLYCOLS				
Intact glycol compounds	10% SE-30	Chromosorb W	Temperature programmed at 5°/minute; 200–320	117
DIACYL WAXES	1% SE-30	Gas Chrom P	Temperature programmed; 270–325	13
UROPYGIOLS Acetonides	3% SE-30	Gas Chrom P (100–140 mesh)	150 or 250	12
DIHYDROXY FATTY ACIDS	5% SE-30	Chromosorb W (60–80 mesh)	187	125
	15% EGSS-X	Gas Chrom P (100–120 mesh)	180	125
ALKANE-1,2-DIOLS Isopropylidenes	10% EGSS-X	Gas Chrom P (100–120 mesh)	190	15
TMS	10% EGSS-X	Gas Chrom P (100–120 mesh)	180	15
LONG CHAIN FATTY ALDEHYDES				
Intact	15% EGSS-X	Gas Chrom P (100–120 mesh)	Temperature programmed at 3°/minute; 130–180	70
Intact	5% SE-30	Chromosorb W (60–80 mesh)	160	70
Dimethyl acetals	Apiezon-M	—	197	115

REFERENCES

1. Snyder, F. *Progress in the Chemistry of Fats and Other Lipids,* Vol. 10. Part 3 Ed. by R. T. Holman (Oxford: Pergamon Press, 1969), pp 287–335.
2. Rapport, M. M., and N. Alonzo. J. Biol. Chem. **217,** 193 (1955).
3. Thompson, G. A., Jr. Biochemistry **6,** 2015 (1967).
4. Hallgren, B., and G. Ställberg. Acta Chem. Scand. **21,** 1519 (1967).
5. Rapport, M. M., and W. T. Norton. Ann. Rev. Biochem. **31,** 103 (1962).
6. Klenk, E., and H. Debuch. *Progress in the Chemistry of Fats and Other Lipids,* Vol. 6. Ed. by R. T. Holman, W. O. Lundberg, and T. Malkin (Oxford: Pergamon Press, 1963), pp 3–29.
7. Kates, M., P. S. Sastry, and L. S. Yengoyan. Biochim. Biophys. Acta **70,** 705 (1963).
8. Hirschmann, H. J. Biol. Chem. **235,** 2762 (1960).
9. Oswald, E. O., C. Piantadosi, C. E. Anderson, and F. Snyder. Chem. Phys. Lipids **1,** 270 (1967).
10. Bergelson, L. D. *Progress in the Chemistry of Fats and Other Lipids,* Vol. 10. Part 3 Ed. by R. T. Holman (Oxford: Pergamon Press, 1969), pp 239–286.
11. Kubistova, J., and D. Seth. Science **154,** 1461 (1966).
12. Haahti, E. O. A., and H. M. Fales. J. Lipid Res. **8,** 131 (1967).
13. Nikkari, T., and E. Haahti. Biochim. Biophys. Acta **164,** 294 (1968).
14. Baumann, W. J., H. H. O. Schmid, H. W. Ulshöfer, and H. K. Mangold. Biochim. Biophys. Acta **144,** 355 (1967).
15. Blank, M., and F. Snyder. Biochim. Biophys. Acta **187,** 154 (1969).
16. Wood, R., and F. Snyder. Lipids **2,** 161 (1967).
17. Mangold, H. K., and W. J. Baumann. *Lipid Chromatographic Analysis 1.* Ed. by G. V. Marinetti (New York: Marcel Dekker, Inc., 1967), pp 339–359.
18. Viswanathan, C. V. Chromatog. Rev. **10,** 18 (1968).
19. Thompson, G. A., Jr., and V. M. Kapoulas. *Methods in Enzymology,* Vol. 14, Ed. by J. M. Lowenstein (New York: Academic Press, 1969), 668–678.
20. Snyder, F. Exptl. Med. Biol. **4,** 609–621 (1969).
21. Gray, G. M. *Lipid Chromatographic Analysis 1.* Ed. by G. V. Marinetti (New York: Marcel Dekker, Inc., 1967), pp 401–463.
22. Snyder, F., B. Malone, and R. L. Wykle. Biochem. Biophys. Res. Commun. **34,** 40 (1969).
23. Snyder, F., R. L. Wykle, and B. Malone. Biochem. Biophys. Res. Commun. **34,** 315 (1969).
24. Tietz, A., M. Lindberg, and E. P. Kennedy. J. Biol. Chem. **239,** 4081 (1964).
25. Pfleger, R. C., C. Piantadosi, and F. Snyder. Biochim. Biophys. Acta **144,** 633 (1967).

26. Warner, H. R., and W. E. M. Lands. J. Biol. Chem. **236**, 2404 (1961).
27. Ansell, G. B., and S. Spanner. Biochem. J. **94**, 252 (1965).
28. Ellingson, J. S., and W. E. M. Lands. Lipids 3, 111 (1968).
29. Snyder, F., and C. Piantadosi. Biochim. Biophys. Acta **152**, 794 (1968).
30. Snyder, F., and C. Piantadosi. Federation Proc. **27**, 458 (1968).
31. Waku, K., and W. E. M. Lands. J. Biol. Chem. **243**, 2654 (1968).
32. Kiyasu, J. Y., and E. P. Kennedy. J. Biol. Chem. **235**, 2590 (1960).
33. Thompson, G. A., Jr. Biochim. Biophys. Acta **152**, 409 (1968).
34. Wood, R., and F. Snyder. Arch. Biochem. Biophys. **131**, 478 (1969).
35. Snyder, F., and M. L. Blank. Arch. Biochem. Biophys. **130**, 101 (1969).
36. Snyder, F., and R. Wood. Cancer Res. **29**, 251 (1969).
37. Snyder, F., and R. Wood. Cancer Res. **28**, 972 (1968).
38. Wood, R., and F. Snyder. Lipids 3, 129 (1968).
39. Baumann, W. J., and H. K. Mangold. Biochim. Biophys. Acta **116**, 570 (1966).
40. Deuel, H. J., Jr. *The Lipids: Their Chemistry and Biochemistry 1.* (New York: Interscience, 1951), pp 392–396.
41. Hilditch, T. P., and P. N. Williams. *The Chemical Constitution of Natural Fats,* 4th ed. (New York: John Wiley and Sons, Inc., 1964), pp 670–672.
42. Schmid, H. H. O., H. K. Mangold, W. O. Lundberg, and W. J. Baumann. Microchem. J. **11**, 306 (1966).
43. Stegerhoek, L. J., and P. E. Verkade. Rec. Trav. Chim. **75**, 143 (1956).
44. Chacko, G. K., and D. J. Hanahan. Biochim. Biophys. Acta **164**, 252 (1968).
45. Baer, E., and H. O. L. Fischer. J. Biol. Chem. **140**, 397 (1941).
46. Baumann, W. J., V. Mahadevan, and H. K. Mangold. Z. Physiol. Chem. **347**, 52 (1966).
47. Cymerman-Craig, J., D. P. G. Hamon, K. K. Purushothaman, S. K. Roy, and W. E. M. Lands. Tetrahedron **22**, 175 (1966).
48. Schmid, H. H. O., W. J. Baumann, and H. K. Mangold. Biochim. Biophys. Acta **144**, 344 (1967).
49. Schmid, H. H. O., W. J. Baumann, and H. K. Mangold. J. Am. Chem. Soc. **89**, 4797 (1967).
50. Piantadosi, C., and F. Snyder. J. Pharm. Sci. (in press, 1970).
51. Snyder, F., and C. Piantadosi. *Advances in Lipid Research 4* (New York: Academic Press, 1966), pp 257–283.
52. Piantadosi, C., and A. F. Hirsch. J. Pharm. Sci. **50**, 978 (1961).
53. Baumann, W. J., H. H. O. Schmid, J. K. G. Kramer, and H. K. Mangold. Z. Physiol. Chem. **349**, 1677 (1968).
54. Wood, R., and F. Snyder. J. Lipid Res. 8, 494 (1967).
55. Cymerman-Craig, J., and D. P. G. Hamon. J. Org. Chem. **30**, 4168 (1965).

56. Ryhage, R., and E. Stenhagen. J. Lipid Res. **5**, 361 (1960).
57. Carter, H. E., D. B. Smith, and D. N. Jones. J. Biol. Chem. **232**, 681 (1958).
58. Debuch, H. Z. Physiol. Chem. **317**, 182 (1959).
59. Wood, R., C. Piantadosi, and F. Snyder. J. Lipid Res. **10**, 370 (1969).
60. Warner, H. R., and W. E. M. Lands. J. Am. Chem. Soc. **85**, 60 (1963).
61. Slotboom, A. J., G. H. de Haas, and L. L. M. van Deenen. Chem. Phys. Lipids **1**, 192 (1967).
62. Slotboom, A. J. *Druk: V.R.B.-Offsetdrukkerij–Kleine der A 4–Groningen* (1968), pp 1–61.
63. Schmid, H. H. O., and H. K. Mangold. Biochem. Z. **346**, 13 (1966).
64. Piantadosi, C., A. F. Hirsch, C. L. Yarbro, and C. E. Anderson. J. Org. Chem. **28**, 2425 (1964).
65. Piantadosi, C., M. F. Frosolono, C. E. Anderson, and A. F. Hirsch. J. Pharm. Sci. **53**, 1024 (1964).
66. Serdarevich, B., and K. K. Carroll. Can. J. Biochem. **44**, 743 (1966).
67. Wood, R., and W. J. Baumann. J. Lipid Res. **9**, 733 (1968).
68. Guyer, K. E., W. A. Hoffman, L. A. Horrocks, and D. G. Cornwell. J. Lipid Res. **4**, 385 (1963).
69. Hanahan, D. J. J. Lipid Res. **6**, 350 (1965).
70. Wood, R., and R. D. Harlow. J. Lipid Res. **10**, 463 (1969).
71. Schmid, H. H. O., and H. K. Mangold. Biochim. Biophys. Acta **125**, 182 (1966).
72. Owens, K. Biochem. J. **100**, 354 (1966).
73. Horrocks, L. A. J. Lipid Res. **9**, 469 (1968).
74. Viswanathan, C. V., M. Basilio, S. P. Hoevet, and W. O. Lundberg. J. Chromatog. **34**, 241 (1968).
75. Viswanathan, C. V., F. Phillips, and W. O. Lundberg. J. Chromatog. **35**, 66 (1968).
76. Anderson, R. E., R. D. Garrett, M. L. Blank, and F. Snyder. Lipids **4**, 327 (1969).
77. Thompson, G. A., Jr., and P. Lee. Biochim. Biophys. Acta **98**, 151 (1965).
78. Lovern, J. A. *The Chemistry of Lipids of Biochemical Significance* (New York: John Wiley & Sons, Inc., 1957).
79. Dawson, R. M. C. Biochem. J. **75**, 45 (1960).
80. Dawson, R. M. C., N. Hemington, and J. B. Davenport. Biochem. J. **84**, 497 (1962).
81. Wells, M. A., and J. C. Dittmer. Biochemistry **5**, 3405 (1966).
82. Bevan, T. H., D. A. Brown, G. I. Gregory, and T. Malkin. J. Chem. Soc. **1953**, 127.
83. Hanahan, D. J. *Lipid Chemistry* (New York: John Wiley & Sons, Inc., 1960).
84. Pietruszko, R., and G. M. Gray. Biochim. Biophys. Acta **56**, 232 (1962).

85. Yurkowski, M., and H. Brockerhoff.   Biochim. Biophys. Acta **125**, 55 (1966).
86. Desnuelle, P., and P. Savary.   J. Lipid Res. **4**, 369 (1963).
87. Mattson, F. H., and R. A. Volpenhein.   J. Lipid Res. **2**, 58 (1961).
88. Mattson, F. H., and R. A. Volpenhein.   J. Lipid Res. **9**, 79 (1968).
89. de Haas, G. H., L. Sarda, and J. Roger.   Biochim. Biophys. Acta **106**, 638 (1965).
90. Wykle, R. L., and F. Snyder.   *USAEC Report ORAU-107* **1969**, 211.
91. Deenen, L. L. M., van, and G. H. de Haas.   Ann. Rev. Biochem. **35**, 157 (1966).
92. Marinetti, G. V., J. Erbland, and E. Stotz.   Biochim. Biophys. Acta **33**, 403 (1959).
93. Gottfried, E. L., and M. M. Rapport.   J. Biol. Chem. **237**, 329 (1962).
94. Warner, H. R., and W. E. M. Lands.   J. Am. Chem. Soc. **85**, 60 (1963).
95. Ansell, G. B., and S. Spanner.   Biochem. J. **97**, 375 (1965).
96. Lands, W. E. M., and P. Hart.   Biochim. Biophys. Acta **98**, 532 (1965).
97. Hartree, E. F., and T. Mann.   Biochem. J. **80**, 464 (1961).
98. Hack, M. H., and V. J. Ferrans.   Z. Physiol. Chem. **315**, 157 (1959).
99. Golde, L. M. G., van, and L. L. M. van Deenen.   Chem. Phys. Lipids **1**, 157 (1967).
100. Ramachandran, S., H. W. Sprecher, and D. G. Cornwell.   Lipids **3**, 511 (1968).
101. Privett, O. S., and E. C. Nickell.   J. Am. Oil Chemists' Soc. **39**, 414 (1962).
102. Hanahan, D. J., J. Ekholm, and C. M. Jackson.   Biochemistry **2**, 630 (1963).
103. Rudloff, E., von.   Can. J. Chem. **34**, 1413 (1956).
104. Hallgren, B., and S. Larsson.   J. Lipid Res. **3**, 31 (1962).
105. Karnovsky, M. L., and A. F. Brumm.   J. Biol. Chem. **216**, 689 (1955).
106. Baumann, W. J., H. H. O. Schmid, and H. K. Mangold.   J. Lipid Res. **10**, 132 (1969).
107. Brockerhoff, H.   J. Lipid Res. **8**, 167 (1967).
108. Slakey, P. M., W. E. M. Lands, and R. A. Pieringer.   Federation Proc. **25**, 521 (1966).
109. Blomstrand, R., and J. Gürtler.   Acta Chem. Scand. **13**, 1466 (1959).
110. Renkonen, O.   Biochim. Biophys. Acta **125**, 288 (1966).
111. Wood, R., W. J. Baumann, F. Snyder, and H. K. Mangold.   J. Lipid Res. **10**, 128 (1969).
112. Wood, R., and F. Snyder.   Lipids **1**, 62 (1966).
113. Wood, R.   Lipids **2**, 199 (1967).
114. Hardegger, E., L. Ruzicka, and E. Tagmann.   Helv. Chim. Acta **26**, 2205 (1943).
115. Farquhar, J. W.   J. Lipid Res. **3**, 21 (1962).
116. Malins, D. C., and H. K. Mangold.   J. Am. Oil Chemists' Soc. **37**, 576 (1960).

117. Bergelson, L. D., V. A. Vaver, N. V. Prokazova, A. N. Ushakov, and G. A. Popkova. Biochim. Biophys. Acta **116**, 511 (1966).
118. Gray, G. M., and M. G. MacFarlane. Biochem. J. **70**, 409 (1958).
119. Hoevet, S. P., C. V. Viswanathan, and W. O. Lundberg. J. Chromatog. **34**, 195 (1968).
120. Renkonen, O. J. Lipid Res. **9**, 34 (1968).
121. Morris, L. J. J. Lipid Res. **7**, 717 (1966).
122. Roy, G. L., A. L. Laferriere, and J. O. Edwards. J. Inorg. Nucl. Chem. **4**, 106 (1957).
123. Kuksis, A., and W. C. Breckenridge. J. Lipid Res. **7**, 576 (1966).
124. Kuksis, A., L. Marai, and D. A. Gornall. J. Lipid Res. **8**, 352 (1967).
125. Wood, R., E. L. Bever, and F. Snyder. Lipids **1**, 399 (1966).
126. Morris, L. J., and B. W. Nichols, in *Progress in Thin-Layer Chromatography and Related Methods*, Vol. 1. Ed. by A. Niederwieser and G. Pataki (Ann Arbor, Michigan: Ann Arbor-Humphrey Science Publishers, 1970), pp 75–93.

Chapter 5

Thin-Layer Chromatographic Analysis of Subclasses and Molecular Species of Polar Lipids

by O. Renkonen[*]

The number of different polar lipid molecules is very large in nature; thus, they have to be fractionated in a stepwise manner (Figure 1). Marshalling all the different steps to separate the molecules according to one structural feature only and not according to several has proved highly advantageous. For instance, when we want to separate lecithins from sphingomyelins, we must use a method that gives maximal resolution between the two lipid classes. But at the same time the method should not reveal differences among the molecular species of lecithins (and sphingomyelins) having different fatty acids. Only this type of method guarantees a complete separation of all lecithin molecules from all sphingomyelin molecules.

The structural differences of lipids may be grouped roughly into variations in the polar groups, the fatty chains, or the linkages between

[*]Research grants from Sigrid Jusélius Foundation, Helsinki, and from the Finnish Research Council for Sciences are acknowledged.

them. The complete fractionation of natural lipids requires the use of all these categories of structural differences, and they could, at least in theory, be employed in any order. However, it is customary to start by separating the lipids according to their polar groups.

Chromatography on silica gel, alumina, or DEAE-cellulose is the principal method used to separate polar lipids (phospholipids and glycolipids) according to differences in the polar groups. The resulting fractions (lecithins, phosphatidic acids, galactosyl diglycerides, lactosyl ceramides, etc.) will be called lipid classes in this paper (Figure 1).

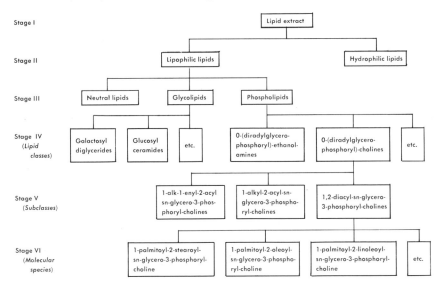

Figure 1. Fractionation of natural lipids.

Within these numerous polar lipid classes are subclasses which differ from one another in the linkages between the fatty chains and the polar group. Figure 2 shows examples of three subclasses of lecithins: (1) diacyl; (2) alkenyl-acyl; and (3) alkyl-acyl glycerophosphoryl cholines. During chromatography on silica gel, alumina, and DEAE-cellulose, no useful separation of the different subclasses takes place. But recently some successful methods have been developed which depend on the differences in the linkages. A given class or subclass contains many molecular species which show differences in the fatty chains proper. Several approaches have recently been presented for their study.

In this review I shall present and discuss the TLC methods available for separation and analysis of subclasses and molecular species of given polar lipid classes. To put these problems into proper perspective, a flow scheme of an idealized lipid fractionation is presented in Figure 1.

gl—Fig 2—Chap 5

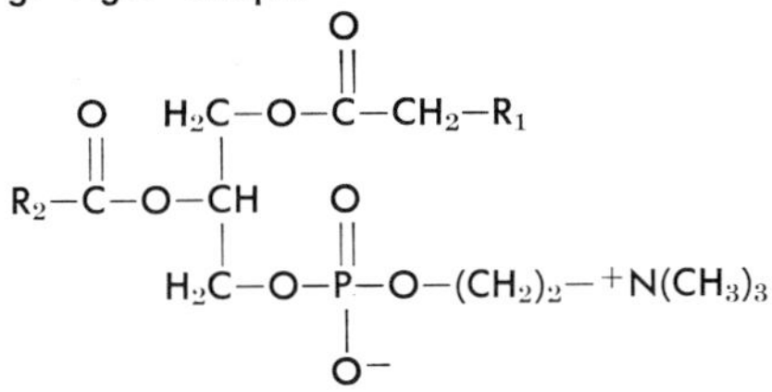

I
1,2-diacylglycerophosphorylcholines

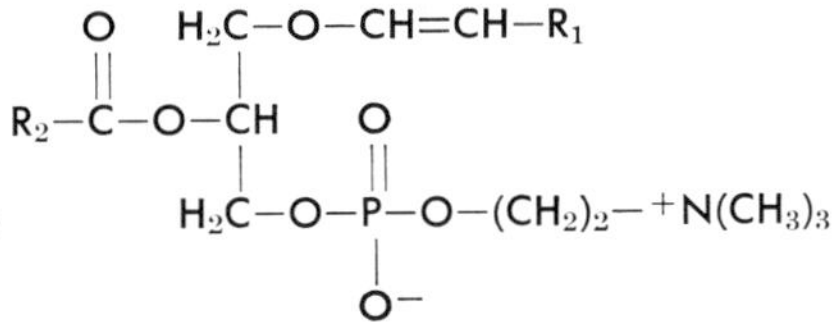

II
1-alkenyl-2-acyl-glycerophosphorylcholines

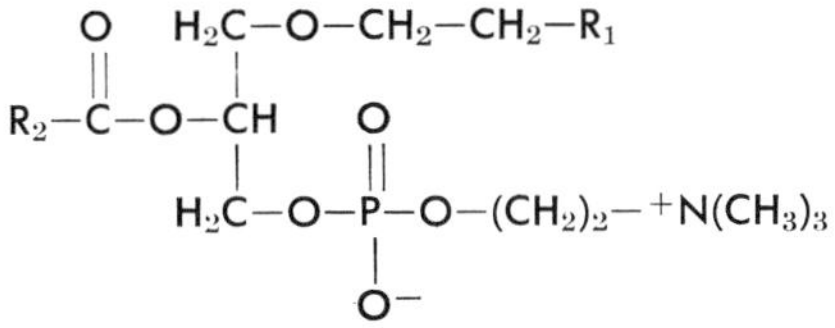

III
1-alkyl-2-acyl-glycerophosphorylcholines

Figure 2. Subclasses of O-(diacylglycerophosphoryl)-cholines or lecithins.

A SURVEY OF DIFFERENT APPROACHES*

The various linkages between glycerol and the fatty chains at C-1 in the three subclasses of glycerolipids (Figure 2) have widely differing chemical properties. This has helped to create procedures of selective destruction. Different agents can be used to hydrolyze one subclass faster than the other two; the slowly hydrolyzed one can then be isolated intact and in pure form from the partial hydrolysate. Table I lists suitable hydrolyzing agents and relative rates of hydrolysis of the different subclasses. The majority of the selective hydrolysis methods suffer a disad-

Table I
Relative Rates of Hydrolysis of Glycerolipid Subclasses[1]

Hydrolyzing agent	*1-alkenyl-2- acyl lipids*	*1-alkyl-2- acyl lipids*	*1,2-diacyl lipids*
Phospholipase A$_2$	Slow	Slow	Fast
Phospholipase C	Slow	Slow	Fast
Phospholipase D	Slow	Fast	Fast
Pancreatic lipase (or Phospholipase A$_1$)	Slow	Slow	Fast
Base	Slow	Slow	Fast
Acid	Fast	Slow	Slow

*Compare also page 110 *et seq.*

vantage in that they hydrolyze all subclasses to some extent, which means that only partial yields can be recovered. During recent years, therefore, chromatographic methods for the separation of the three subclasses have been studied. This work has been based mainly upon the different "polarity" of the ether and ester linkages in suitable derivatives of the polar lipids.

The olefinic double bonds of the unsaturated fatty acids or the hydroxyl groups of some glycolipid fatty acids represent polar structures which affect chromatographic mobility and make the molecules, even within a lipid class, slightly different from one another. The size of the fatty chains varies, too, and affects the apparent polarity of the lipids. All these subtle differences can be used to separate certain molecular species by adsorption or partition chromatography. Differences in the degree of olefinic unsaturation of the individual molecular species can be used for efficient separations of the intact polar lipids when silver ions are used to enhance the polar character of the double bonds. The methods currently used are based on Arvidson's work in Lund, Sweden. Arvidson has also developed a reversed-phase technique which allows separation of intact lecithins according to molecular size of the fatty chains.

All the above examples represent fractionation of the polar lipids in intact form. These lipids, however, have a great tendency to associate and form multimolecular aggregates, which decreases the efficiency of any chromatographic separation. Accordingly, we have studied chromatography of the subclasses and molecular species of polar lipids after removing or "masking" of the polar groups. With these chemical modifications we convert the polar lipids into a nonassociating form which can be chromatographed with improved resolution.

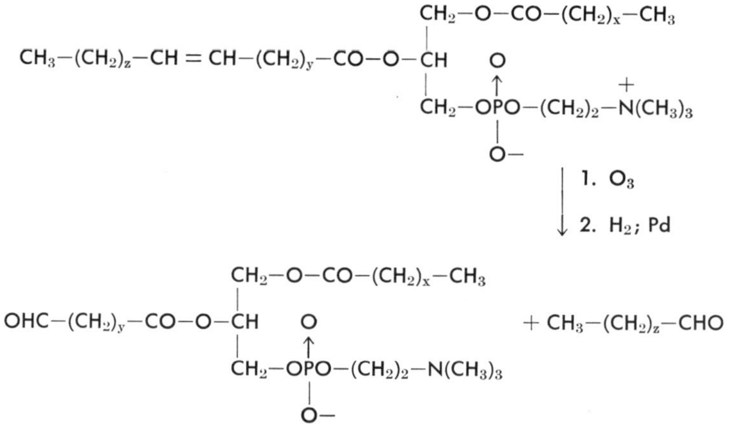

$$CH_3-(CH_2)_z-CH=CH-(CH_2)_y-CO-O-\underset{\substack{|\\ CH_2-O\overset{\uparrow}{P}O-(CH_2)_2-\overset{+}{N}(CH_3)_3 \\ |\\ O-}}{\overset{\overset{\displaystyle CH_2-O-CO-(CH_2)_x-CH_3}{|}}{CH}}\quad O$$

$$\downarrow \quad \begin{array}{l} 1.\ O_3 \\ 2.\ H_2;\ Pd \end{array}$$

$$OHC-(CH_2)_y-CO-O-\underset{\substack{|\\ CH_2-O\overset{\uparrow}{P}O-(CH_2)_2-N(CH_3)_3 \\ |\\ O-}}{\overset{\overset{\displaystyle CH_2-O-CO-(CH_2)_x-CH_3}{|}}{CH}}\quad O \qquad + CH_3-(CH_2)_z-CHO$$

Figure 3.   Oxidative analysis of lecithins.

A different approach through chemically modified polar lipids was described in Privett's laboratory.[2] This group accentuated the differences of olefinic unsaturation by oxidizing the polar lipids as shown in Figure 3. Their approach has been elaborated, for example, by Wurster and Copenhaver,[3] who could separate four groups of lecithins from one another. These were the intact saturated lecithin species and the different "aldehydic" lecithins resulting from unsaturated fatty acids at C-1 or C-2, or at both positions.

Some of these approaches are described in detail in the subsequent sections, whereas others are treated less extensively. The presentation is not exhaustive, but it tries to be critical. Compare also the foregoing chapter, pages 110–118 and 129–132.

SEPARATION OF SPECIES OF INTACT PHOSPHATIDYL CHOLINES AND OTHER GLYCEROPHOSPHOLIPID CLASSES

Argentation-TLC*

Kaufmann *et al.*[4] were the first to report separation of egg and soya lecithins into several components on silver nitrate-impregnated Silica Gel G plates. However, they did not report any experimental evidence on the composition of the different fractions. Pelick *et al.*[5] could not reproduce the work of the Kaufmann group, but in 1965 van Golde and co-workers[6] reported a complete separation of two different subfractions of rat liver lecithins with this method. Both fractions were recovered and their fatty acids analyzed; results showed that the more rapidly moving fraction contained principally palmitic, stearic and octadecenoic acid on C-1 of glycerol, and octadecadienoic, octadecenoic and palmitic acid on C-2. The more slowly moving lecithin fraction contained C_{20}-polyenes, mainly arachidonic acid, on C-2, whereas stearic, palmitic and octadecenoic acid were the principal components on C-1. Thus, the slow fraction of lecithins appeared to be a relatively simple mixture of tetraenoic and pentaenoic species, whereas the rapid fraction was more complex and probably contained molecules of zero to three double bonds. Arvidson finally reported superb and well-documented separations of intact lecithin species on silver nitrate-impregnated silica gel.[7] He described the separation of monoenoic, dienoic, trienoic, tetraenoic, pentaenoic, and hexaenoic species from one another; only the saturated and monoenoic species were not well-separated. The general approach of Arvidson was the same as that of van Golde *et al.*, but the improved separations were

---

*For a review on argentation-TLC of lipids, see Volume I of this series, pages 74–93. See also this volume, pages 130 and 131.

obtained by using gypsum-free silica gel, and by activating the plates quite strongly.

Arvidson's first report dates back to 1965; the following details are taken from his paper of 1968.[8] This procedure has been selected to guarantee successful application of the method, yet to avoid unnecessary precautions.

The isolated samples of phosphatidyl cholines are fractionated on plates (20 × 20 cm) coated with a 0.8-mm thick layer of Silica Gel H (E. Merck, AG, Darmstadt, Germany) containing 15 g of $AgNO_3$ per 50 g of silica gel. The plates are activated at 190–195°C for 2.5–4.0 hours and then stored over P_2O_5 in a vacuum desiccator to which they are transferred while still hot. A maximal amount of 10 mg of rat liver phosphatidyl cholines is applied as a band to each plate. The solvent for TLC is chloroform–methanol–water (60:30:5, v/v). After chromatography the plates are sprayed with a 0.2% solution of dichlorofluorescein in ethanol, and the different fractions are located under ultraviolet light. They are marked out and scraped off into small sintered glass funnels, and the lipids are eluted three times with a 4-ml mixture of chloroform–methanol–acetic acid–water (50:39:1:10, v/v). To each eluate 4 ml of 4M ammonia is added and the mixtures are shaken and then centrifuged. The upper phases containing dichlorofluorescein but no lipid are sucked off and discarded. The chloroform phases are washed once with 4 ml of 50% v/v methanol in water containing 0.5% w/v NaCl which precipitates remaining traces of silver ions. In this way lipid fractions free from dye and silver ions are obtained.

Through this procedure rat liver phosphatidyl cholines are separated into four subfractions with different degree of total unsaturation (Figure 4). Fraction I is monoenoic, II is dienoic, III is tetraenoic, and IV is hexaenoic (Table II). Recovery of phosphatidyl cholines (P) from the $AgNO_3$-impregnated plates ranges between 90 and 95%. Close agreement is found among the specific radioactivities of the unfractionated samples, the specific radioactivities calculated from the total amounts of P, and radioactivity recovered in the four fractions. This indicates that no preferential loss of any subfractions occurs. At the beginning of his work Arvidson used methanol or chloroform–methanol–water (5:4:1) for the elution of the lecithin fractions, but this led to low and variable recoveries of 60–80%.

Many other laboratories have used Arvidson's procedure or its modifications with remarkable success. Tinoco et al.[9] reproduced Arvidson's procedure almost exactly, and they too obtained quite clear separation of monoenes, dienes, trienes, and tetraenes. In a later report,[10] even the tetraenes were further separated from the pentaenes and hexaenes. Methanol was used in the extraction of the lecithins from the adsorbent, but the yields (75%) were clearly inferior to those of Arvidson. This

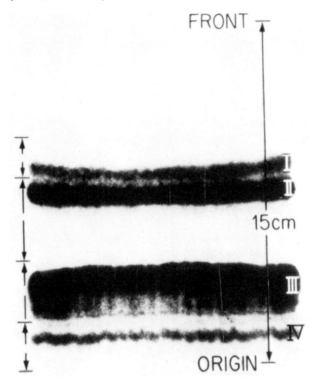

Figure 4. Argentation-TLC of intact lecithins from rat liver: (I) monoenoic fraction; (II) dienoic fraction; (III) tetraenoic fraction; and (IV) hexaenoic fraction. Experimental conditions are listed in the text. According to Arvidson.[8] (Reproduced by permission of Springer-Verlag.)

Table II

Composition of Rat Liver Phosphatidyl Cholines*

Sex	Sub-fraction	Per cent of total recovered P^a	Fatty acid composition (moles %)[b]						
			16:0	16:1	18:0	18:1	18:2	20:4	22:6
Male	Monoenoic	11.5±1.3	46.7	5.0	7.7	37.2	3.5	—	—
	Dienoic	25.9±0.5	36.7	2.0	11.0	3.5	46.8	—	—
	Tetraenoic	49.6±1.8	26.0	—	24.6	3.0	—	46.5	—
	Hexaenoic	13.0±0.7	36.9	—	18.6	2.9	2.2	3.9	35.5
Female	Monoenoic	12.8±1.4	46.0	2.3	9.4	38.6	3.7	—	—
	Dienoic	24.5±1.8	32.9	1.3	14.3	4.0	47.4	—	—
	Tetraenoic	42.7±2.0	18.4	—	30.5	2.9	—	48.2	—
	Hexaenoic	20.1±1.6	30.4	—	23.8	3.0	—	3.1	39.8

[a]Six male and six female rats were used. Values are means ± S.D.
[b]Pooled samples from rats for each subfraction.
*According to Arvidson.[8] (Courtesy of Springer-Verlag.)

group showed that the label of $^{14}CH_3$-methionine was incorporated more to the tetraenoic than to the less unsaturated lecithin species of rat liver *in vivo*.

Rat liver lecithins were separated into three subgroups—mono + dienoic, tetraenoic, and hexaenoic fractions—by Kyriakides and Balint.[11] These authors activated the plates far less than Arvidson did; they also used calcium sulfate-containing adsorbent, yet their separations must have been excellent as judged by the reported GLC data. Silver nitrate was eliminated from the lecithins with a cation exchange resin (AG 50W-88; 200–400 mesh, H$^+$ form, Bio-Rad Laboratories, Richmond, California). The appropriate areas of the adsorbent were scraped into small columns containing 1–2 g of resin, and the lipids were then eluted with methanol–acetic acid–water (94:1:5).

Nakayama and Kawamura[12] studied biliary lecithins by using low-activity plates of calcium sulfate type. The separations were remarkable in some cases, *e.g.*, between the species containing 20:4 or 20:5 as component fatty acids; but as a whole these lecithin mixtures contained rather saturated species which proved to separate poorly on this type of plates. Resolution between monoenes and dienes that made up 70–80% of the total would have been significant, but it was not obtained.

Using Arvidson's technique, Rytter *et al.*[13] separated microsomal lecithins of rat liver into four fractions. However, close examination of the reported fatty acid compositions revealed certain inconsistencies. The hexaenoic fraction was obtained in satisfactory purity, but the linoleate and arachidonate-containing fractions appeared to grossly contaminate each other, as did the linoleate and oleate-containing fractions. Fortunately the purity of the hexaenoic subfractions enabled the authors to see clear differences in the incorporation of radioactive choline and ethanolamine into the lecithins. An earlier report of Balint *et al.*[14] had already shown that labeled choline incorporates quickly into the dienoic lecithin species, whereas the tetraenoic species are labeled more easily from methyl-^{14}C derived from methionine than from 1-^{14}C-choline.

Glycerophosphatides other than lecithins have been studied relatively little. Haverkate and van Deenen[15] separated phosphatidyl glycerols of spinach leaves into two subfractions on argentation plates. The slower fraction contained three to four double bonds per molecule, and the faster zero to two. An interesting molecular species—(1-linolenoyl-2-Δ^3-*trans*-hexadecenoyl)-phosphatidyl glycerol—accounted for about half of all phosphatidyl glycerols of spinach leaves. Arvidson[8] separated phosphatidyl ethanolamines with his system making only a small change in the solvent; chloroform–methanol–water (55:35:7) was suitable for these lipids. Figure 5 shows the separations obtained, and the fatty acid compositions of the subfractions are given in Table III. The work of Lundberg and associates (page 154) suggests that alkenyl-acyl phospholipids,

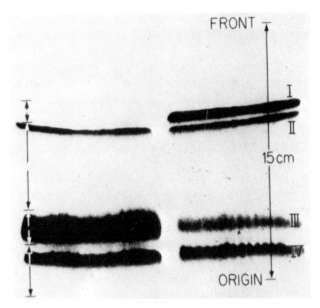

Figure 5. Argentation-TLC of intact phosphatidyl ethanolamines from rat liver (left sample) and from egg yolk (right sample): (I) monoenoic fraction; (II) dienoic fraction; (III) tetraenoic fraction; and (IV) hexaenoic fraction. According to Arvidson.[8] (Reproduced by permission of Springer-Verlag.)

too, are separated into molecular species with this method. Our group has fractionated phosphatidic acids after their conversion into dimethyl esters (page 171).

Table III
Composition of Rat Liver Phosphatidyl Ethanolamines*

Sex	Sub-fraction	Per cent of total recovered P[a]	\multicolumn{7}{Fatty acid composition (moles %)[b]}						
			16:0	16:1	18:0	18:1	18:2	20:4	22:6
Male	Monoenoic	3.6±0.6	35.6	4.4	16.4	37.3	6.3	—	—
	Dienoic	18.5±1.8	27.3	—	25.2	6.1	41.5	—	—
	Tetraenoic	49.7±1.4	12.8	—	36.7	5.3	—	45.2	—
	Hexaenoic	28.2±1.4	36.9	—	19.6	2.2	—	3.4	37.9
Female	Monoenoic	3.6±0.8	33.0	3.0	19.4	38.5	6.1	—	—
	Dienoic	16.3±1.9	23.9	—	31.2	3.8	41.0	—	—
	Tetraenoic	40.4±1.7	11.5	—	42.3	—	—	46.2	—
	Hexaenoic	39.7±1.0	29.1	—	26.6	1.8	—	—	42.5

[a]Five male and six female rats were used. Values are means ± S.D.
[b]Pooled samples from three rats for each subfraction.
*According to Arvidson.[8] (Courtesy of Springer-Verlag.)

The experience of these different groups leads me to the following conclusions: (1) argentation-TLC can be used to separate intact molecular species; (2) it appears likely that Arvidson's system needs only minor modifications in the solvents to separate phosphatidyl inositols, phosphatidyl glycerols, phosphatidyl serines, etc.; (3) separation of the less unsaturated molecules—monoenes, dienes, and trienes—seems to require very highly activated plates; (4) saturated and monoenoic molecules have not yet been separated. It is curious that this latter separation is harder to obtain than the fractionation, for example, of a tetraene and pentaene.

Reversed-Phase TLC

In 1967 Arvidson[16] made another breakthrough by describing reversed-phase separations of intact phosphatidyl cholines. Each of the four fractions he had obtained from rat liver lecithins by argentation-TLC contained essentially two molecular species which were homologs to each other. For instance, the monoenoic fraction contained palmitoyl-oleoyl- and stearoyl-oleoyl-glycerophosphoryl choline. The dienoic fraction contained in the same way a palmitoyl-linoleoyl and a stearoyl-linoleoyl lecithin. The new fractionation system of Arvidson was now designed to resolve these binary mixtures.

At the beginning of the experiment an inert and nonadsorptive support for reversed-phase partition-TLC was obtained by repeatedly washing Kieselguhr G (E. Merck, AG, Darmstadt, Germany) with 2N HCl until it was free from sulfate. The absence of sulfate was determined by adding a few drops of a saturated solution of $Ba(NO_3)_2$ to a centrifuged aliquot of the Kieselguhr suspension. The sulfate-free material was then repeatedly suspended in distilled water until free from chloride (no precipitate with a saturated silver nitrate solution). The sulfate- and chloride-free Kieselguhr was then washed with methanol and dried at 120°C. The dry powder was exposed to the vapors of dichlorodimethyl-silane (Fluka AG, Buchs, Switzerland) in a desiccator. When completely hydrophobic (after 1–2 days, judged from shaking a sample with water in a test tube) the powder was again washed with methanol on a sintered glass filter under suction. The filter cake was then suspended in diethyl ether. All lumps and coarse particles that rapidly sedimented from the ether suspension were rejected. The remaining material was air-dried and stored until needed for preparing plates. To 50 g of this Kieselguhr was added 20 ml of undecane (Kistner AB, Gothenburg, Sweden) and enough hexane to give a rather thin slurry which was spread to a thickness of 0.5 mm on 10 × 15-cm glass plates. The plates were left at room temperature for 2 hours and then stored in a desiccator. (The closed vessel prevents evaporation of undecane.)

Aliquots of the four lecithin fractions were applied to the plates as spots or bands. The load of phosphorus was 0.5–1 μg per spot or 20–25 μg over a band 7 cm long. Seven parts of methanol–water (9:1) that had been equilibrated with undecane in a separatory funnel was diluted with three parts of pure methanol–water (9:1) and the mixture used as solvent. Chromatography took place at 18°C in tanks lined with filter paper moistened with the solvent. Immediately after chromatography, while the plate was still wet, the fractions could be seen as grayish areas against a white background both in reflected and transmitted light. The bands were scraped off into conical centrifuge tubes containing 10 ml of chloroform–methanol (2:1). The tubes were shaken and centrifuged. The clear supernatant solution was decanted into a second tube and the solvent was evaporated under nitrogen. As illustrated in Figure 6, each lecithin fraction applied to the undecane-impregnated plate was resolved into two subfractions. From GLC analysis it became evident that the four pairs of spots on the plate in Figure 6 represent the eight major molecular species found in rat liver lecithins.

Arvidson tested several types of plates and found that silica gel was entirely unsatisfactory. Also, on plates made by conventional procedures from untreated Kieselguhr, severe trailing obscured possible separations. This necessitated a somewhat tedious washing and silanizing procedure.

The results obtained by reversed-phase partition chromatography were temperature-dependent. TLC at 4°C increased the degree of resolution of all four lecithin samples into their subfractions, but the monoenoic lecithins occasionally exhibited some streaking. At 25°C the Rf-values of all fractions were increased to more than 0.9. At 18°C, separations were satisfactory as long as the water content of the solvent was between 5 and 15%. Below 5% water the Rf-values became too high for resolution, above 15% too low. It is noteworthy that the unsaturated fatty acid moiety of the lecithin molecule had little influence on the Rf-values, especially of the polyunsaturated lecithins (Figure 6, B, C, and D). Thus, the partition coefficient in the undecane–methanol–water system was largely determined by the saturated fatty acid at the 1-position.

Arvidson made several interesting biochemical observations with his methods. He showed, for instance, that after injection of radioactive choline the palmitoyl lecithins achieved a much higher specific activity than the corresponding stearoyl lecithins of rat liver. Tinoco *et al.*[17] in their methylation studies have recently applied Arvidson's reversed-phase technique with remarkable success to rat liver lecithins.

Lipid classes other than lecithins have been studied very little. Arvid-

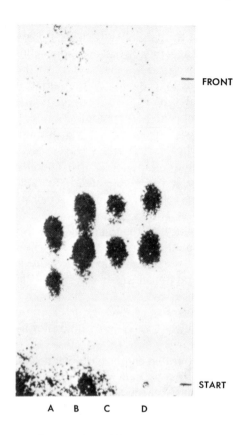

FRONT

Figure 6. Reversed-phase TLC of the four subfractions of rat liver lecithins obtained by argentation-TLC: (A) monoenes; (B) dienes; (C) tetraenes; (D) hexaenes. According to Arvidson.[16] (Reproduced by permission of the American Institute of Biological Sciences.)

START

A   B   C   D

son has reported[18] that the reversed-phase separation of phosphatidyl ethanolamine species has met with difficulties not yet solved. Phosphatidic acids have been studied by both reversed-phase and argentation techniques after conversion into dimethyl esters (see page 171).

ATTEMPTS TO SEPARATE INTACT SUBCLASSES OF LECITHINS AND RELATED PHOSPHOLIPID CLASSES

Methods of selective hydrolysis of the three subclasses of glycerophospholipids were mentioned in the Survey of Different Approaches (page 145). This section will discuss a recent attempt described by Lundberg and associates of the Hormel Institute, Austin, Minnesota.

Hoevet et al.[19] were encouraged by the beautiful argentation separations of intact diacyl glycerophosphoryl cholines reported by Kaufmann et al.[4] and by Arvidson.[7] They pointed out many reports indicating that alkenyl-acyl phosphatides (plasmalogens) generally contain very small amounts of saturated fatty acids and that the main fatty acids are polyenes. (It would have been better to emphasize similarities of plasmalogens and diacyl phosphatides in relation to the C-2 fatty acids.) They also emphasized that the vinyl ether linkage introduces additional olefinic unsaturation to the alkenyl-acyl phosphatides as compared to the diacyl phosphatides. These considerations led them to think that it might be possible to fractionate a natural mixture of alkenyl-acyl and diacyl choline phosphatides by using argentation-adsorption-TLC.

As experimental procedure this group prepared the silver nitrate-impregnated plates by putting activated Silica Gel G plates (layer thickness 250 μ, area 20 × 20 cm) in a chromatographic chamber containing a saturated solution of silver nitrate in 95% ethanol. After the solution rose to the top of the plates, the plates were removed, air-dried for 10 minutes, and activated for 2 hours at 100°C. Subfractionation of a mixture of alkenyl-acyl and diacyl choline phosphatides (10 mg per plate) was carried out with chloroform–methanol–water (70:25:3) as solvent. The different bands were detected with 0.2% alcoholic solution of 2′,7′-dichlorofluorescein; they were scraped off separately into 125-ml Erlenmeyer flasks and eluted three times with 50 ml of chloroform–methanol (1:2). The purity of the fractions was verified by argentation-TLC and also by adsorption-TLC on Silica Gel G with chloroform–methanol–ammonia (70:30:5) as solvent.

The fractions obtained were analyzed by acid-catalyzed methanolysis and subsequent TLC separation of resulting fatty acid methyl esters and dimethyl acetals. These were recovered and subjected to GLC analysis. The content of alkenyl-acyl lipids in the fractions was assayed by densitometry of the dimethyl acetals and methyl esters of the methanolysates. The separation obtained with ox-heart glycerophosphoryl choline lipids is shown in Figure 7. The methanolysate of subfraction A released lesser amounts of dimethyl acetals than the other two fractions. This is shown qualitatively in Figure 7, and the quantitative analyses are presented in Table IV. Composition of the fatty chains is presented in Table V.

Table IV
Plasmalogen Content of a Mixture of Alkenyl-acyl and
Diacyl Choline Phosphatides, and the Fractions Thereof Obtained
by Argentation-TLC*

| | Per cent plasmalogen content | | | |
| | Original mixture | Fraction A | Fraction B | Fraction C |
Estimation				
Densitometry	55.6	8.0	84.4	65.0
Quantitative weighing	59.8	—	88.6	—

*According to Hoevet et al.[19] (Courtesy of Elsevier Publishing Co.)

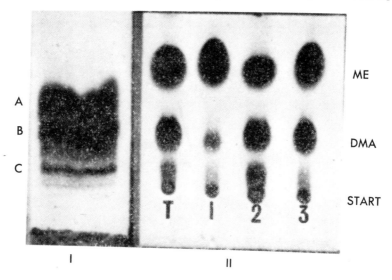

Figure 7. (I) Argentation-TLC of ox-heart lecithins. (II) Methanolysis products of the original lecithins (T), and the different fractions thereof; 1 derives from fraction (A), 2 from (B), and 3 from (C). According to Hoevet et al.[19] (Reproduced by permission of Elsevier Publishing Co.)

Summarizing the above results it appears that Fraction A contained mainly diacyl choline lipids 16:0–18:1 and 16:0–18:2, and Fraction B alkenyl-acyl choline lipid 16:0–18.2.* Fraction C seemed to contain mainly polyenoic diacyl and alkenyl-acyl choline lipids. If this proves to be true, it means that on argentation plates the plasmalogenic lecithins run behind the corresponding molecular species of diacyl lecithins. It should be possible to verify this conclusion by using simpler mixtures of choline lipids, *e.g.,* plasmalogenic concentrates, and plasmalogen-free lecithins prepared by selective destruction procedures (page 145).

In a more recent paper the same authors presented evidence of essentially similar separations of subclasses of ethanolamine phospholipids.[20] Four fractions were obtained from ox-heart glycerophosphoryl ethanolamine lipids on argentation plates. The fastest-moving Fraction 1 probably contained monoenoic and dienoic diacyl lipids, Fraction 2 mainly dienoic alkenyl-acyl lipids, Fraction 3 tetraenoic diacyl lipids, and Fraction 4 the corresponding tetraenoic plasmalogens. The Hormel group emphasizes the possibility of subclass separation by this method (*i.e.,* separation of plasmalogens from diacyl lipids), but I feel that the simultaneous separation of molecular species and subclasses leads to confusion.

---

*The degree of unsaturation refers here to the number of olefinic bonds in the chains proper and excludes the double bond of the linkage.

Table V

Fatty Acid and Fatty Aldehyde Composition of Beef Heart Alkenyl-acyl and Diacyl Choline Phosphatides*

	Per cent fatty acid composition				Per cent fatty aldehyde composition			
	Original sample	Fraction A	Fraction B	Fraction C	Original sample	Fraction A	Fraction B	Fraction C
13:0	—	—	0.5	—	2.4	1.5	—	—
14:0	tr	0.5	—	0.8	2.6	—	2.6	—
14:1	tr	tr	0.6	.1.2	2.1	2.4	4.1	—
15:0	tr	0.7	tr	tr	2.6	8.3	3.7	12.3
15:1	tr	tr	1.1	1.2	2.1	1.8	2.7	1.3
16:0	30.8	38.8	6.7	14.6	69.4	64.6	66.3	55.0
16:1	1.7	3.1	0.5	1.3	3.1	4.2	3.8	3.5
17:0	tr	0.8	1.5	tr	1.2	2.2	2.5	6.8
17:1	tr	1.4	—	—	—	—	—	—
18:0	5.8	7.5	14.8	5.9	12.1	11.8	11.4	19.8
18:1	19.1	23.4	12.8	3.1	2.4	3.1	3.0	1.2
18:2	32.3	24.0	57.6	8.6	—	—	—	—
20:0	—	—	—	0.9	—	—	—	—
20:1	tr	—	tr	3.9	—	—	—	—
20:3	4.2	—	4.0	14.8	—	—	—	—
20:4	6.2	—	—	32.1	—	—	—	—
Unidentified	—	—	—	1.0	—	—	—	—
20:5	—	—	—	2.1	—	—	—	—
24:0	—	—	—	2.5	—	—	—	—
Unidentified C22?	—	—	—	1.4	—	—	—	—
Unidentified C22?	—	—	—	4.7	—	—	—	—

*According to Hoevet et al.[19] (Courtesy of Elsevier Publishing Co.)

The findings of the Hormel group agree with our observations on diglyceride acetates. When the diglyceride acetates derived from alkenyl-acyl and alkyl-acyl choline lipids of ox-brain were compared on argentation plates, it became apparent that the fully saturated alkyl-acyl derivative moves ahead of its alkenyl-acyl counterpart which contains fully saturated chains but has one olefinic linkage that belongs to the alkenyl linkage (Figure 8). Similarly, the alkyl-acyl derivatives having one double bond in the fatty chains proper move faster than the corresponding alkenyl-acyl lipids which have one double bond somewhere in the chains and one more in the alkenyl linkage (Figure 8). The same also holds true with more unsaturated pairs.

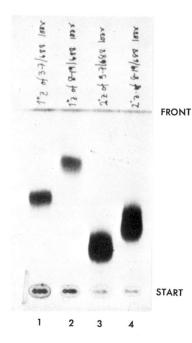

Figure 8.   Argentation-TLC of diglyceride acetates:

(1) "Saturated" alkenyl-acyl diglyceride acetate*
(2) Saturated alkyl-acyl diglyceride acetate
(3) "Monoenoic" alkenyl-acyl diglyceride acetate*
(4) Monoenoic alkyl-acyl diglyceride acetate.

Solvent: benzene–chloroform (9:1).

*The degree of unsaturation refers to the number of olefinic bonds in the chains proper and excludes the double bond of the linkage.

Comparison of these two diglyceride acetate subclasses with 1,2-diacyl derivatives has shown that the alkyl-acyl derivatives move fastest, the diacyl derivatives hold an intermediate position, and the alkenyl-acyl derivatives are slowest. The differences between the alkenyl-acyl and diacyl derivatives are not too prominent with aromatic solvents, but the separation appears to improve when aliphatic solvents are used.

In conclusion, it seems obvious that the double bond of the alk-1-enyl group forms a silver complex. The potential use of this observation for separation of the subclasses will be hampered by the fact that all elements of unsaturation of the individual molecular species affect the mobility of the lipids in the argentation systems.

SUBFRACTIONATION OF INTACT SPHINGOLIPID CLASSES

Sphingolipid studies present suitable examples of separations based on polarity differences among individual molecular species. With sphingomyelins, for instance, one sees a double spot on the TLC plates almost regularly. Wood and Holton[21] as well as Eldin and Sloane-Stanley[22] showed that the fast fraction contains sphingomyelins made up of very long-chain fatty acids (C_{22}–C_{26}), whereas the slower fraction contains molecules of medium-chain fatty acids (C_{16}–C_{18}). Glucosyl ceramides as well as lactosyl ceramides of serum are likewise separated into two subfractions on TLC plates[23, 24] (Figure 9). Svennerholm[23] showed that this separation was caused by differences in the fatty acids: in each double spot the faster fraction contained glycolipid made up of unsubstituted fatty acids, and the slower fraction contained the same glycolipid class but made up of α-hydroxy acids. Similar findings have been recorded

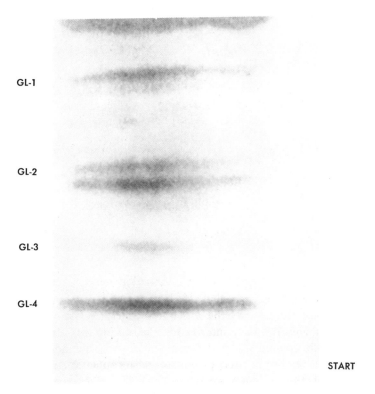

GL-1

GL-2

GL-3

GL-4

START

Figure 9. TLC of the glycosyl ceramides from human plasma. GL-1, cerebrosides; GL-2, dihexosyl ceramides; GL-3, trihexosyl ceramides; GL-4, globosides. Solvent: chloroform–methanol–water (100:42:6). According to Vance and Sweeley.[24] (Reproduced by permission of the American Institute of Biological Sciences.)

with a number of ceramide glycosides, *e.g.,* sulfatides[25] and brain ceramide galatosides and ceramide dihexosides.[26] It often remains obscure,
however, whether a double spot seen in sphingolipid chromatograms depends on the presence of normal and hydroxy acids or on the differences
in chain length of the fatty acids. Hooghwinkel *et al.*[27] have analyzed a
sample of spinal cord cerebrosides which was heterogeneous in both
ways.

It is interesting that glycerolipids show less tendency than sphingolipids
to separate into subfractions on silica gel plates. The increase in chain
length of glycerolipid fatty acids is generally accompanied by a simultaneous increase in unsaturation. These two changes have reciprocal
effects on the chromatographic mobility of the lipids, which explains why
the glycerolipids move as one spot. In the sphingolipids the increase of
fatty acid chain length is not compensated for by increasing unsaturation,
and more diverging mobilities result.

SEPARATION OF SUBCLASSES AND MOLECULAR SPECIES OF GLYCEROPHOSPHATIDES THROUGH TLC OF DIGLYCERIDE ACETATES

In 1964/65 it was found that in unpolar form, as diglyceride acetates,
the glycerophosphatides can be fractionated far more effectively than in
native form. This became evident as the separation of the three subclasses, alkenyl-acyl, alkyl-acyl, and diacyl derivatives succeeded; further,
the different molecular species could be separated with exceptionally
good resolution. The explanation of this observation is simple: native
polar lipids tend to associate and form multimolecular aggregates in
organic solvents. This counteracts their chromatographic separation. On
the other hand, the nonpolar derivatives of polar lipids do not associate;
they remain molecularly dispersed and can be chromatographed very
efficiently.

Conversion of Glycerophosphatides into Diglyceride Acetates

Two methods have been used to achieve this conversion, which is
shown in Figure 10. Acetolysis with a mixture of acetic acid and acetic
anhydride is suitable, and so is enzymic cleavage to diglycerides followed
by acetylation. The acetolysis reaction, which was originally described by
Bevan *et al.*[28] gives 1,2-diglyceride acetates from a variety of glycerophosphatides.[29] This reaction was used successfully also by Elovson[30]
who studied the molecular species of rat liver phosphatides. However,
some formation of 1,3-diglyceride acetates seems to take place during
the acetolysis,[31, 32] which has made the reaction unpopular for the past
two or three years. Admittedly, the 1,3-isomers may disturb argentation

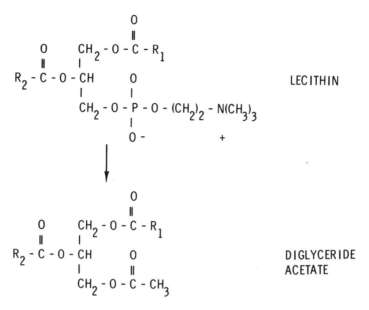

Figure 10. Conversion of lecithins into diglyceride acetates.

analysis of the 1,2-diglyceride acetates because the two isomers have different mobilities on silica gel. But this difference also allows removal of the disturbing isomeric form before the actual analysis. Furthermore, GLC on nonpolar phases does not separate the two isomers;[33] thus, it should be possible to use acetolysis in analyzing individual molecular species by GLC without development of any complications.

The enzymic hydrolysis of glycerophosphatides is carried out by phospholipase C (EC 3.1.4.3). The enzyme obtained from *Clostridium welchii* hydrolyzes lecithins easily but does not attack pure acidic phospholipids. Therefore, the enzymes obtained from *Bacillus cereus* culture filtrates are preferable. This preparation is known to attack glycerophosphoryl glycerol lipids,[34] glycerophosphoryl ethanolamine and glycerophosphoryl serine lipids,[35] glycerophosphoryl inositol lipids,[36] and even cardiolipin[37] as well as phosphatidyl glycerophosphate.[37] The last reaction requires Zn^{++}-ions for activation of the enzyme.[38] The polyphospho-inosites are attacked by a brain enzyme.[39] Thus, it seems that eventually all glycerophosphatide classes can be enzymatically converted into diglycerides. Only about 1% isomerization of 1,2- to 1,3-diglycerides takes place during the hydrolysis of diacyl glycerophosphoryl cholines.[40] This isomerization, however, is a possible source of difficulties that should be kept in mind when phospholipase C hydrolyses are carried out. In the hydrolysis of different subclasses of glycerophosphatides the *Clostridium welchii* enzyme attacks alkenyl-acyl, alkyl-acyl, and diacyl glycerophosphoryl choline lipids,[40] and the diacyl lipids are more rapidly cleaved than the alkenyl-acyl lipids.[41]

When the parent phosphatide is completely hydrolyzed, the diglycerides are extracted and acetylated with acetic anhydride and pyridine at room temperature.[42] TLC on Silica Gel G should be used to ascertain that only 1,2-diglyceride acetates have been obtained. These derivatives run more slowly than the corresponding 1,3-isomers. This has been clearly demonstrated with diacyl and alkenyl-acyl lipids,[40] and it is probably true with alkyl-acyl lipids as well.

Separation of Subclasses of Diglyceride Acetates

The first great advantage of converting the phosphatides into diglyceride acetates became evident in 1965, when we succeeded in separating 1-alkenyl-2-acyl-3-acetins, 1-alkyl-2-acyl-3-acetins, and 1,2-diacyl-3-acetins into three distinct fractions.[43, 44] These diglyceride acetates were derived from the three subclasses of ox-heart lecithin and ox-brain glycerophosphoryl ethanolamine lipids by procedures outlined above. When a mixture of the three subclasses of diglyceride acetates was chromatographed on Silica Gel G with hexane–diethyl ether, two fractions were obtained. The fast one contained the alkenyl-acyl and alkyl-acyl derivatives, and the slow one the diacyl derivatives. The fast fraction was resolved into the two subclasses with aromatic solvents like toluene. All three subclasses could be separated from one another in a convenient way when these observations were combined and the diglyceride acetates subjected to chromatography first with aliphatic and then with aromatic solvents (Figure 11). The IR-spectra shown in Figure 12 support the identification of the three subclasses. Wood and Snyder have recently confirmed our findings.[45]

Of considerable interest was the fact that the alkenyl-acyl derivatives were seen to move *faster* than their alkyl-acyl counterparts on Silica Gel G plates, even though the alkenyl derivatives have one olefinic double bond more. This is contrary to general experience, which shows that olefinic double bonds increase the polarity and slow down the migration of molecules on silica gel plates.

In the following years Schmid et al.[46–48] confirmed our findings to a large extent. They worked with ordinary triacyl glycerols, alkyl-diacyl glycerols, and alkenyl-diacyl glycerols. In their hands, too, the alkenyl derivatives moved faster than the corresponding alkyl lipids, and those in turn were faster than the acyl lipids. However, these authors did not use aromatic solvents and the separation between the alkenyl and the alkyl derivatives was rather slight (Figure 13).

The aromatic solvents incorporated into our chromatographic system serve two purposes: they bring about the selectivity required to separate alkenyl-acyl lipids from their alkyl counterparts, and they make the three

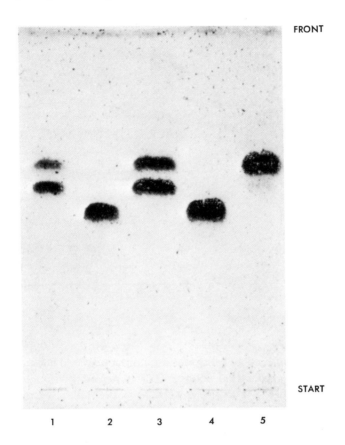

Figure 11. TLC of subclasses of diglyceride acetates: (1) alkenyl-acyl and alkyl-acyl diglyceride acetates; (2) diacyl diglyceride acetates; (3) same as 1; (4) same as 2; (5) alkenyl-acyl diglyceride acetates. Solvents: hexane–ether (1:1), followed by toluene. According to Renkonen.[43] Reproduced by permission of Societas Medicorum Finnicae.)

subclasses of diglyceride acetates migrate as compact spots. It is well-known that unsaturated molecules tend to migrate more slowly on silica gel plates than their saturated analogs. In our experience this difference is more pronounced with aliphatic than with aromatic solvents. Therefore, we think that the use of aromatic solvents tends to keep together all molecules that differ from one another only in unsaturation. This is naturally of paramount importance for clear separations among classes or subclasses of lipids.

Separation of Molecular Species of Diglycerides

Comparatively much is known about the separation of the molecular species of 1,2-diacyl-3-acetins. The very first attempts already had led

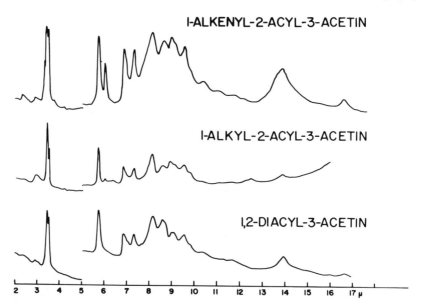

Figure 12. Infrared spectra (oil on KBr windows) of diglyceride acetate subclasses.

to successful separation of fully saturated, monoenoic, dienoic, and polyenoic species on argentation plates.[29] This separation was achieved with benzene–chloroform (9:1) as solvent. A more polar solvent, chloroform–methanol (97:3), was then found to separate the polyenes into trienes, tetraenes, pentaenes, and hexaenes.[33] More recent work led to recognition of even more unsaturated species in Baltic herring lecithins. TLC analysis of the diglyceride acetates derived from these lecithins proved the existence of species containing up to 12 double bonds. These diglyceride acetates were conveniently separated on argentation plates with chloroform–methanol–water (65:25:4) as solvent.[49]

The separations discussed above are all based on different numbers of olefinic bonds, but the selectivity of argentation-TLC is sufficient to separate some species of diglyceride acetates even when their degrees of unsaturation are identical. For instance, two common dienoic species, 1-palmitoyl-2-linoleoyl-3-acetin and 1,2-dioleoyl-3-acetin are separable with aliphatic though not with aromatic solvents; the 1,2-dioleoyl derivative runs faster than the palmitoyl-linoleoyl lipid.[40] Similarly, a common pair of trienoic species, namely 1-oleoyl-2-linoleoyl-3-acetin and 1-palmitoyl-2-linolenoyl-3-acetin also separate, the former running faster.[1] Further, 1-oleoyl-2-arachidonoyl-3-acetin runs ahead of diglyceride acetates that represent a combination of saturated and pentaenoic fatty acid.[1] Similar separations are well-known among the ordinary triglycerides.[50]

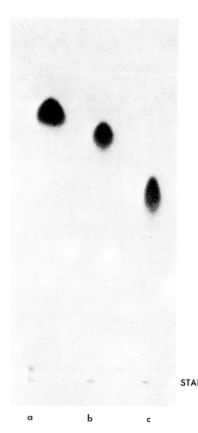

Figure 13. TLC of subclasses of triglycerides: (a) alkenyl-diacyl glycerols; (b) alkyl-diacyl glycerols; (c) triacyl glycerols. Solvent: hexane–ether (9:1). According to Schmidt *et al.*[48] (Reproduced by permission of Elsevier Publishing Co.)

START

a   b   c

Still other types of isomeric diglyceride acetates are formed when diacyl phosphatides are dephosphorylated. For instance, oleic acid can be esterified both at C-1 and C-2 positions of phosphatide glycerol, which means that among others 1-oleoyl-2-palmitoyl, as well as 1-palmitoyl-2-oleoyl species may exist. It has proved possible to separate the monoenoic triglyceride isomers of type "1-0-0" and "0-1-0" on silver nitrate-containing silica gel.[51] But with 1,2-diglyceride acetates derived from natural phosphatides, we could never observe the analogous separation. To elaborate this we synthetized two series of triglycerides and compared their chromatographic properties. The triglycerides synthetized were *rac.* 1-stearoyl-2-olein and *rac.* 1-oleoyl-2-stearin, each of which contained a variable acyl group (acetyl, hexanoyl, decanoyl or tetradecanoyl) at the third hydroxyl of glycerol. The results[52] of argentation-TLC experiments with these molecules are summarized in Table VI. The important finding was that the two isomeric acetates, SOAc and OSAc, were indeed very difficult to separate, whereas separation of the corresponding hexanoates, decanoates, and tetradecanoates was compara- tively easy. This means that the acetyl group that we have used to "mask" the third hydroxyl group of phosphatide glycerol is not the best choice; a larger group would be better. In all cases shown in Table VI, the isomer that had oleate in the outer (C-1) position was slower. In other words, the outer oleate double bond seems to be exposed to the environment more than the inner one.

Table VI

Argentation-TLC of *rac.* 1-stearoyl-2-olein (SO)
and *rac.* 1-oleoyl-2-stearin (OS) in Acylated Form

Acyl group at C-3	*Separation of the isomers*
Acetyl (C_2)	Difficult
Hexanoyl (C_6)	Easy
Decanoyl (C_{10})	Easy
Tetradecanoyl (C_{14})	Easy

The argentation separations obviously do not yield pure molecular species, and other methods must be used to complete the separations. Partition methods aimed primarily at separations according to molecular size are of particular importance here. Reversed-phase TLC of diglycer- ide acetates has been used in our laboratory,[1] but GLC methods are much more convenient. [45, 53, 54]

The final identification of individual diglyceride acetates requires that the component fatty acids be analyzed and their positions within the molecules determined. Hydrolysis of the original phospholipids with phospholipase A_2 gives positional information which helps to identify the major species of derived diglyceride acetates. Moreover, the diglycer- ide acetates can be analyzed by hydrolysis with pancreatic lipase. In our laboratory we have obtained reliable results with this enzyme; they agree with the findings from phospholipase A_2 hydrolysis of the parent phos- phatides.[40, 55] Also, Kleiman *et al.*,[56] who worked with sn-1,2-diacyl-3- acetyl glycerols from *Euonymus verrucosus* seed oil, found pancreatic lipolysis a reliable method for analyzing the positional distribution of fatty acids in these molecules.

Many derivatives of diglycerides besides acetates have been used for analysis of phosphatide species. Van Golde *et al.* in Utrecht have used free diglycerides in a number of elegant papers.[6,57–60] The separations ob- tained are similar to those observed with diglyceride acetates (Figure 14). The Dutch group carries out the quantitative analysis of the different sub- fractions with GLC by adding known amounts of heptadecanoic acid to each fraction as an internal standard. Other approaches include that of

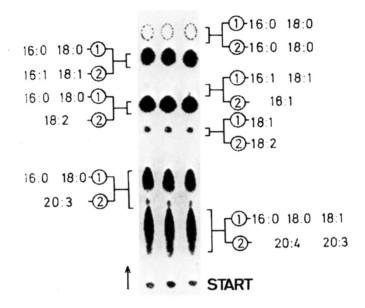

Figure 14. Argentation-TLC of 1,2-diacyl glycerols derived from rat liver lecithins. Solvent: chloroform–ethanol (94:6). According to van Golde *et al.*[60] (Reproduced by permission of Elsevier Publishing Co.)

Bergelson's group, which converted the diglycerides into trityl derivatives;[61] these molecules are particularly easy to quantitate after the argentation-TLC. Lands and Hart[62] have acetylated the diglycerides with heptadecanoyl anhydride and fractionated the resulting triglycerides on silver nitrate-impregnated plates. The experiences of our laboratory (Table VI) suggest that these derivatives are better than the acetates in bringing about certain separations among isomeric molecules.

In the separation of molecular species of alkenyl-acyl and alkyl-acyl diglycerides, the accumulated experience is still scanty. As acetates these lipids are separated quite as well as the ordinary diglyceride acetates.[40] GLC of course is a tailor-made method for separation of homologs of these lipids.[53, 63] See also pages 132–136.

ANALYSIS OF SPHINGOMYELIN SPECIES AS FREE AND ACETYLATED CERAMIDES

Other examples of efficient separations obtainable with nonpolar derivatives are available in recent adsorption, argentation, and partition studies of ceramides or ceramide diacetates. The conversion of sphingomyelins into ceramides (Figure 15) is conveniently carried out with

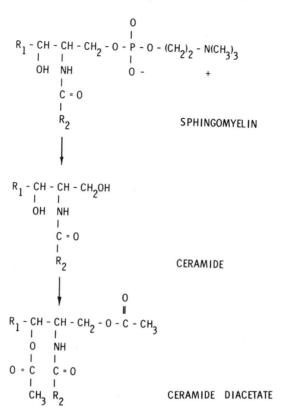

Figure 15. Conversion of sphingomyelins into ceramides and ceramide diacetates.

commercially available phospholipase C of *Clostridium welchii*. The
details of a suitable procedure have been outlined by Renkonen,[42] and
Karlsson has recently described[64] a micromodification of it. Karlsson[64]
also verified that many different molecular species of sphingomyelin are
really degraded by this enzyme (Table VII). The ceramides can be
studied as such, and indeed many laboratories do this. We have acetylated them, much like the diglycerides, with a mixture of pyridine and
acetic anhydride, but I wish to emphasize that the ceramide acetates
are very easy to deacetylate back to free ceramides through mild alkaline
methanolysis.[65]

The adsorption chromatographic behavior of different molecular
species of ceramides on Silica Gel G has been studied by Karlsson.[64]
Figure 16 shows separations obtained with chloroform–methanol (95:5).
The separations are based largely on the number of free hydroxyl groups,
of which sample A has only one, samples B and C two, samples D

Table VII

Behavior of Different Sphingomyelin Species
Toward Treatment with Phospholipase C (*Cl. welchii*) *

Composition of ceramide part		Hydrolysis
Fatty acid	*Long-chain base*	
Normal acid	Monohydroxy base (Sphingine)	+
Normal acid	Dihydroxy base	+
Normal acid	Trihydroxy base	+
Normal acid	Dihydroxy base acetylated in position 3	−
2-Hydroxy acid (D, L)	Dihydroxy base	+
2-Acetoxy acid (D, L)	Dihydroxy base	−

*According to Karlsson.[64] (Courtesy of Munksgaard International Forlag.)

through G three, and sample H four. Also, the chain length of the fatty acid can vary enough to influence the mobility (samples B and C). This is, however, far less important than the effect of the hydroxyl groups. Isomeric species having hydroxyl groups of different configuration or at different positions may have clearly different mobilities. Particularly interesting is the behavior of sample G, which represents the species derived from phytosphingosine-containing sphingomyelins;[66] this molecule appears to have a relatively high mobility compared to other trihydroxy ceramides.

Our group has studied the molecular species of human plasma sphingomyelins by fractionating the corresponding ceramide acetates with argentation-TLC.[42, 65] All these ceramides were of the dihydroxy type. Six bands were obtained when acetates of these ceramides were subjected to argentation-TLC (Figure 17). The structural differences among the molecular species could be identified as follows: the fastest fraction (A) was comprised of saturated fatty acids and monoenoic sphingosines; the second fraction contained *trans*-monoenoic fatty acids and monoenoic sphingosines; and the third (B) in turn was comprised of *cis*-monoenoic fatty acids and monoenoic sphingosines. Thus, in these three fractions the fatty acids varied and the bases were similar. The fourth fraction (C) contained saturated fatty acids and dienoic sphingosines. The fifth subfraction was comprised of *trans*-monoenoic fatty acids and dienoic bases. The slowest fraction (D) contained *cis*-monoenoic fatty acids and dienoic sphingosines. Thus, even the last three fractions formed an understandable pattern; saturated, *trans*-, and *cis*-monoenoic acids combined with the same sphingosine base. Samuelsson and Samuelsson[67] have recently made similar observations, except that they did not report the presence of ceramides containing *trans*-monoenoic fatty acids in plasma.

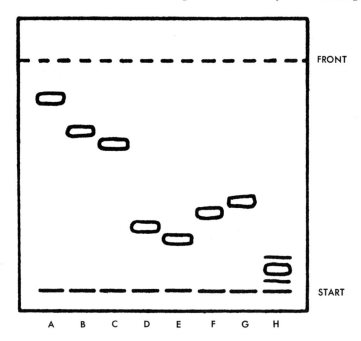

Figure 16. TLC of ceramides with the following fatty acid and long-chain base composition: (A) normal fatty acid and monohydroxy base (sphingine); (B) normal, C_{24}, fatty acid and monounsaturated dihydroxy base; (C) normal, C_{18}, fatty acid and monounsaturated dihydroxy base; (D) 2-D-hydroxy, C_{24}, fatty acid and monounsaturated dihydroxy base; (E) 2-D-hydroxy, C_{18}, fatty acid and monounsaturated dihydroxy base; (F) 2-L-hydroxy, C_{18}, fatty acid and saturated dihydroxy base; (G) normal, mostly C_{24}, fatty acid and saturated trihydroxy base; (H) 2-hydroxy, mostly C_{26}, fatty acid and saturated trihydroxy base. Combination (H) is from cerebrin of *Torulopsis utilis*. Silica Gel G; solvent: chloroform-methanol (95:5, v/v). According to Karlsson.[64] (Reproduced by permission of Munksgaard International Forlag.)

Morrison has recently fractionated ceramides on borate-containing silica gel plates.[84] He could thereby separate the ceramides containing saturated dihydroxy bases from those containing monoenoic dihydroxy bases. As these two groups do not separate on argentation-TLC the two methods should be used together.

To put these separations into proper perspective, it should be remembered that intact sphingomyelins (and the ceramides) can be separated into two fractions differing mainly in the chain length of the component fatty acids. Two research groups have recently described GLC of trimethylsilyl derivatives of ceramides,[67, 68] which is naturally a valuable method for separation of homologs.

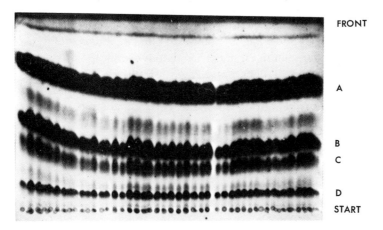

FRONT

A

B

C

D

START

Figure 17. Argentation-TLC of ceramide diacetates (1 mg) derived from human serum sphingomyelins. Layer activated at 160°C. Solvent: chloroform–methanol (99:1); three ascents. According to Hirvisalo and Renkonen.[65] (Reproduced by permission of the American Institute of Biological Sciences.)

Finally, it should be emphasized that good methods are available for chemical or enzymic conversion of cerebrosides and gangliosides into ceramides;[69, 70, 71, 85] the molecular species of these lipids, too, can therefore be analyzed with the above methods.

TLC OF POLAR LIPIDS AFTER MASKING THEIR POLAR GROUPS

The successful fractionation of the dephosphorylated forms of phospholipids confirmed that the use of nonpolar derivatives in TLC is basically sound. However, to become practical, this approach has to be modified so that even the polar group is conserved in the derivatives. In other words, it is necessary to study derivatives that have been obtained by "masking" the polar groups instead of removing them. The first report on such derivatives in fractionation studies was that of Wurster and Copenhaver, who subjected dimethyl phosphatidates to reversed-phase TLC in 1966.[72] In subsequent years these as well as other derivatives of phospho- and glycolipids have been studied by TLC on plain silica gel and by argentation-TLC in several laboratories.

Separations Obtainable with Dimethyl Phosphatidates

The dimethyl phosphatidates, or phosphatidic acid dimethyl esters are obtainable from several glycerophospholipid classes by direct diazomethanolysis[73, 77] or by simple methylation of phosphatidic acids.[72] Phosphatidic acids exist as such probably in all cells, but they can also be obtained by hydrolyzing other phosphatide classes with cabbage phospholipase D. This enzyme is known to attack phosphatidyl cholines, phosphatidyl ethanolamines, and phosphatidyl serines,[75] as well as phosphatidyl glycerols.[34] It does not cleave phosphatidyl glycerophosphates or cardiolipins.[37] The reaction takes place readily also with alkyl-acyl glycero-phosphoryl cholines,[40] but the corresponding plasmalogens are hydrolyzed only very slowly.[40]

The reversed-phase system of Wurster and Copenhaver consisted of Kieselguhr G plates dipped in a 5% solution of *n*-tetradecane in ether. Chromatography was performed with acetonitrile–acetone–water (8:1:1) saturated with *n*-tetradecane. The spots were detected by spraying the plates with water or 0.005% Rhodamine 6G. Separations were obtained when the dimethyl phosphatidates differed by two methylene groups or one double bond. It is not clear whether the polyenoic molecules behaved even in this system in the anomalous way described by Arvidson for lecithins.[16]

Adsorption chromatography of dimethyl phosphatidates has been studied in our laboratory as a means to separate the subclasses of alkenyl-acyl, alkyl-acyl, and diacyl phosphatidic acid esters. It proved quite easy to separate the more slowly moving diacyl type of molecules from the two other subclasses on Silica Gel G.[76] This simple experiment represented the first case where two subclasses of glycerophosphatides could be clearly and quantitatively separated from each other.

A little later it proved possible to separate all three subclasses of dimethyl phosphatidates by using multiple chromatography.[77] When the dimethyl phosphatidates were chromatographed on Silica Gel G plates by using 6–7 successive ascents of hexane–chloroform, the separation depicted in Figure 18 was achieved. The alkenyl-acyl dimethyl phosphatidates (VE-GPMM) moved fastest, the alkyl-acyl derivatives (AE-GPMM) were intermediate, and the corresponding diacyl lipids (EE-GPMM) were the slowest.

Argentation-TLC of the dimethyl phosphatidates resulted in very good separations among molecular species.[76, 77] Only the diacyl lipids have been studied so far, but it seems very likely that the other two subclasses will behave in a similar manner. The less unsaturated dimethyl phosphatidates are separated on silver nitrate-impregnated Silica Gel G plates by using chloroform–methanol (98:2) as shown in the left chromatogram of Figure 19. Experiments with a hydrogenated sample showed that this system also separates saturated and monoenoic dimethyl phosphatidates. Molecules containing four, five, and six double bonds per molecule were separated with chloroform–methanol–water (90:10:1) as shown in the right chromatogram of Figure 19.

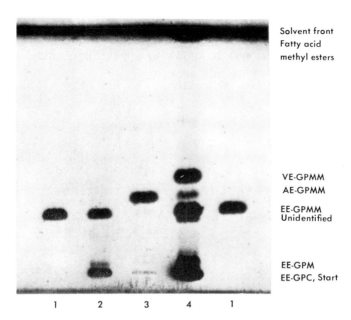

Figure 18. TLC of different suoclasses of phosphatidic acid dimethyl esters. VE-GPMM, alkenyl-acyl derivative; AE-GPMM, alkyl-acyl derivative; EE-GPMM, ordinary diacyl derivative. Silica Gel G; solvent: seven ascents of hexane–chloroform (1:1). Samples: (1) ordinary diacyl dimethylphosphatidate (EE-GPMM) prepared enzymatically from egg lecithin; (2) diazomethanolysate of egg lecithin; (3) dimethylphosphatidate of the alkyl acyl type (AE-GPMM) prepared enzymatically from lecithin sample B; (4) diazomethanolysate of ox heart lecithin. According to Renkonen.[77] (Reproduced by permission of Elsevier Publishing Co.)

The results of fatty acid analysis, which correspond to Figure 19, are shown in Table VIII. These results confirm the qualitative identifications shown in Figure 19. The high resolution obtained is exemplified by the fact that the dienes containing two monoenoic chains run ahead of those containing a saturated and a dienoic chain. Even with the pentaenes a similar separation was observed: the fatty acid composition of the pentaenoic molecules shown in Table VIII suggests that the smaller pentaene contained one monoenoic acid (18:1) and one tetraenoic acid (20:4); the main pentaene appeared to contain one saturated (16:0 or 18:0) and one pentaenoic acid (22:5). Figure 19 shows that the small fraction ran ahead of the large one. Thus, the separations obtained with dimethyl phosphatidates are as good as those with diglyceride acetates; in both cases the degree of *cis*-unsaturation is of prime importance, but the localization of the double bonds also affects the separation. Possmayer *et al.*[78] have recently confirmed many of these results.

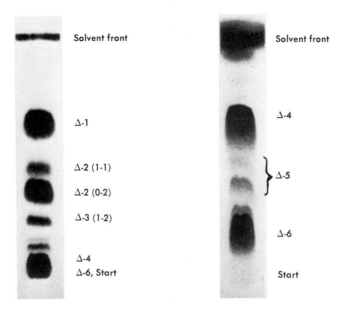

Figure 19. Argentation-TLC of diacyl phosphatidic acid dimethyl esters. Left chromatogram, separation of less unsaturated species with chloroform–methanol (98:2). Right chromatogram, separation of highly unsaturated species with chloroform–methanol–water (90:10:1). According to Renkonen.[77] (Reproduced by permission of Elsevier Publishing Co.)

Table VIII

Fatty Acid Composition of the Principal Subfractions
of Dimethyl Phosphatides from Egg Lecithin*

	Relative amounts of principal fatty acids†							
Fraction	*16:0*	*16:1*	*18:0*	*18:1*	*18:2*	*20:4*	*22:5*	*22:6*
Monoenes	38		11	51				
Dienes (1-1)‡	4	9	1	86	1			
Dienes (0-2)‡	29		19	1	50			
Trienes (1-2)‡	5			40	52			
Tetraenes	18		34	1		45		
Pentaenes	30		17	9		10	34	
Hexaenes	38		18	1				44

*According to Renkonen.[77] (Courtesy of Elsevier Publishing Co.)
†The identification of the polyenoic acids is based on GLC as well as argentation-TLC.
‡(1-1) signifies molecules containing two monoenoic acids, (0-2) those of a saturated and a dienoic acid, and (1-2) a combination of a monoenoic and a dienoic acid.

The wide applicability of dimethyl phosphatidates is further exemplified by the results obtained in analyzing Baltic herring lecithins.[49] In conformity with the analysis carried out by using diglyceride acetates, the dimethyl phosphatidates also revealed the existence of molecular species containing up to 12 double bonds per molecule. In other words, argentation-TLC of dimethyl phosphatidates covers the whole range of unsaturation from 0 to 12 double bonds.

The positional analysis of fatty acids in diacyl phosphatidic acid dimethyl esters is possible by use of pancreatic lipase, which liberates primarily fatty acids occupying position C-1 of the dimethyl phosphatidates.[77] Elovson, Åkesson and Arvidson[79] have also found that phospholipase A digestion of the phosphatidic acids and pancreatic lipase hydrolysis of the derived dimethyl phosphatidates give comparable results.

Separations Obtainable with Dinitrophenylated and Methylated Glycerophosphoryl Ethanolamine Lipids

A more thorough example of masking than the methylation of phosphatidic acids has been studied in our laboratory by O-methylating and N-dinitrophenylating glycerophosphoryl ethanolamine lipids. The resulting derivatives are depicted in Figure 20. In these cases, only one hydrogen atom has been removed from the parent lipids during the derivatization.

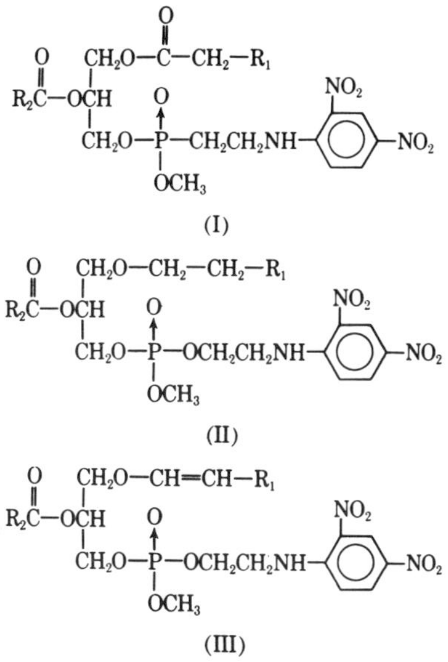

Figure 20. Methylated DNP-derivatives of the three subclasses of ethanolamine glycerophosphatides. (I) phosphatidyl ethanolamines; (II) alkyl-acyl derivative; (III) alkenyl-acyl derivative.

The preparation of the methylated DNP-derivatives is simple. Our procedure, which has been adapted from the work of Collins,[80] is as follows. A sample of 0.5–1 mg of the original lipid is dissolved in 2 ml of benzene; 40 μl of triethylamine and 4 μl of fluoro-2,4-dinitrobenzene are added. After 2 hours at 20°C the reaction mixture is evaporated to dryness and the excess reagent is removed by heating at 90°C *in vacuo* at 1 mm Hg under a cold finger. (Alternative chromatographic procedures may be used.) The dinitrophenylated lipids are then methylated by dissolving them in chloroform and adding an excess of ethereal diazomethane. After 30 minutes at 20°C the excess reagent is finally evaporated, which leaves the derivatives ready for analysis.

Adsorption-TLC of these derivatives on unmodified Silica Gel G easily separated the alkenyl-acyl or the alkyl-acyl derivatives from the more slowly moving diacyl lipids.[76, 81] Already this represented an obvious advantage over the existing chromatographic separations of the parent lipids. But eventually still better separations, like those shown in Figure 21, were obtained, where the alkenyl-acyl, alkyl-acyl and diacyl glycerophosphoryl ethanolamine lipids are nicely separated from one another.[82] The order of migration is the same as with diglyceride acetates and di-

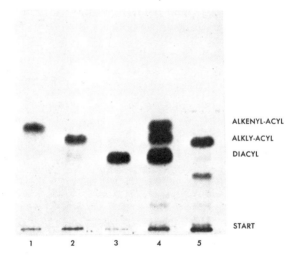

Figure 21. TLC of methylated DNP-derivatives of the three subclasses of ethanolamine glycerophospholipids. Solvent: Five ascents of hexane–chloroform (4:6) followed by five ascents of toluene–chloroform (4:6). Samples: (1) derivatives of plasmalogens from ox-brain; (2) derivatives of alkyl-acyl lipids from hen's eggs; (3) derivatives of diacyl lipids from hen's eggs; (4) mixture of 1, 2 and 3; (5) derivative of 1-hexadecyl-2-stearoyl-GPE. According to Renkonen.[82] (Reproduced by permission of the American Institute of Biological Sciences.)

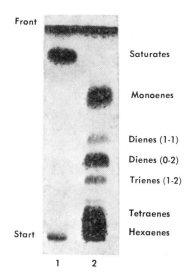

Figure 22. Argentation-TLC of methylated DNP-derivatives of phosphatidyl ethanolamines. Solvent: chloroform–methanol (98:2). Samples: (1) methylated DNP-derivative of 1,2-dipalmitoyl-phosphatidyl ethanolamine; (2) methylated DNP-derivatives of egg phosphatidyl ethanolamines. According to Renkonen.[81] (Reproduced by permission of Munksgaard International Forlag.)

methyl phosphatidates. The new TLC system has already shown the presence of all these subclasses in the glycerophosphoryl ethanolamine lipids of ox-brain, hen's eggs, and human plasma.[82]

Argentation-TLC has been used so far with the diacyl and the alkyl-acyl derivatives only, but we believe that the alkenyl-acyl lipids will eventually behave like the other two subclasses. Figure 22 shows an example of an early separation of molecular species obtained in our laboratory;[81] the dinitrophenylated and methylated ethanolamine lipids (diacyl type) were separated as effectively as the diglyceride acetates and the dimethyl phosphatidates. The separations are again based primarily

Table IX
Fatty Acid Composition of Subfractions of Methylated DNP-Derivatives of Ethanolamine Lipids*

| | Relative amounts of principal acids (%) | | | | | | |
Fraction	*16:0*	*18:0*	*18:1*	*18:2*	*18:3*	*20:4*	*22:6*
Monoenes	13	35	52				
Dienes (1-1) †	2	6	82	5			
Dienes (0-2) †	7	40	2	51			
Trienes (1-2) †	5	5	35	47	7		
Tetraenes	5	41	1		3	49	
Hexaenes	24	26	3			3	44

*According to Renkonen.[81] (Courtesy of Munksgaard International Forlag.)
†(1-1) signifies molecules containing two monoenoic fatty acids, (0-2) those of a saturated and a dienoic acid, and (1-2) a combination of a monoenoic and a dienoic acid.

on the number of *cis*-double bonds per molecule, but isomeric molecules containing equal numbers of double bonds can also be separated in certain cases. The identifications of Figure 22 were all confirmed by analysis of the component fatty acids (Table IX).

CONCLUSION

Several techniques are now available for the analysis of subclasses and individual molecular species of polar lipids in biological materials. For studies where it is important to use the intact molecules, Arvidson's approach, based on a combination of argentation and partition methods, is the most promising one. However, when emphasis must be put on high resolution or on easily mastered techniques, it seems that our approach, based on the use of nonpolar derivatives, has many advantages.

It appears quite possible that both approaches can eventually be extended to cover all polar lipids found in nature. At present the derivative technique has been applied more extensively. It has been used in connection with adsorption, argentation, and partition chromatography, working with all degrees of unsaturation from 0 to 12 double bonds per molecule. It works with glycerolipids as well as sphingolipids, and it appears to work with glycolipids as well as phospholipids.[83]

Lately, our interest has been focused on the methods which conserve the polar parts of the molecules, but analysis of diglycerides or ceramides and their simple derivatives may well become the most important method in this field. This belief is based on the possibility of combining two easy methods—argentation chromatography and GLC—with these lipids. Also, the increasing use of labeled glycerol and fatty acids in biochemical studies allows removal of the polar parts of the molecules without removing the label. The findings of Arvidson and others have clearly indicated that the metabolic schemes currently accepted are not yet sufficiently refined to account for the metabolism of the individual species of polar lipids. This means that the work on molecular species will go on.

REFERENCES

1. Renkonen, O.   Advan. Lipid Res. **5**, 329 (1967).
2. Privett, O. S., and M. L. Blank.   J. Am. Oil Chemists' Soc. **40**, 70 (1963).
3. Wurster, C. F., and J. H. Copenhaver, Jr.   Biochim. Biophys. Acta **98**, 351 (1965).
4. Kaufmann, H. P., H. Wessels, and C. Bondopadhyaya.   Fette, Seifen, Anstrichmittel **65**, 543 (1963).
5. Pelick, N., T. L. Wilson, M. E. Miller, F. M. Angeloni, and J. M. Steim. J. Am. Oil Chemists' Soc. **42**, 393 (1965).

6. van Golde, L. M. G., R. F. A. Zwaal, and L. L. M. van Deenen. Koninkl. Ned. Akad. Wetenschap. Proc. Ser. **B68,** 255 (1965).
7. Arvidson, G. A. E. J. Lipid Res. **6,** 574 (1965).
8. Arvidson, G. A. E. Eur. J. Biochem. **4,** 478 (1968).
9. Tinoco, J., S. M. Hopkins, D. J. McIntosh, G. Sheehan, and R. L. Lyman. Lipids **2,** 479 (1967).
10. Lyman, R. L., S. M. Hopkins, G. Sheehan, and J. Tinoco. Biochim. Biophys. Acta **176,** 86 (1969).
11. Kyriakides, E. C., and J. A. Balint. J. Lipid Res. **9,** 142 (1968).
12. Nakayama, F., and S. Kawamura. Clin. Chim. Acta **17,** 53 (1967).
13. Rytter, D., J. E. Miller, and W. E. Cornatzer. Biochim. Biophys. Acta **152,** 418 (1968).
14. Balint, J. A., D. A. Beeler, D. H. Treble, and H. L. Spitzer. J. Lipid Res. **8,** 486 (1967).
15. Haverkate, F., and L. L. M. van Deenen. Biochim. Biophys. Acta **106,** 78 (1965).
16. Arvidson, G. A. E. J. Lipid Res. **8,** 155 (1967).
17. Tinoco, J., R. Babcock, D. J. McIntosh, and R. L. Lyman. Biochim. Biophys. Acta **164,** 129 (1968).
18. Arvidson, G. A. E. Thesis, University of Lund, Sweden (1968).
19. Hoevet, S. P., C. V. Viswanathan, and W. O. Lundberg. J. Chromatog. **34,** 195 (1968).
20. Viswanathan, C. V., S. P. Hoevet, and W. O. Lundberg. J. Chromatog. **35,** 113 (1968).
21. Wood, P. D. S., and S. Holton. Proc. Soc. Exp. Biol. Med. **115,** 990 (1964).
22. Eldin, A. K., and G. H. Sloane-Stanley. Biochem. J. **92,** 40P (1964).
23. Svennerholm, E., and L. Svennerholm. Biochim. Biophys. Acta **70,** 432 (1963).
24. Vance, D. E., and C. C. Sweeley. J. Lipid Res. **8,** 621 (1967).
25. Wagner, H., L. Hörhammer, and P. Wolff. Biochem. Z. **334,** 175 (1961).
26. Rouser, G., G. Kritchevsky, and A. Yamamoto, in *Lipid Chromatographic Analysis.* Ed. by G. V. Marinetti (New York: Marcel Dekker, 1967) p 99.
27. Hooghwinkel, G. J. M., P. Borri, and J. C. Riemersma. Rec. Trav. Chim. **83,** 576 (1964).
28. Bevan, T. H., D. A. Brown, G. I. Gregory, and T. Malkin. J. Chem. Soc. **1953,** 127.
29. Renkonen, O. Acta Chem. Scand. **18,** 271 (1964).
30. Elovson, J. Biochim. Biophys. Acta **106,** 480 (1965).
31. Renkonen, O. Lipids **1,** 160 (1966).
32. Nutter, L. J., and O. S. Privett. Lipids **1,** 234 (1966).
33. Renkonen, O. Ann. Med. Exptl. Biol. Fenniae (Helsinki) **44,** 356 (1966).
34. Haverkate, F., and L. L. M. van Deenen. Biochim. Biophys. Acta **84,** 106 (1964).

35. Robinson, D. S., P. M. Harris, and J. C. F. Poole.　Quart. J. Exptl. Physiol. **42**, 285 (1957).
36. Slein, M. W., and G. F. Logan, Jr.　J. Bacteriol. **90**, 69 (1965).
37. De Haas, G. H., P. P. M. Bonsen, and L. L. M. van Deenen.　Biochim. Biophys. Acta **116**, 114 (1966).
38. Ottolenghi, A. C.　Federation Proc. **23**, 549 (1964).
39. Thompson, W., and R. M. C. Dawson.　Biochem. J. **91**, 237 (1964).
40. Renkonen, O.　Biochim. Biophys. Acta **125**, 288 (1966).
41. Warner, H. R., and W. E. M. Lands.　J. Am. Chem. Soc. **85**, 60 (1963).
42. Renkonen, O.　J. Am. Oil Chemists' Soc. **42**, 298 (1965).
43. Renkonen, O., S. Liusvaara, and A. Miettinen.　Ann. Med. Exptl. Biol. Fenniae (Helsinki) **43**, 200 (1965).
44. Renkonen, O.　11th Intern. Conf. Biochem. Lipids, Nordwijk, The Netherlands, 1965.
45. Wood, R., and F. Snyder.　Arch. Biochem. Biophys. **131**, 478 (1969). (1969).
46. Schmid, H. H. O., and H. K. Mangold.　Biochem. Z. **346**, 13 (1966).
47. Schmid, H. H. O., and H. K. Mangold.　Biochim. Biophys. Acta **125**, 182 (1966).
48. Schmid, H. H. O., W. J. Baumann, and H. K. Mangold.　Biochim. Biophys. Acta **144**, 344 (1967).
49. Renkonen, O.　Lipids **3**, 191 (1968).
50. Gunstone, F. D., and F. B. Padley.　J. Am. Oil Chemists' Soc. **42**, 957 (1965).
51. Barret, C. B., M. S. J. Dallas, and F. B. Padley.　Chem. Ind. (London) **1962**, 1050.
52. Renkonen, O., and L. Rikkinen.　Acta Chem. Scand. **21**, 2282 (1967).
53. Renkonen, O.　Biochim. Biophys. Acta **137**, 575 (1967).
54. Kuksis, A., W. C. Breckenridge, L. Marai, and O. Stachnyk.　J. Am. Oil Chemists' Soc. **45**, 537 (1968); J. Lipid Res. **10**, 25 (1969).
55. Renkonen, O.　Ann. Med. Exptl. Biol. Fenniae (Helsinki) **43**, 194 (1965).
56. Kleiman, R., R. W. Miller, F. R. Earle, and I. A. Wolff.　Lipids **2**, 473 (1967).
57. van Golde, L. M. G., and L. L. M. van Deenen.　Biochim. Biophys. Acta **125**, 496 (1966).
58. van Golde, L. M. G., and L. L. M. van Deenen.　Chem. Phys. Lipids **1**, 157 (1967).
59. van Golde, L. M. G., V. Tomasi, and L. L. M. van Deenen.　Chem. Phys. Lipids **1**, 282 (1967).
60. van Golde, L. M. G., W. A. Pieterson, and L. L. M. van Deenen.　Biochim. Biophys. Acta **152**, 84 (1968).
61. Dyatlovitskaya, E. V., V. E. Volkova, and L. D. Bergelson.　Bull. Acad. Sci. USSR, Div. Chem. Sci. English Transl. **1966**, 946.
62. Lands, W. E. M., and P. Hart.　J. Am. Oil Chemists' Soc. **43**, 290 (1966).

63. Wood, R., W. J. Baumann, F. Snyder, and H. K. Mangold. J. Lipid Res. **10**, 128 (1969).
64. Karlsson, K. A. Acta Chem. Scand. **22**, 3050 (1968).
65. Hirvisalo, E. L., and O. Renkonen. J. Lipid Res. **11**, 54 (1970).
66. Karlsson, K. A., and G. O. Steen. Biochim. Biophys. Acta **152**, 798 (1968).
67. Samuelsson, B., and K. Samuelsson. J. Lipid Res. **10**, 47 (1969).
68. Casparrini, G., E. C. Horning, and M. G. Horning. Chem. Phys. Lipids **3**, 1 (1969).
69. Carter, H. E., J. A. Rothfuss, and R. Gigg. J. Lipid Res. **2**, 228 (1961).
70. Brady, R. O., A. E. Gal, J. N. Kanfer, and R. M. Bradley. J. Biol. Chem. **240**, 3766 (1965).
71. Hajra, A. K., D. M. Bowen, Y. Kishimoto, and N. S. Radin. J. Lipid Res. **7**, 379 (1966).
72. Wurster, C. F., Jr., and J. H. Copenhaver, Jr. Lipids **1**, 422 (1966).
73. Baer, E., and J. Maurukas. J. Biol. Chem. **212**, 39 (1955).
74. Crone, H. D. Biochim. Biophys. Acta **84**, 665 (1964).
75. Kates, M. Can. J. Biochem. Physiol. **34**, 967 (1956).
76. Renkonen, O. Scand. J. Clin. Lab. Invest. **19**, Suppl. 95, 48 (1967).
77. Renkonen, O. Biochim. Biophys. Acta **152**, 114 (1968).
78. Possmayer, F., G. L. Scherphof, T. M. A. R. Dubbelman, L. M. G. van Golde, and L. L. M. van Deenen. Biochim. Biophys. Acta **176**, 95 (1969).
79. Elovson, J., N. Akesson, and G. Arvidson. Biochim. Biophys. Acta **176**, 214 (1969).
80. Collins, F. D., in *New Biochemical Separations*. Ed. by A. T. James, and L. J. Morris (Princeton, New Jersey: D. van Nostrand Company, Inc., 1964), p 378.
81. Renkonen, O. Acta Chem. Scand. **21**, 1108 (1967).
82. Renkonen, O. J. Lipid Res. **9**, 34 (1968).
83. Renkonen, O. Unpublished data.
84. Morrison, W. R. Biochim. Biophys. Acta **176**, 537 (1969).
85. Klenk, E., and R. T. C. Huang. Z. Physiol. Chem. **350**, 1081 (1969).

Chapter 6

Thin-Layer Chromatography in Pharmacognosy

by E. Tyihák and G. Held

The concept of chromatography in general first became widely known through Tswett's experimental work[242] on plant dyestuffs. Similarly, the first thin-layer chromatographic experiments—by Ismailov and Schraiber in 1938[114] and later by Kirchner, Miller, and Keller[131] and by Stahl[213]—were also carried out on plant substances. This may be easily understood if we bear in mind that it is the demand for a reliable analysis of complex systems such as plant extracts that has brought into being the varieties of chromatography, including the most recent—thin-layer chromatography (TLC).

At the time of the first publications on TLC, paper chromatography (a type of partition chromatography) was being widely applied to the analysis of practically all kinds of natural substances. This represented a considerable step forward in the microanalysis of many such materials, although with respect to certain hydrophobic substances—the terpenoids, for example—results were negligible. It may be sufficient to refer here to the book by Hais and Macek,[89] which offers an excellent survey of the literature on paper chromatography: of the 10,290 sources cited, not more than 7 deal with essential oils and 7 with azulenes. In contrast to this is Stahl's book[217] which sums up the first brief period of TLC application, including use of the "chromato-strip" and "chromato-plate" methods which are more or less the precursors of TLC. In this latter book 59 citations referring to the analysis of essential oils, resins, and balsams appear; in the second edition[218] the number of these citations has reached 334.

While in the beginning TLC was applied primarily to the analysis of substance classes which were either too cumbersome or impossible to analyze by paper chromatography, a later attempt was made to transfer the advantages of the method to analysis of other substance classes, such as amino acids,[179] alkaloids,[218] steroids,[218] etc. Today TLC is used in the analysis of the most diverse types of organic and inorganic compounds.

In pharmacognosy TLC has far surpassed the limits of earlier expectations; it may be enough to refer here to appropriate chapters in textbooks by Stahl,[217, 218] Kirchner,[132] Randerath,[187] and Luckner[150] or to the reviews by Háznagy et al.[94, 95] To reveal adequate active ingredient sources, it is necessary to have a method available by which large numbers of plant species can be examined simply and rapidly. In these so-called screenings, TLC is gradually becoming the most extensively applied method. The requirement of chemotaxonomy to classify members of the vegetable kingdom according to chemical marks also involves the necessity of rapid and easy examination of a great many plant species. The results of chemotaxonomy, on the other hand, may be utilized directly in the search for significant active ingredient sources. The discovery of chemical identities and deviations among species and within a certain species may provide useful information about plant improvement with respect to active ingredient content.

Up-to-date knowledge of medicinal plants and drugs requires the supplementation of chemotaxonomy by ontogenetical and ecological investigation and by an increasingly thorough acquaintance with the formation mechanism of active ingredients. The manufacture of modern pharmaceutical products demands more pure-vegetable active substances. In this work considerable help may be gained by the application of TLC, as manifested by the number of publications on the isolation of new vegetable substances.

APPLICATION OF TLC TO THE ASSAY OF ACTIVE PLANT INGREDIENTS

As shown in Table I, the number of data on the analysis of active ingredients of vegetable origin have risen tremendously as a result of the spreading of TLC methods. In order to include the greatest possible number of publications in the table, we used abridged literature citations; the key to the abbreviations may be found in the table footnote; any literature citation mentioned in another section is quoted with its own reference number. It should be mentioned further that Table I contains only those publications on alkaloids which have already been mentioned in this chapter—mainly in the paragraphs on screening and chemotaxonomy—in order to complement data in the text. TLC of alkaloids will be discussed in detail by Tyihák and Vágujfalvi in Volume III of this series.

APPLICATION OF TLC TO THE ANALYSIS OF THE MAIN SUBSTANCE GROUPS OF VEGETABLE ORIGIN

Table II briefly sums up those publications which deal with TLC analysis of pure active ingredients isolated from several plants. The ingredients are classified according to their related substance structures. Obviously, the results of such works may be applied directly or after some modifications to the same substance in plants of widely differing species. The table does not include results of TLC analysis of therapeutically less important constituents of plants and drugs (*e.g.,* organic acids, sugars, amino acids), well-known substances (*e.g.,* vitamins), or the components of microbes.

APPLICATION OF TLC IN SCREENING AND CHEMOTAXONOMY

Popular medicine may be considered the most ancient and simplest form of screening of plants for use in medicine. This basic type of screening may provide some useful information even for modern scientific research; the modern test methods allow us to check such information thoroughly and quickly in the laboratory.

The primary aim of screening is a practical one—the search for therapeutically useful compounds by means of studying plants in whose family the occurrence of the sought compound has already been indicated. In addition, screening has a theoretical target, namely the study and recognition of the chemical aspects of phytotaxonomy based on morphological features that were recorded at a time when the state of development of chemistry did not permit the revelation of internal content conditions. A relatively new branch of phytotaxonomy, called chemotaxonomy, is now engaged in the study of these problems.

In the beginning of the development of scientific plant screening, simpler methods, such as test-tube or drop tests,[9] were used. Persinos and Quimby,[180] for example, used drop tests for screening the entire flora of Nigeria for alkaloids, tannins, and saponins. Of the screening methods described in the literature, spectrophotometric methods where characteristic peaks in the IR- or UV-spectra are supposed to indicate

(*Text Continues on page 205.*)

Table I
The Application of TLC to the Assay of Plant Principles
(for key to abbreviations, see page 199)

Family of plants	Genus or species of plants	Substance class investigated	Purpose of investigation	Reference
Aceraceae	Acer platanoides	carotenoids	biosynthesis	61, 62
Agavaceae	Agave americana	steroid sapogenins	identification	Y. Chen: C. A. **61**, 4150b (1964)
Altingiaceae	Liquidambar orientale	triterpenes	isolation	S. Huneck: Tetrah. **19**, 479 (1963)
Anacardiaceae	Rhus typhina	gallotannin	biosynthesis	D. Cornthwaite[a]: J. Ch. Soc. **1965**, 3008
Apocynaceae	Apocynum cannabinum	glucosides	isolation	H. Gerlach[b]: Pharm. **20**, 450 (1965)
	Cerbera	glucosides	structure elucidation	J. Cable[b]: Aust. J. Ch. **18**, 1079 (1965)
	Pachypodium	glucosides	isolation	Z. Meyer[b]: H. Ch. Ac. **47**, 2330 (1964)
	Strophantus kombe	cardenolids	biosynthesis	H. H. Sauer[b]: Phytoch. **7**, 1543 (1968), 202
Aquifoliaceae	Wallaris solanacea	glucosides	isolation	H. Kaufmann[b]: H. Ch. Ac. **48**, 65 (1965)
	Ilex latifolia	triterpenes	isolation	S. Yamada: B. Ch. Soc. Jap. **39**, 2313 (1966)
Araliaceae	Hedera helix	triterpenes	isolation, structure	R. Tschesche[b]: Z. Naturforsch. **20b**, 708 (1965)
Aristolochiaceae	Panax Ginseng	principles (general)	isolation	L. Hörhammer[b]: Ph. Ztg. **106**, 1307 (1961)
	Aristolochia clematitis	triterpenes	ecology	W. Schunack[b]: Pharm. **22**, 118 (1967)
	Asarum canadense	triterpenes	isolation	R. W. Doskotch[a]: Lloydia **30**, 141 (1967)
	Asarum europeum	sterols	isolation	L. Gracza: PM. **12**, 440 (1964)
	Asarum europeum	terpenes	identification	L. Gracza: Pharm. **20**, 740 (1965)
	Asarum europeum	essential oil	separation, chemotaxonomy	B. Dános[b]: Ac. Agr. Hung. **15**, 421 (1966), 223
Asclepiadaceae	Asclepias curassavica	principles (general)	isolation	S. M. Kupchan[b]: Science **146**, 1635 (1964)
	Cynanchum vincetoxicum	principles (general)	isolation	L. Ferenczy[b]: Ac. Microbiol. Hung. **12**, 337 (1965)
	Cynanchum wilfordi	pregnane	isolation	H. Mitsuhashi[b]: Ch. Ph. B. **14**, 712 (1966)
	Cynanchum caudatum	principles (general)	structure elucidation	Y. Shimizu[a]: Tetrah. **24**, 4143 (1968)
	Dregea volubilis	glucosides	isolation	H. H. Sauer[b]: H. Ch. Ac. **49**, 1625 (1966)
	Gongronema gazense	cardenolids	isolation	M. L. Lewbart[b]: H. Ch. Ac. **46**, 505 (1963)

186

Family	Plant	principles	method	reference
	Gymnema sylvestre	principles (general)	isolation	W. Stöcklin[b]: H. Ch. Ac. 50, 474 (1967)
	Metaplexis japonica	steroid sapogenins	isolation	H. Mitsuhashi[b]: Syoyakugaku Zasshi. 20, 9 (1966), 169
	Stapelia gigantea	glucosides	isolation	U. Eppenberger[b]: H. Ch. Ac. 49, 1492 (1966)
Aspidiaceae	Dryopteris	phloroglucine	(two-dim. TLC)	M. von Shantz[b]: PM. 10, 98 (1962)
	Dryopteris	phenols	composition	F. Fish[a]: J. Chr. 36, 383 (1968)
Berberidaceae	Podophyllum	lignane	isolation	M. Kuhn[a]: H. Ch. Ac. 46, 2127 (1963)
	Podophyllum	N-lignane	isolation	H. Auterhoff[a]: Arch. Ph. 297, 488 (1966)
Betulaceae	Betula	triterpenes	isolation	H. Rimpler[b]: Arch. Ph. 299, 422 (1966)
Boraginaceae	Symphytum	principles (general)	isolation	K. R. Fell[a]: PM. 16, 411 (1968)
Burseraceae	Bursera macrophylla	lignane	isolation	E. Bianchi[b]: J. Ph. Sci. 57, 696 (1968)
Cactaceae	Thelocactus bicolor	triterpenes	isolation	X. A. Dominguez[b]: PM. 16, 458 (1968)
Campanulaceae	Lobelia	principles (general)	pharmacopoeia	M. Luckner[b]: Arzn.-Standard 11, 121 (1967)
Cannabiaceae	Cannabis	principles (general)	chemotaxonomy	134, 135
	Cannabis sativa	principles (general)	isolation	R. Mechoulam[a]: Tetrah. 21, 1223 (1965)
	Cannabis sativa	principles (general)	screening	B. Caddy[a]: J. Chr. 31, 584 (1967)
Caprifoliaceae	Viburnum	principles (general)	identification	L. Hörhammer[b]: D. Apoth. Z. 105, 1371 (1965)
	Sambucus ebulus	triterpenes	isolation	E. Domagalina[a]: Diss. Ph. Phc. 19, 391 (1967)
Caryophyllaceae	Vaccaria segatilis	glucosides	isolation	K. Amanmuradova[a]: Khim. Prir. Soed. 1965, 372
Chenopodiaceae	Bassia butyracea	alkaloids	screening	196
	Beta vulgaris v. conditiva	anthocyanins	isolation, structure	D. Kumari[b]: Curr. Sci. 35, 223 (1966)
	Spinacea oleracea	principles (general)	identification	E. Tyihák: Sci. Ph. 31, 51 (1963), 242
		quinones	isolation	M. D. Henninger: Plant Phys. 39, 598 (1964)
Compositae		lignane	chemotaxonomy	R. Hänsel[b]: Z. Naturforschg. 19b, 727 (1964)

Table I (continued)

Family of plants	Genus or species of plants	Substance class investigated	Purpose of investigation	Reference
Compositae (continued)	Achillea	terpenes	chemotaxonomy	127, 128
	Achillea	sterols	isolation, identific.	Z. Kasprzyk[a]: Roczniki Ch. **41**, 201 (1967)
	Achillea asplenifolia	azulenes	chemotaxonomy	P. Tétényi[b]: Pharm. **17**, 463 (1962)
	Achillea fragrantissima	polyins	isolation	30
		azulenes	separation	E. Tyihák[b]: Pharm. 18, 566 (1963)
		essential oil	separation	A.-F. Shalaby[a]: J. Ph. Sci. 53, 1502 (1964)
	Achillea millefolium	principles (general)	pharmacopoeia	154
	Ambrosia	germacranolids	isolation	T. A. Geissman[b]: J. Org. Ch. **31**, 2269 (1966), 70
	Ambrosia artemisifolia	sesquiterpenes	isolation	E. Bianchi[b]: Austr. J. Ch. **21**, 1109 (1968)
	Ambrosia confertiflora	guajanolids	isolation	N. H. Fischer[a]: Tetrah. **23**, 2529 (1967)
	Anaphalis	polyins	isolation, structure	33
	Anthemis	polyins	isolation	34, 37
	Anthemis austriaca	polyins	synthesis	F. Bohlmann[b]: Ch. Ber. **100**, 1200 (1967)
	Anthemis carpatica	polyins	synthesis	31
	Anthemis saguramica	polyins	isolation	F. Bohlmann[b]: Ch. Ber. **99**, 1642 (1966)
	Arnica	principles (general)	pharmacopoeia	M. Luckner[b]: Pharm. **20**, 681 (1965)
	Arnica montana	polyins	isolation	K. E. Schulte[a]: Arch. Ph. **299**, 468 (1966)
	Arnica montana	principles (general)	isolation, separation	A. Saner[a]: Ph. Ac. H. **41**, 431 (1966)
	Artemisia	sesquiterpenes	isolation	M. A. Irwin[a]: Phytoch. **8**, 305 (1969)
	Artemisia abrotanum	flavones	isolation	P. Schmersahl: Naturw. **52**, 498 (1965)
	Artemisia absinthium	essential oil	separation	E. Tyihák[a]: Herba Hung. **2**, 156 (1963)
	Artemisia judaica	bitter principles	identification	S. M. Khafagy: PM. **16**, 446 (1968)
	Artemisia pedemontana	polyins	isolation	F. Bohlmann[a]: Ch. Ber. **99**, 2416 (1966)
	Artemisia spicata	terpenes	isolation	P. Sanciu: Phytoch. **8**, 267 (1969)
	Aster pilosus	flavones	isolation	N. R. Farnsworth[b]: J. Ph. Sci. **57**, 1059 (1968)

188

Species	Type	Study	Ref.	Citation
Berkheya adlamii	polyins	isolation		F. Bohlmann[b]: Ch. Ber. 100, 1193 (1967)
Calendula officinalis	triterpenes	isolation		Z. Kasprzyk[a]: Phytoch. 6, 69 (1967)
Calendula officinalis	steroids	isolation		Z. Kasprzyk[b]: Ac. Biochim. Pol. 15, 149 (1968)
Calendula officinalis	principles (general)	isolation	84	
Chrysanthemum anethifolium	essential oil, flavones	isolation		S. M. A. Wahab[b]: PM. 16, 426 (1968)
Chrysanthemum cinerariifolium	pyretrins	separation		E. Stahl: Arch. Ph. 293, 531, (1960); Naturw. 52, 620 (1965); E. Tyihák: Herba Hung. 5, 306 (1966)
Chrysanthemum frutescens	polyins	biosynthesis		F. Bohlmann[a]: Ch. Ber. 99, 995 (1966)
Chrysanthemum maximum	polyins	isolation, structure	32	
Chrysanthemum serotinum	polyins	isolation		F. Bohlmann[a]: Ch. Ber. 99, 1830 (1966)
Cnicus benedictus	germacranolids	isolation	245	E. Tyihák[a]: Herba Hung. 3, 468 (1964),
Cosmos sulphureus	polyins	structure elucidation		F. Bohlmann[b]: Ch. Ber. 99, 142 (1966)
Cousinia hystrix	polyins	isolation		F. Bohlmann[a]: Ch. Ber. 99, 590 (1966)
Crossostephium chinense	triterpenes	isolation	201	
Cynareae	sesquiterpenes	isolation, chemotaxon.	35	
Cynara scolymus	sesquiterpenes	isolation	36	
Echinacea	polyins	isolation	35	
Farfara	principles (general)	isolation		L. Hörhammer[b]: D. Apoth. Z. 103, 429 (1963)
Gaillardia pulchella	sesquiterpenes	isolation		137; Kupchan, S. M.[b]: J. Am. Ch. Soc. 88, 5292 (1966)
Helichrysum bracteatum	pigments	isolation		H. Rimpler[a]: Arch. Ph. 298, 838 (1965)
Hymenoclea monogyra	sesquiterpenes	isolation		F. P. Toribio[a]: Phytoch. 8, 313 (1969)

Table I (continued)

Family of plants	Genus or species of plants	Substance class investigated	Purpose of investigation	Reference
	Inula helenium	sesquiterpenes	isolation	126
	Jurinea cyanoides	germacranolids	isolation	M. Suchy[b]: Coll. 34, 229 (1969)
	Matricaria	polyins	isolation, chemotaxon.	38
	Matricaria chamomilla	flavones	isolation	L. Hörhammer[b]: Arzn.-Forsch. 13, 33 (1963), 88
	Matricaria chamomilla	principles (general)	pharmacopoeia	151
	Matricaria chamomilla	azulenes	separation	246
	Matricaria chamomilla	sesquiterpenes	identification	113
	Petasites hybridus	terpenes	isolation	L. Novotny[b]: Coll. 34, 336 (1969)
	Phagnalon saxitale	quinones	isolation	F. Bohlmann[a]: Ch. Ber. 99, 885 (1966)
	Serratula radiata	polyins	isolation	39
	Solidago	diterpenes	isolation	71
	Tagetes	essential oil	chemotaxonomy	W. F. Schenkel[a]: C. A. 66, 108173 (1967)
	Tagetes minuta	polyins	isolation	R. E. Atkinson: J. Ch. Soc. 1965, 7109
	Tanacetum vulgare	essential oil	chemotaxonomy	221, 224, 225
	Taraxacum officinale	triterpenes	biosynthesis	3
Cornaceae	Cornus mas	phenols	separation	G. Juhász[a]: Ac. Agr. Hung. 15, 349 (1966)
Cruciferae		triterpenes	screening, chemotaxon.	48, 78, 81
		oils	industrial	166
		alkaloids	screening, chemotaxon.	47
	Camelina sativa	steroids	isolation	I. Zyczynska: Roczniki Ch. 40, 1225 (1966)
	Erysimum	cardenolids	isolation	80
	Erysimum crepidifolium	cardenolids	separation	G. Reuter[a]: Ph. Zhalle 105, 597 (1966)
Cucurbitaceae	Byronia alba	triterpenes	isolation	J. Konopa[b]: Neoplasma 13, 335 (1966)
	Byronia dioica	triterpenes	isolation	57, 79

Family	Species	Compound	Activity	Reference
	Citrullus colocynthis	triterpenes	isolation	H. El Khadem[a]: J. Ch. Soc. 1963, 4991 (1957)
	Coccinia	Δ⁷ sterins	isolation	229
	Luffa operculata	triterpenes	isolation	J. B. DaSilva: C. A. 63, 12969e (1965)
	Luffa operculata	triterpenes	isolation	P. Kloss: Arch. Ph. 299, 351 (1966)
	Marah oreganus	triterpenes	isolation	S. M. Kupchan[b]: J. Med. Ch. 10, 337 (1967)
Dioscoreaceae	Momordica charantia	Δ⁷ sterins	isolation	W. Sucrow: Ch. Ber. 99, 3559 (1966)
	Dioscorea	steroid sapogenins	separation	G. Blunden[a]: J. Chr. 15, 273 (1964)
	Dioscorea deltoidea	steroid sapogenins	biosynthesis	B. Kaul[a]: Lloydia 31, 171 (1968)
	Dioscorea tenuipes	steroid sapogenins	isolation	6
	Dioscorea tokor	steroid sapogenins	ecology	7
	Tamus communis	steroid sapogenins	isolation	99
	Tamus communis	principles (general)	isolation, structure	231
Ericaceae	Arctostaphylos	principles (general)	separation	G. H. Constantine, Jr.[b]: J. Ph. Sci. 55, 1378 (1966)
	Chimaphila umbellata	principles (general)	isolation	K. Sheth[b]: Lloydia 30, 78 (1968)
Erythroxylaceae	Erythroxylum monogynum	diterpenes	isolation	A. H. Kapadi[b]: Tetrah. L. 1965, 2725
Euphorbiaceae		cocarcinogenic principles	chemotaxonomy, screening	97
	Euphorbia esula	sterins	isolation	N. R. Farnsworth[b]: J. Ph. Sci. 57, 933 (1968)
	Euphorbia lateriflora	sterins	isolation	D. Lavie[a]: Phytoch. 7, 657 (1968)
	Mallotus philippinensis	cardenolids	isolation	K. D. Roberts[b]: H. Ch. Ac. 46, 2886 (1963)
Gramineae	Zea mays	sterins	ontogenesis	R. J. Kemp[b]: Phytoch. 6, 1609 (1967)
Guttiferae	Calophyllum apetatum	triterpenes	isolation	S. K. Nigam[a]: Phytoch. 8, 323 (1969)
	Calophyllum scribif.	xanthines	isolation	B. Jackson[b]: J. Ch. Soc. 1967, 2500
	Garcinia cola		separation	I. U. W. Osisliogu: C. A. 62, 1967c (1965)

Table I (continued)

Family of plants	Genus or species of plants	Substance class investigated	Purpose of investigation	Reference
	Heronga madagascariensis	antraquinones	determination	W. Messerschmidt: D. Apoth. Z. 106, 1209 (1966)
Hippocastanaceae	Aesculus Hippocast.	triterpenes	isolation	B. Akačič[a]: Ac. Ph. Jug. 16, 111 (1966)
	Aesculus Hippocast.	triterpenes	isolation	A. R. Wellburn[b]: Biochem. J. 102, 313 (1967)
	Aesculus Hippocast.	triterpenes	biosynthesis	125
Hydrocotylaceae	Centella asiatica	terpenes	isolation	T. Dutta[a]: Ind. J. Ch. 5, 586 (1967)
Juglandaceae	Juglans nigra	triterpenes	isolation	U. C. Bhargava: J. Ph. Sci. 57, 1728 (1968)
	Juglans regia	quinones	biosynthesis	145
Labiatae	Lavandula angustifolia	essential oil	chemotaxonomy	149
	Majorana hortensis	essential oil	separation	148
	Melissa officinalis	essential oil	separation	G. Phokas: C. A. 65, 3663 (1966)
	Mentha	essential oil	separation, pharmacop.	228
	Mentha aquatica	essential oil	biosynthesis	98
	Mentha piperita	essential oil	separation, identific.	116, 192–194
	Rosmarinus officinalis	triterpenes	separation	C. H. Brieskorn[b]: Arch. Ph. 299, 663 (1966)
	Thymus	essential oil	separation	W. Messerschmidt: PM. 12, 501 (1964), 165
	Thymus serpyllum	essential oil	separation	E. Schratz[a]: Pharm. 20, 710 (1965)
Lauraceae	Cinnamomum	essential oil	separation	A. Bhramaramba[a]: Anal. Abstr. 12, 776 (1965)
	Lindera strychnifolia	triterpenes	isolation	K. Takeda[b]: J. Ch. Soc. 1964, 4578; Tetrah. 20, 2665 (1964)
Leguminosae	Acacia	sterins	isolation	J. W. Clark-Lewis[a]: Aust. J. Ch. 20, 1961 (1967)
	Cassia	anthraquinones	identification	R. Anton[a]: Ann. Ph. Franc. 25, 589 (1967)

Plant	Substance	Topic	Reference
Cassia officinalis	glucosides	determination	A. Moes: J. Ph. Belg. 19, 173 (1964)
Cassia officinalis	glucosides	determination	R. Longo[a]: Boll. Chim. Farm. 104, 503 (1965)
Cassia tora	principles (general)	identification	182
Cytisus	principles (general)	identification	74
Cytisus	alkaloids	separation	76
Cytisus laburnum	isoflavones	isolation	J. Chopin[b]: B. Soc. Chim. France 1964, 1038
Genista	alkaloids	chemotaxonomy	25, 26, 64, 75, 174
Glycyrrhiza glabra	triterpenes	isolation	M. H. A. Elgamal[b]: Tetrah. 21, 2109 (1965)
Glycyrrhiza glabra	triterpenes	determination	B. Pasich[b]: Farm. Polska 22, 35 (1966)
Lathyrus	phenols	analysis	K. Brunsberg: C. A. 64, 16277 (1966)
Lotus	phenols	separation	W. F. Grant[a]: J. Chr. 24, 243 (1966)
Lupinus polyphyllus	isoflavones	isolation	L. Hörhammer[a]: Arzn.-Forsch. 12, 1002 (1962)
Medicago sativa	isoflavones	biosynthesis	H. Grisebach[a]: Z. Naturf. 18b, 466 (1963), 16
Medicago sativa	anthocyanins	separation	S. B. Gupta: J. Chr. 36, 115 (1968)
Medicago sativa	flavones	separation	S. B. Gupta: J. Chr. 36, 258 (1968)
Ononis spinosa	glucosides	isolation	Y. Fujise[b]: Ch. Ph. B. 13, 93 (1965)
Pisum sativum	triterpenes	biosynthesis	15
Rhynchosia pyramidalis	androgens	isolation	63
Spartium junceum	oil	isolation	N. L. Gurvich[a]: C. A. 66, 79481b (1967)
Trifolium	isoflavones	chemotaxonomy	206
	steroid sapogenins	screening	252
Liliaceae			
Allium cepa	flavones	identification	P. R. Bhandari: Naturw. 53, 82 (1966)
Allium sativum	principles (general)	analysis	O. E. Schultz[a]: Pharm. 20, 379 (1965)
Allium sativum	amino acids	isolation	107
Aloe	principles (general)	screening, chemotaxon.	T. J. McCarthy[a]: PM. 15, 342 (1967)
Aloe	principles (general)	separation	H. Böhme[a]: D. Apoth. Z. 103, 505 (1963)

Table I (continued)

Family of plants	Genus or species of plants	Substance class investigated	Purpose of investigation	Reference
	Aloe ferox	principles (general)	determination	B. Janiak[a]: Arzn.-Forsch. 12, 431 (1962)
	Aloe ferox	principles (general)	pharmacopoeia	M. Luckner[b]: Arzn.-Standard 14, 117 (1968)
	Colchicum autumnale	flavones	isolation	L. Skrzypczakowa: Diss. Ph. Phc. 20, 551 (1968)
	Colchicum hungaricum	alkaloids	identification	160
	Convallaria majalis	glucosides	structure elucidation	R. Tschesche[b]: Ch. Ber. 94, 1699 (1961); M. M. Kimura[b]: Ch. Ph. B. 15, 1204, 1699 (1967); 129
	Convallaria majalis	glucosides	isolation	F. Kaczmarek: Herba Pol. 14, 115 (1968)
	Hosta	steroid sapogenins	isolation	K. Takeda[b]: Tetrah. 21, 2089 (1965)
	Hosta kiyosumiensis	steroid sapogenins	biosynthesis	K. Takeda[b]: Ch. Ph. B. 16, 275 (1968)
	Smilax sieboldi	steroid sapogenins	structure elucidation	T. Okanishi[b]: Ch. Ph. B. 13, 545 (1965); W. Steidle: PM. 9, 435 (1961)
	Urginea maritima	glucosides	determination	W. Steidle: Ann. 662, 126 (1963)
Linaceae	Linum maritimum	glucosides	isolation	O. H. Volk[a]: Z. Naturforsch. 23b, 1017 (1968)
Loganaceae	Strychnos nux vomica	alkaloids	separation	D. F. Monache[b]: J. Chr. 32, 178 (1968)
Malvaceae	Malva silvestris	amines	isolation	G. K. Phokas: Farm. Deltion 3, 14 (1963)
Meliaceae	Aglaia odorata	triterpenes	isolation	D. Shiengthong[b]: Tetrah. 21, 917 (1965)
	Melia azedarach	terpenes	structure elucidation	D. Lavie[b]: J. Ch. Soc. 1967, 1347
Monimiaceae	Peumus boldus	essential oil	separation	R. Washicky: Anal. Abstr. 11, 3772 (1964)
Moraceae	Ficus elastica	principles (general)	identification	K. J. Stone[b]: Biochem. J. 102, 325 (1967)
	Humulus lupulus	flavones	identification	P. R. Bhandari: J. Chr. 16, 130 (1964)
	Streblus asper	glucosides	isolation	A. R. Manzetti[a]: H. Ch. Ac. 47, 2303 (1964)
Myrtaceae	Eucalyptus sieberiana	phenols	screening	W. E. Hillis: Biochem. J. 92, 516 (1964)
Ochanaceae	Lophira lanceolata	principles (general)	screening	G. J. Persinos[b]: PM. 15, 361 (1967)

Family	Species	Compound	Investigation	Reference
Onagraceae	Oenothera biennis	flavones	isolation	Z. Kowalewski[b]: Diss. Ph. Phc. 20, 573 (1968) 24
Palmae	Phoenix dactylifera	estrone	isolation	R. Berthold[b]: H. Ch. Ac. 48, 1634 (1965)
Periplocaceae	Parquetina nigrescens	cardenolids	isolation	L. J. Goad[a]: European J. Biochem. I, 357 (1967)
Pinaceae	Larix decidua	steroids	biosynthesis	
Piperaceae	Piper cubeba	lignane	isolation	R. Hänsel[a]: Arch. Ph. 294, 699 (1961)
	Piper futokadzura	futoxide	isolation	Sh. Takahashi: Phytoch. 8, 321 (1969)
	Piper methysticum	dyestuffs	isolation	R. Hänsel[b]: 294, 739 (1961)
	Piper methysticum	pyrones	separation	R. L. Young[b]: Phytoch. 5, 795 (1966) 227
Polemoniaceae	Polemonium	principles (general)	isolation	F. Kaczmarek: Herba Pol. 14, 3 (1968)
Polygonaceae	Fagopyrum sagittatum	principles (general)	isolation	
	Polygonum bistorta	principles (general)	isolation	G. Gstirner[a]: Arch. Ph. 299, 640 (1966) 69
	Rheum	phenols	chemotaxonomy	H. Friedrich[a]: Arch. Ph. 299, 857 (1966) 91
	Rheum palmatum	phenols	isolation	241
Primulaceae	Primula veris	flavones	biosynthesis	A. Poláková[a]: Cesk. Farm. 14, 307 (1965)
Ranunculaceae	Adonis vernalis	triterpenes	isol., structure	P. G. Kritikos[a]: Sci. Ph. 31, 290 (1963)
	Helleborus	cardenolids	isolation	M. El-Dakhakhny: PM. 11, 465 (1963)
	Nigella sativa	lipids, steroids	separation	A. Ulubelen[b]: J. Ph. Sci. 31, 249 (1968)
	Paeonia decora	essential oil	isolation	R. Longo[a]: C. A. 64, 15675a (1966)
Rhamnaceae	Cascara sagrada	anthocyanins	isolation	R. Longo: C. A. 64, 15675 (1966)
	Rhamnus alpina	anthrone	identification	R. Longo: C. A. 63, 11251b (1965)
	Rhamnus frangula	anthrone	separation, determin.	L. Hörhammer[b]: D. Apoth. Z. 107, 563 (1967)
	Rhamnus frangula	anthrone	identification	
		principles (general)		
Rosaceae	Crataegus monogyna	glucosides	chemotaxonomy	E. Steinegger[a]: Ph. Ac. H. 41, 102 (1966)
	Crataegus oxyacantha	glucosides	ecology	H. Flück[a]: P.M. 16, 377 (1968)
		principles (general)	separation	L. Hörhammer[b]: D. Apoth. Z. 103, 1302 (1963)
Rosaceae	Filipendula ulmaria	phenols	isolation	H. Thieme: Pharm. 20, 113 (1965)
	Rosa canina	essential oil	separation	S. Juvonen: PM. 12, 488 (1964)

Table I (continued)

Family of plants	Genus or species of plants	Substance class investigated	Purpose of investigation	Reference
Rubiaceae	Rosa canina	hydrocarbons	separation	V. Wollrab[b]: Coll. 30, 1654 (1965)
	Cephaelis ipecacuancha	principles (general)	pharmacopoeia	152
	Coffea arabica	triterpenes	isolation	H. P. Kaufmann[b]: Fette, Seifen, Anstr. 66, 461 (1964)
	Rubia tinctorum	anthraquinones	biosynthesis	E. Leistner[a]: Z. Naturforsch. 22b, 865 (1967)
Rutaceae		alkaloids	chemotaxonomy	89
	Citrus aurantifolia	furocoumarins	isolation	W. L. Stanley[a]: Phytoch. 6, 585 (1967)
	Citrus aurantium	coumarins	separation	A. Kunkar: C. A. 63, 14631c (1965)
	Citrus aurantium	flavones	separation	R. F. Albach[a]: Phytoch. 8, 127 (1969)
	Citrus maxima	essential oil	separation	G. Rispoli[b]: C. A. 59, 8541a (1963)
	Citrus maxima	principles (general)	separation	J. F. Fisher[b]: J. Food Sci. 31, 947 (1966)
	Citrus maxima	anthocyanins	separation	J. D. Conradie[a]: J. Chr. 34, 419 (1968)
	Dictamnus albus	furocoumarins	isolation	230
	Fagara	alkaloids	screening	43
	Ruta graveolens	furocoumarins	isolation	I. Novák[b]: PM. 13, 226 (1965), 175, 188
				G. Schneider[b]: Arch. Ph. 300, 73 (1967)
Salicaceae	Ruta pinnata	furocoumarins	isolation	R. E. Reyes[a]: C. A. 63, 14837a (1965)
	Populus tremula	triterpenes	separation	B. O. Lindgren[a]: Ac. Ch. Scand. 20, 1763 (1966)
Sapotaceae	Mimusops manilkara	triterpenes	isolation	G. Misra[a]: Phytoch. 8, 249 (1969)
Sauraceae	Anemopsis californica	essential oil	separation	R. N. Acharya[a]: J. Ph. Sci. 57, 1020 (1968)
				A. D. Morton: J. Chr. 28, 480 (1967)
Saxifragaceae	Ribes nigrum	anthocyanins	separation	M. A. El-Keiy[b]: C. A. 66, 22255b (1966)
Scrophulariaceae	Digitalis	glucosides	separation, identific.	J. Zurkowska[b]: Ac. Pol. Ph. 20, 115 (1963)
				T. Wada[a]: Ch. Ph. B. 13, 308 (1965)
				W. Hauser[b]: Sci. Ph. 36, 237 (1968)

Family	Species		Investigation	Reference
Scrophulariaceae	Digitalis canariensis	glucosides	separation, isolation	P. Studer[b]: H. Ch. Ac. 46, 23 (1963)
	Digitalis canariensis	glucosides	isolation	R. Tschesche[b]: Ann. 663, 157 (1963)
	Digitalis grandiflora	glucosides	extraction	A. Ulubelen[a]: J. Ph. Sci. 53, 1123 (1964)
	Digitalis lanata	glucosides	determination	J. Zurkowska[a]: PM. 12, 222 (1964)
	Digitalis purpurea	sapogenins	isolation	R. Tschesche[a]: Ch. Ber. 94, 2019 (1961)
	Digitalis purpurea	saponins	isolation	T. Kawasaki[a]: Ch. Ph. B. 12, 1311 (1964)
	Digitalis viridifolia	anthraquinones	isolation	S. Imre: Phytoch. 8, 315 (1969)
	Gratiola officinalis	triterpenes	structure elucidation	R. Tschesche[b]: Ann. 674, 196 (1964), 82
	Scrophularia smithii	triterpenes	isolation	J. L. Breton[a]: J. Ch. Soc. 1963, 1401
Simarubaceae	Ailanthus altissima	principles (general)	structure	J. Polonsky[a]: Tetrah. L. 52, 3983 (1964)
	Hannoa klaineana	bitter principles	isolation	J. Polonsky[a]: B. Soc. Chim. Franc. 1965, 2793
Solanaceae	Simaruba glauca	principles (general)	structure	183
	Atropa belladonna	principles (general)	pharmacopoeia	E. Steinegger[a]: Ph. Ac. H. 37, 343 (1962)
	Atropa belladonna	glucosides	structure elucidation	E. Steinegger[a]: Ph. Ac. H. 39, 450 (1964)
	Capsicum	flavones	separation	P. H. List[a]: Arch. Ph. 298, 107 (1965)
	Capsicum annuum	pungent principles	chemotaxonomy	120
	Capsicum annuum	pungent principles	isolation	K. Jentzsch[b]: Monatshefte F. Ch. 99, 661 (1968)
	Capsicum annuum	essential oil	separation	J. Tatár: Herba Hung. 3, 455 (1964)
	Jaborosa integrifolia	flavones	isolation	188
	Petunia hybrida	steroid sapogenins	structure elucidation	R. Tschesche[b]: Tetrah. 24, 5169 (1968)
		anthocyanins	separation	L. Birkofer[b]: Z. Naturforsch. 17b, 352 (1962)
Solanaceae	Physalis	principles (general)	screening	W. Völksen: Arch. Ph. 294, 337 (1961)
	Solanum	steroid sapogenins	isolation	204, 249, 250
	Solanum dulcamara	steroid sapogenins	chemotaxonomy	196, 198, 259
	Solanum paniculatum	steroid sapogenins	isolation	H. Ripperger[b]: Ch. Ber. 100, 1741 (1967)
	Solanum sisymbriifolium	steroid sapogenins	isolation	240
	Solanum sodomeum	steroid sapogenins	isolation	H. Sander: Naturw. 48, 303 (1961)
	Solanum tuberosum	steroids	isolation	K. Schreiber[a]: Tetrah. 20, 2575 (1964)

Table I (continued)

Family of plants	Genus or species of plants	Substance class investigated	Purpose of investigation	Reference
	Withania somnifera	withanolids	structure	141–143
	Withania somnifera	withanolids	chemotaxonomy	A. Abraham[b]: Phytoch. 7, 957 (1968)
Taxaceae	Taxus baccata	principles (general)	separation	184
	Taxus baccata	triterpenes	structure	R. Fr. Preuss[a]: Pharm. 20, 698 (1965)
Taxodiaceae	Metasequoia glyptostroboides	flavones	separation	S. Beckmann[a]: Phytoch. 7, 1667 (1968)
	Sequoia sempervirens	phenols	isolation	B. Balogh[a]: Phytoch. 4, 569 (1965)
Tiliaceae	Tilia	principles (general)	separation	E. Steinegger[a]: Sci. Ph. 31, 298 (1963)
Thymelaeaceae	Daphne mezereum	coumarins	isolation	R. Tschesche[b]: Naturw. 50, 521 (1963)
Umbelliferae		essential oil	pharmacopoeia	L. Hörhammer[b]: D. Apoth. Z. 104, 1398 (1964)
	Ammi	principles (general)	pharmacopoeia	C. K. Atal[a]: C. A. 62, 6343g (1965)
		principles (general)	pharmacopoeia	L. Hörhammer[a]: D. Apoth. Z. 102, 733 (1962)
	Ammi visnaga	furocoumarins		B. Kaul[a]: PM. 15, 145 (1967)
	Angelica silvestris	principles (general)	isolation	L. Hörhammer[b]: Z. Naturforschg. 18b, 639 (1963)
	Bupleurum falcatum	sapogenins	isolation	Sh. Shibata[b]: Ch. Ph. B. 14, 1023 (1966)
	Centella asiatica	anthrone	separation	T. Rahandraha[b]: Ann. Ph. Franc. 21, 561 (1963)
	Coriandrum sativum	essential oil	ecology	K. Lörincz[a]: Herba Hung. 4, 191 (1965)
	Coriandrum sativum	essential oil	separation	S. Lassányi: Ac. Agr. Hung. 14, 135 (1965)
	Coriandrum sativum	essential oil	isolation	J. Reisch[b]: Naturw. 52, 642 (1965)
	Coriandrum sativum	essential oil	separation	J. Reisch[b]: PM. 14, 326 (1966)
	Coriandrum sativum	essential oil	identification	E. Schratz[a]: PM. 14, 310 (1966)
	Daucus carota	essential oil	chemotaxonomy	222
	Foeniculum vulgare	terpenes	biosynthesis	122
	Foeniculum vulgare	lipids	separation	123
	Foeniculum vulgare	essential oil	identification	237, 238
	Lomatium nuttallii	coumarins	isolation	K.-H. Lee[a]: J. Ph. Sci. 57, 865 (1968)

	Myrrhis odorata	essential oil	separation	H. Gertig[a]: C. A. 66, 10817h (1966) 220
	Petroselinum hortense	essential oil	chemotaxonomy	A. V. Ananchiev[a]: Med. Prom. SSSR 20, 5 (1966)
	Peucedanum morisoni	furocoumarins	separation	
	Sanicula europea	principles (general)	isolation	102
	Sanicula europea	saponins	isolation	104
Valerianaceae	Nardostachys jatamansi	terpenes	isolation	S. N. Shanberg[b]: Tetrah. 20, 2605 (1964)
	Valeriana collina	essential oil	separation	255
	Valeriana wallichii	flavones	isolation	P. W. Thies: PM. 16, 361 (1968) 117
Zingiberaceae	Balanites aegyptiaca	pigments	screening, chemotaxon.	
Zygophyllaceae	Tribulus terrestris	steroid sapogenins	structure	A. A. M. Davidar[a]: Phytoch. 8, 261 (1969)
		flavones	structure	S. P. Bhutani[b]: Phytoch. 8, 299 (1969)

Table II

TLC of the Main Plant Substance Classes

(for key to abbreviations see page 204)

Substance class	Layer material	Solvents number used	Solvents example	Detection	Reference
Amines					
aliphatic amines	Silica Gel G, cellulose	6	EtOH–25% NH$_4$OH (80:20)	ninhydrin; sodium nitroprusside, nitric acid	235
quaternary amines	Aluminum oxide G	3	BuOH–H$_2$O–HCOOH (12:7:1)	iodoplatinate; iodine; Dragendorff; dipicrylamine	234
Indoles	Silica Gel G, Silica Gel G + Kieselguhr G	5	PrOH–5% NH$_4$OH (5:2)	Ehrlich reagent	147
Lipids					
neutral lipids	Silica Gel G	3	petrol ether–ether–AcOH (90:10:1)	dichlorofluoresceine	158
fatty and wax acids	Kieselguhr G	3	90% AcOH satur. tetradecane	alk. KMnO$_4$	124
phospho- and glucolipids	Silica Gel G	3	CHCl$_3$–MeOH–H$_2$O (65:25:4)	iodine; ninhydrin; Dragendorff; Schiff reagent	146
Phenolic compounds					
phenols	Silica Gel G	4	benzene–MeOH (95:5) benzene	diazot. benzidine; alk. KMnO$_4$	178
phenols	Supergel + CaSO$_4$	4	CHCl$_3$–AcOH (5:1)	*p*-nitrobenzene–diazonium–fluoroborate	208
phenols	polyamide		benzene–dioxane–HCOOH (70:25:5)	*o*-diphenyloxidase	53
phenolic glucosides	Silica Gel G polyamide + cellulose	8	ethyl acetate–MeOH (9:1) (two-dimensional)	4% H$_2$SO$_4$; AgNO$_3$	11

Substance	Sorbent		Solvent system	Detection	Ref.
coumarins	Silica Gel G		benzene–acetone (9:1) benzene–ethyl acetate (9:1)	UV or 0.5% J_2-KJ	1
furocoumarins	Silica Gel G Silica Gel H	4	CHCl$_3$	UV; alcoholic KOH	27
depsids and depsidons	Eastman Chromagram K 301 R2	9	toluene–acetone–AcOH (7:2:1)	UV; benzidine; Echtblausalz	200
lignane	Silica Gel G		1st-dim. CHCl$_3$–MeOH (90:10) 2nd-dim. CHCl$_3$–acetone (65:35)	H$_2$SO$_4$–AcOH (1:3)	216
chromones	Silica Gel G	4	xylene–acetone (40:10)	10% NaOH; 20% HCl; chlorosulfonic acid–AcOH (1:3)	14
flavones	polyamide		MEK–EtOH–AcOH–H$_2$O (15:15:5:65)	UV	59
quinones	polyamide	4	MeOH–H$_2$O (1:1)	UV	82
hydroxyquinones	acetyl cellulose MN300 Ac		THF–ethyl acetate–H$_2$O (35:6:47)	UV; 0.5N NaOH in EtOH; Ni-acetate	159
anthraquinones	Silica Gel G	2	benzene–ethyl formiate–HCOOH (75:25:1)	UV; 5% KOH or NaOH	139
polyhydroxy-anthraquinones	Silica Gel G Kieselguhr G		CH$_2$Cl$_2$–MeOH (10:3) CCl$_4$–benzene (1:1)	UV; Borntraeger reagent; nitroso-dimethylaniline in pyridine	209
anthocyanins	Silica Gel G		ethyl acetate–HCOOH–H$_2$O (85:6:9) or acetone–0.5N HCl (1:3)		101
	cellulose MN300 + silica gel		acetone–0.5N HCl (1:3)		10
anthocyanidins	Avicel SF (two-dimensional)	8	AcOH–H$_2$O–conc. HCl (30:10:3) MeOH–H$_2$O–conc. HCl (90:10:1)		172

Table II (continued)

Substance class	Layer material	Solvents number used	Solvents example	Detection	Reference
Terpenoids					
monoterpenes	Silica Gel G		hexane hexane–ethyl acetate (85:15)	conc. H₂SO₄; SbCl₃; SbCl₅; KMnO₄	72
monoterpene hydrocarbons	Silica Gel G + AgNO₃		benzene	SbCl₅	144
terpene aldehydes and ke-tones	Silica Gel G	4	benzene–ethyl acetate–AcOH (90:5:5) benzene	UV; monohydrazine sulfate	134
thujyl compounds	Silica Gel G	9	benzene–ethyl acetate (95:5) benzene	vanillin–conc. H₂SO₄	17
monoterpene alcohols terpene alcohols	Silica Gel G Kieselguhr G impregnated with paraffin Silica Gel G		hexane–benzene (1:1) acetone–H₂O (65:25) benzene–ethyl acetate (80:20)	vanillin–conc. H₂SO₄ anisaldehyde–conc. H₂SO₄	2
sesquiterpene hydro-carbons	Silica Gel G		benzene–acetone (95:5)	chlorosulfonic acid–AcOH (1:2)	87
farnesole isomers	silica gel + CaSO₄		benzene–ethyl acetate (95:5)	vanillin–conc. H₂SO₄	243
gibberellins	Silica Gel G Kieselguhr G	3	diisopropyl ether–AcOH (95:5) H₂O–H₂SO₄ (3:7)	EtOH–conc. H₂SO₄ (15:5)	156
neutral triterpenes	Silica Gel G		cyclohexane; benzene; CH₂Cl₂ diisopropyl ether	chlorosulfonic acid–AcOH (1:2)	239

Compound	No.	Stationary phase	Mobile phase	Detection	Ref.
triterpene isomers		Anasil-B; Anasil-B + AgNO₃; Silica Gel G; Silica Gel G + AgNO₃; Silica Gel G + AgNO₃	hexane–benzene (2:1), (4:1); hexane–ether (97:3)	H_2O–H_3PO_4–H_2SO_4 (100:1:1)	66
tetracycl. triterpenes		Silica Gel G	hexane–benzene–EtOH (50:50:0.5)	$SbCl_3$; $SbCl_5$	112
triterpene esters	4	Silica Gel G	CH_2Cl_2	chlorosulfonic acid–AcOH (1:2)	239
triterpene acids		Silica Gel G	diisopropyl ether–acetone (5:2)	chlorosulfonic acid–AcOH (1:2)	239
cucurbitacins	5	Silica Gel GF₂₅₄	diisopropyl ether–acetone (5:2)	aldehydes in EtOH; FeCl₃; iodine	262
Resins and Balsams					
resin acids		Silica Gel G; Silica Gel G	MeOH–H_2O (70:30); 1st dimension: hexane–ethyl acetate (70:30); 2nd dimension: CHCl₃–acetone (90:10)	SbCl₃; SbCl₅; anisaldehyde; vanillin–conc. H_2SO_4	120; 45
Carotinoids					
carotinoids	9	Silica Gel G + MgO (1:1); Silica Gel G; MgO; Ca(OH)₂ + Silica Gel G (6:1)	petrol ether–benzene (90:10)		40
carotinoids		polyamide + cellulose MN300 (85:15)	petrol ether 100–120°C; MEK–MeOH (50:50)		58
Ubiquinones					
		Silica Gel G	benzene–CHCl₃ (1:1)	UV; Rhodamine B	256
Steroids					
steroids	10	impregnated Florisil	benzene–EtOH (98:2); benzene	conc. H_2SO_4	207
free sterols		Silica Gel H + AgNO₃	CHCl₃–acetone (95:5)	blue tetrazolium	51
free sterols		Silica Gel G impregnated with undecane	acetone–AcOH (60:20)	dibromofluoresceine	46

Table II (continued)

Substance class	Layer material	Solvents		Detection	Reference
		number used	example		
cardiac glucosides	Silica Gel G		CH_2Cl_2–MeOH–formamide (80:19:1)	chloramine–trichloroacetic acid	216
cardiac glucosides	Silica Gel G		benzene–95% EtOH (70:30)	diluted $HClO_4$	119
cardiac glucosides	Silica Gel G		1st dimension: ethyl acetate–MeOH–H_2O (16:1:1) 2nd dimension: $CHCl_3$–pyridine (6:1) one dimens.: $CHCl_3$–MEK–formamide (2:5:1)	anisaldehyde	210
sapogenins	Wakogel B-5	22	$CHCl_3$–MeOH (18:2) benzene–EtOH (85:15)	conc. H_2SO_4; AcOH–H_2SO_4; $SbCl_3$; chlorosulfonic acid–EtOH (1:2)	163
sapogenins	Wakogel	6	$CHCl_3$–MeOH (95:5)	conc. H_2SO_4; $SbCl_3$; chlorosulfonic acid–AcOH (1:2)	232
sapogenins	Silica Gel G Kieselguhr G Silica Gel G + Kieselguhr G (1:1)	3	CH_2Cl_2–MeOH–HCOOH (93:6:1)	50% H_2SO_4	23
sapogenins and steroid alkaloids	Silica Gel G + $AgNO_3$		$CHCl_3$–MeOH (90:10), (5:5) $CHCl_3$–ether–AcOH (97:2.5:0.5)	iodine + KI; KBr; $CeSO_4$ in H_2SO_4	191
withanolids	Silica Gel G		benzene–EtOH (90:10)	$SbCl_3$; $FeCl_3$	247
Polyins	Silica Gel G		petrol ether petrol ether–ether (8:2), (85:15)	1st dicobaltoctacarbonyl; 2nd 1N HCl	205

Abbreviations: AcOH = glacial acetic acid; BuOH = butyl alcohol; EtOH = ethyl alcohol; MEK = methyl ethyl ketone; MeOH = methyl alcohol; PrOH = propyl alcohol; THF = tetrahydrofuran; UV = ultraviolet light.

204

the presence of the sought compound should also be mentioned. Wall et al.[257] used drop tests for the screening of neutral steroid saponins, while Schreiber et al.[204] screened more than 120 *Solanum* species for steroid alkaloids by means of preparative analysis.

As a first step in the informative analysis of substances of known structure or for the rapid series analysis of small samples, it is advantageous to use qualitative or semiquantitative methods such as paper or thin-layer chromatography. The results of chromatographic screening, however, may not be certain. In some cases it will be necessary to isolate the substance whose presence has been indicated by screening and to investigate its structure. Chromatographic methods have several advantages, nevertheless, among them that of providing information not merely on the compound sought, but also on the presence of related and other substances. Screenings by other methods may fail to discover many, perhaps valuable, substances.

The expediency of TLC is confirmed by the continuously increasing number of publications on results of TLC screening tests. TLC screening requires appropriate extraction and partial purification of the sample. Hultin[108–111] studied solvent mixtures using this method for the analysis of plant extracts.

Study of Infraspecific Chemical Taxa

TLC plays an important role in the achievement of results in modern chemotaxonomy with respect to the discovery of both the chemical deviations within the same species (infraspecific chemical taxa) and the relationships or deviations among different species (interspecific chemical taxa).

One of the important criteria that justify the use of chemical taxa is hereditary character. During cultivation trials of *Chrysanthemum vulgare,* for example, it was established that the composition of the essential oil is independent of environmental factors.[221, 224, 225]

Stahl et al. have established the taxa of several plant species by screening with TLC. In the case of *Asarum europeum* these authors established four chemical taxa[223] from the components of essential oils by means of the usual TLC method for essential oils.[217, 218] In parsley the presence of one myristicin and one apiol taxon was discovered in the same way. In addition, Stahl investigated the ripe fruits of European and Japanese culture varieties of *Daucus carota* subsp. *sativus* by so-called low temperature TLC at $-9\,°C$ on Silica Gel HF_{254},[222] and he recently described a special method[226] applicable to the investigation of plants containing essential oils. From a small 1–25-mg drug sample he distilled the essential oil onto the adsorbent layer in an appropriate apparatus (the so-called TAS technique) and performed the chromatographic procedure in the usual manner.

The essential oils of clones of *Lavandula angustifolia* were examined by Lörincz and Tyihák.[149] Considerable differences were discovered with respect to their morphological character, too, among the clones belonging to the main chemical types. The Lörincz-Tyihák group used Silica Gel G and Silica Gel H as adsorbents for the separation of terpene alcohols, terpenic acids and esters, ketones, aldehydes, and hydrocarbons (Figure 1). The fatty acids of low carbon number bound by ester bonds were determined in the form of hydroxamic acids on layers of cellulose MN 300 and MN 300 G.

Sander[198] and Rozumek and Sander[195] studied the infraspecific differentiation of *Solanum dulcamara*. From screening of wild species growing in various localities they established three taxa. Both the steroid glucosides and the aglucons were investigated on Silica Gel G. Willuhn[259] studied the unripe fruit by TLC. It was noted that two compounds characteristic of the vegetative organs are present in the ripe soladulcidine and tomatidenol types in addition to only a small quantity of solaso-

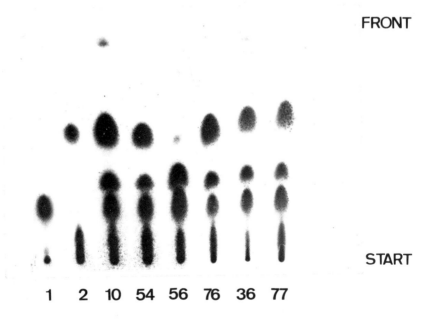

Figure 1. Thin-layer chromatogram of essential oils of clones of *Lavandula angustifolia*.[149] (1) linalool; (2) linalyl acetate; at the following starting points samples of clone numbers 10, 54, 56, 76, 36, and 77 were subsequently applied. Silica Gel G; benzene–ethyl acetate (98:2, v/v); detection: 1% vanillin in conc. H_2SO_4, 5 minutes at 105°C. (Reproduced from Acta Agron. Acad. Sci. Hung. by permission of the publisher.)

dine. The unripe fruit of the solasodine type contains only solasodine. In addition, screening within a plant species may also be performed for aims other than the search for infraspecific taxa, and the screening itself may be approached in other ways.

Often before a plant has been screened to determine its principles through identification of several active components, a certain physiological activity of the plant species is known. In search of the toxic, pyrogenic, and cocarcenogenic components of *Croton tiglium* seed oil, for example, Hecker[97] screened first the hydrophilic fraction of croton oil by preparing various compounds. And in investigating the ethanolic extract of *Rhynchosia pyramidalis,* a popular medicinal plant, Farnsworth *et al.*[63] found catechin tannins, organic acids, and phenols after the removal of fats (but the flavone test was negative).

Pharmacological trials were performed along with these TLC tests. Korte and Sieper[135, 136] investigated the chemical substances in hashish, a procedure which involved the separation of cannabidiolic acid, cannabidiol, cannabinol, and several of their isomers by means of TLC on dimethylformamide-impregnated Silica Gel G.

Investigations of Higher Taxa
Study of the Interspecific Chemical Taxa

The chemical screening of plants is often limited by the existence of a definite taxonomic unit. In the search for relationships among internal contents of the different species in a genus or tribe, another important category of chemotaxonomy based on identities has been established. Interspecific taxa, as it is called, often subjects the genus itself, as a taxonomic category, to screening tests.

Vágujfalvi *et al.*[249, 250] established with the help of their TLC method that the formation of neutral steroid sapogenins, in addition to the basic steroid sapogenins, characterizes the *Solanum* genus (Figure 2). In all of the 28 species investigated, these neutral sapogenins are present, though in various proportions. Máthé *et al.*[161, 162] and Földesi[67] investigated species of the subgenus *archeosolanum* (genus *Solanum*) also by means of TLC. The steroid-alkaloid glucoside content was investigated on Silica Gel G.

In the course of the chemical screening of plants chemotaxonomic conclusions are sometimes drawn for wide categories such as lipids. Purdy and Truter[185] screened 10 monocotyledonous and 14 dicotyledonous plants for lipids by means of TLC. They drew their conclusions from results obtained with various solvent systems and reagents, but they did not identify the components.

In order to avoid misleading conclusions, screening of plants is usually performed within narrower limits—if possible only for taxonomic units or for well-defined compound types. These latter compounds may be

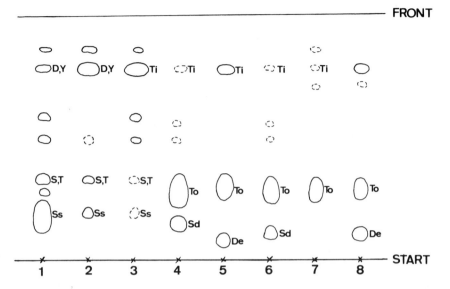

Figure 2.   Thin-layer chromatogram of steroid sapogenins of *Solanum* species according to Reference 249. (1) *S. laciniatum;* (2) *S. nitidibaccatum;* (3) *S. nodiflorum;* (4) *Lesculentum* var. *cerasiforme;* (5) *S. demissum;* (6) *S. simplicifolium;* (7) *S. tomotillo Debrecen;* (8) *S. tomotillo Roma.* (De) Demissidine; (D) diosgenin; (Sd) soladulcidine; (S) solasodien; (Ss) solasodine; (Ti) tigogenin; (T) tomatidenol; (Y) yamogenin. Silica Gel G; chloroform–methanol (19:1, v/v); detection with 20% $SbCl_3$ in chloroform. (Reproduced from Bot. Közlem. by permission of the publisher.)

screened by application of specific reagents for detection; reliable results are quite often accomplished by combining several detecting reagents. Saponins are screened by treating the thin-layer chromatogram with blood gelatin; hemolysis will indicate their presence. This is followed by further preliminary tests using other TLC methods to provide more nearly exact information on the chemical structure of the detected saponins.[12] Several works describe how satisfactory results were obtained by applying a combination of different solvents. For instance, Blunden et al.[28] investigated the steroid components of *Dioscorea* types by two-dimensional TLC.

For the TLC of phenolic compounds, layers of polyamide are often used, *e.g.*, by Friedrich and Höhle[69] in a study of polyphenols of the species of the *Rheum* genus. Other authors have used polyamide layers for the study of isoflavone glucosides of *Trifolium* species.[206] Polyamide combined with cellulose was found to be useful for the separation of the phenolic glucosides in the *Salix* genus.[11] Juhász and Tyihák[121] studied the distribution of capsaicin isomers in the *Capsicum* genus using an alkaline solvent on cellulose MN 300. They found capsaicin a and b in the cultivated species of *Capsicum annuum* and in other species of the genus. Other researchers also used cellulose MN 300 for the study of phenolic components, *e.g.,* in the *Galeopsis* species[41] and the flower dye-stuffs in *Rhododendron* species.[49] Jentzsch[115] classified *Curcuma* species according to the composition of their dyestuff complexes into the *domestica* type and the *xanthorrhiza* type.

Cassia angustifolia, an important medicinal plant in the *Cassia* genus, is an excellent laxative. Anton and Duquénois[8] studied its active substances, the anthraglucosides, by TLC on Silica Gel GF_{254}. In their study of the components of the *Erysimum* genus Gmelin and Bredenberg[80] identified the bitter substance erysimupicrone with k-strophanthidin and described a glycosinolate from the seeds of four *Erysimum* species. The *Matricaria* species contain several substances of therapeutic importance. Six substances of yet unidentified composition, in addition to 38 compounds already known, are present in the 16 species investigated by Bohlmann *et al.*[38] TLC was successfully used for isolation and identification of the compounds; it was possible by this means to isolate polyines from certain *Echinacea* species[35] and several species of the *Carduinae* subtribe.[36]

Several examples of TLC screening for alkaloids of plant species also have been reported. Fejér-Kossey[65] studied the alkaloid content of certain species and hybrids of *Nicotiana* (Figure 3). Ahmed *el al.*[4] screened the *Plantago* species for alkaloids by two-dimensional TLC. Johne and Gröger[118] studied the occurrence of the pyrrolidino-quinazoline alkaloid peganine in the *Linaria* genus and found it in five species. Calderwood and Fish[43] investigated the occurrence of tertiary and quaternary alkaloids in the African *Fagara* species. In studying the phytochemistry of the *Cytisus* genus Gill and Steinegger used TLC to establish the non-uniformity of the species with respect to quinolizidine alkaloid occurrence;[74] sparteine and lupanine occurred the most frequently and were present in all species investigated. The occurrence and distribution of alkaloids in the various species of the *Genista* genus were studied by several authors.[25, 26, 64, 75, 76, 174] Comparison with the botanical system revealed close agreement between chemical and morphological properties.

Screening of Plant Species within the Same Family

Drozdz[55, 56] screened the entire *Cynareae* tribe of the *Compositae* family looking for the occurrence of sesquiterpene lactones. Isolation was performed in conjunction with TLC. The occurrence of sesquiterpene lactones was also studied in *Ambrosia* species.[70] Kasprzyk and Kozierowska[127] also screened the *Compositae* family (24 species in 11 tribes of the *Tubuliflorae* subfamily) for sterols and triterpene alcohols. They established by one- and two-dimensional TLC on Silica Gel G that triter-

FRONT

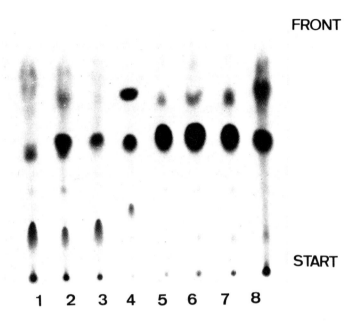

START

1   2   3   4   5   6   7   8

Figure 3. Separation and identification of tobacco alkaloids in certain species and hybrids of *Nicotiana* by TLC.[65] Extracts of nornicotine-type tobacco hybrids (1–3); mixture of authentic alkaloids (4) containing (from start to front): nornicotine, anabasine, nicotine, nicotyrine; extracts of nicotine-type hybrids (5–8). Silica Gel G suspended for spreading in 0.5N KOH; chloroform–ethanol (90:10, v/v). Detection spray of 1% benzidine in ethanol–BrCN vapor. (Reproduced from Acta Biol. Acad. Sci. Hung. by permission of the publisher.)

pene monohydroxy alcohols are characteristic secondary metabolites in the flowers of all members of the *Compositae* family. Gerlach[71] isolated diterpenes from the roots of *Solidago* species (*Solidago canadensis* and *S. gigantea*) and investigated the purity of the isolated substances by TLC on Silica Gel G.

Cucurbitacines are triterpenic substances which were first obtained from plants in the *Cucurbitaceae* family. This family has been subjected to screening,[133] as has the *Cruciferae* family.[78, 81] The occurrence of the triterpene saponins was also studied in *Polemonium* species.[227] Váguj-falvi and Held[252] and Held *et al.*[100] screened the *Liliaceae* family for Δ^5 neutral steroid sapogenins. Cyclohexane–ethyl acetate–water (60:40:0.1, v/v) was found suitable for the separation of the three main steroid types—sterols and basic and neutral sapogenins. Harborne[92, 93] screened the leaves and flowers of 100 species of *Primulaceae* and found correlation between pigmentation and system of classification within the family.

TLC is often applied for preparative purposes in the study of plant substances.[73,100] Bendz *et al.*[20,21,22] employed this method using thick Silica Gel HF layers for the investigation of organic acids in lichen. Ahmed *et al.*[5] investigated the Egyptian species of the *Araceae* family. Phytochemical screening was extended by means of TLC to the mucilage, tannin, unsaturated amine, alkaloid, essential oil, flavonoid, and saponin content. Miller *et al.* screened 102 species in the *Cruciferae* family for industrial oils.[167]

The species of the *Papaveraceae* family contain therapeutically important alkaloids.[181] In this connection the preparative screening of the plants in this family by Slavik *et al.*[212,213] and Maturová *et al.*[164] are of considerable importance (for details see the chapter on alkaloids in Volume 3 of this series). Dreyer[54] has subjected the therapeutically valuable *Rutaceae* family to screening by preparative analysis. Important screening tests for alkaloid occurrence were carried out in the *Chenopodiaceae* family[197] and the *Cruciferae* family.[47,48] The alkaloid content of the *Ranunculaceae* family was studied by screening about 60 species.[68]

Screening of Plant Species within Several Families

Plants of several families were reported screened for one or several types of compounds in still other works. Examples of such TLC screening tests were carried out by Vágujfalvi and Tyihák[248] (Figure 4), who concluded that essential oil components are universally present in plants. They screened 50 species of 45 genera in 27 plant families for essential oil components that had never before been isolated in those plants. The tests were carried out on aboveground vegetative organs. All species contained a certain amount of essential oil; the majority contained 0.0001–0.001%.

Raffauf[186] also performed TLC screenings irrespective of the taxonomic units. He screened 15,000 species for alkaloids, using several solvents and iodoplatinate for detection.

Some general screening tests involving several plant families and various compounds are also known. Nakanishi *et al.*[173] screened 89 species of 82 genera in 40 families of the flora in Malaysia and Singapore for alkaloids, phenolic compounds, amino acids, and reductive sugars, and for acidic and basic substances. Chemical screening was performed together with pharmacological tests, including toxicity tests and the investigation of antimicrobial and cytostatic activity.

A survey of the literature shows that TLC is a preferred, valuable method for screening plants and establishing their chemotaxonomy. TLC is considerably helpful in the important work which tries to elucidate the chemical relationships among plants, while at the same time it discovers new medical plants with special usefulness to man.

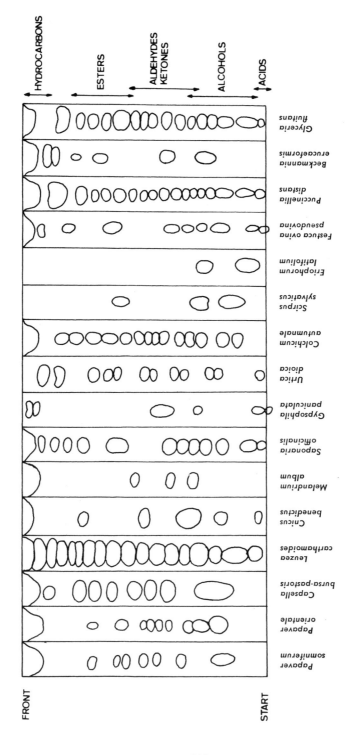

Figure 4. Thin-layer chromatograms of essential oil components in different species of several families; these components were never before described in these plants.[248] Silica gel; benzene; detection: 1% vanillin in H₂SO₄, 5 minutes at 105°C. (Reproduced from Bot. Közlem, by permission of the publisher.)

APPLICATION OF TLC IN THE STUDY OF BIOSYNTHESIS

It appears from the data of Table I that our knowledge of the composition of plant kingdom substances has improved tremendously within the past decade thanks to TLC. Similarly, our knowledge of the formation mechanism of many known and newly isolated plant substances has gained much from the increasing number of biosynthetic studies. In these studies—besides the extensive application of labeled substances and up-to-date instrumental physico-chemical methods—TLC as a simple and versatile separation technique is of considerable help.

The biochemistry of isoprenoids has undergone particularly significant development in the past decade because microanalysis of individual representatives of this group has been made possible by the application of TLC. In the study of the biosynthesis of anethole by *Foeniculum vulgare,* anethole was identified in fennel oil by the chromato-strip method[122] mentioned at the beginning of this chapter. The qualitative and quantitative composition of carotenoids in the leaves of *Acer platanoides* in summer and autumn was studied by means of TLC, and special methods were applied to the analysis of the hypophase and the epiphase.[61] These analytical methods served later on as the basis for preparative methods.[61, 62] In the study of terpene biogenesis by *Mentha piperita*[193] and *M. aquatica*[98] during the vegetative period and ontogenesis, TLC was applied in combination with GC to the analysis of the essential oil. By means of TLC the composition of the essential oil was determined in the fruits of *Coriandrum sativum* from different localities[204] and in samples obtained by steam distillation from the seedlings of the Lucs variety of *Coriandrum sativum* and of *pericarpium* after germination.[140] Changes in the composition of essential oil in the various tissue regions of *Valeriana collina* were also traced by means of TLC.[255]

In the study of the biosynthesis and metabolism of β-sitosterol, β-amyrin, and methyl sterols in the flowers of *Taraxacum officinale,* TLC was used for the determination of nonradioactive β-amyrin.[3] Baisted[15] followed the incorporation of ^{14}C into β-sitosterol, squalene, β-amyrin, and cholesterol exclusively by preparative layer chromatography of the germinating seeds of *Pisum sativum,* and he measured the radioactivity after scraping off the substance zones. The author then identified the compounds by TLC and by preparative layer technique was able to isolate even geraniol-^{14}C from the *Pelargonium graveolens* he had grown in $^{14}CO_2$ atmosphere. After the administration of progesterone-4-^{14}C to *Strophantus kombe* plants, the cardenolides periplogenin, trophyntidin and strophantidol were isolated by preparative TLC and column chromatography on silica gel.[202]

In their study of the biogenesis of plant polyines Bohlmann and Schulz[39] isolated the polyines from fresh leaves of *Chrysanthemum flos-*

culosum by means of TLC. The investigation of the biochemical conversion of gitogenin into 12-oxygenated sapogenin in *Hosta kiyosumiensis* isolated the substances by using preparative layer chromatography, and it was found that the conversion occurs under the action of a plant enzyme.[233] In studying the biosynthesis of umbelliferone in the extracts of leaves of *Hydrangea macrophylla,* the glucoside precursors were isolated on an analytical and preparative scale on cellulose (Whatman CC 41).[13] The incorporation of tritium-labeled daidzein into the isoflavonoids, cumestrol, and formononetin of alpha-alpha preceded isolation and identification by means of TLC; the necessary isoflavone methyl ether derivatives were also purified on thick-layers of silica gel.[16] In a study by Grisebach and Zilg[86] on the biogenetic relationship between isoflavonones and isoflavones, the authors identified the individual flavones partly by paper chromatography, but mainly by employing TLC on polyamide and silica gel; for isolation they used a silica gel column. Kartnig and Hiermann[125] autoradiographically measured the distribution of saponins in the stages of the ontogenesis of *Aesculus hippocastanum* after the administration of 2-^{14}C mevalonic acid lactone to young plants. The biogenesis of juglone was studied in the leaves of *Juglans regia* by administering radioactive precursors and later by isolating and purifying the juglone on silica gel.[144]

APPLICATION OF TLC TO THE IDENTIFICATION AND ISOLATION OF PLANT SUBSTANCES

Thin-layer chromatography offers several ways to identify and isolate plant substances. The most important are:

(1) Preexamination of extracts from various substance classes and identification of the extracts by TLC

(2) Thin-layer chromatographic examination of the fractions arrived at by column chromatography or by other separation methods

(3) Direct application of thin-layer chromatographic separation conditions to column chromatography

(4) Preparative layer chromatography.

Examination of Extracts and Identification by TLC

In the case of pharmacologically active extracts it is advisable to carry out preexaminations by means of TLC before embarking on the isolation procedure. The results of these TLC tests will provide information on the biologically active substances to be expected (alkaloids, steroids, etc.). By means of an analytical method especially devised for the substance group under investigation, it will be possible to identify known substances with the help of several solvents, adsorbents, and specific reactions, in addition to some indispensable test substances. Isolation will thus be limited to the unknown substances only, or if preliminary identification has furnished the desired result, it may even be omitted in some cases. In general, TLC identification alone is advisable and justified when the occurrence of the substance in question is chemotaxonomically probable; isolation of well-known substances from every species would involve an unreasonable amount of work. However, it is advisable to carry out isolation in every doubtful case. If the occurrence of obviously isomeric compounds is suspected, TLC identification results should be treated with particular reservation.

When investigating the components of an essential oil, in general it will only be possible to identify the main components because of the large number of substances present. Such data are available on *Oleum menthae*,[116] *Foeniculum vulgare*,[237, 238] azulene drugs,[246] and Rumanian *Mentha piperita* oil.[192, 193] The combination of TLC with gas chromatography sometimes enables identification of unknown components[237, 238] even without further physico-chemical tests.[165, 237] In general, however, other tests (*e.g.*, spectra) remain necessary for structure elucidation.[148] Two-dimensional thin-layer chromatographic analysis of essential oils has so far been neglected. Figure 5 shows one- and two-dimensional separa-

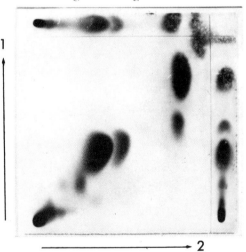

Figure 5. One- and two-dimensional thin-layer chromatograms of essential oil of *Lavender*[251] on Silica Gel G. (1) dimension: benzene–chloroform (75:25, v/v); (2) dimension: cyclohexane–methanol (98:2, v/v); detection: 0.5% anisaldehyde in conc. H_2SO_4, 5 minutes at 105°C.

tions of the essential oil of lavender.[253] The advantage of the two-dimensional technique appears clear. Some further examples are lemon and lime oils[155] and *Thymus* essential oil.[165] These and the two-dimensional analysis of some other essential oils[253] have recently contributed to the extending of TLC tests in the analysis of essential oils.

TLC identification alone was applied to the ether-soluble terpenoids of some *Compositae* species,[128] the flavone glucosides and aglucons (apigenin and luteolin) of *Capsicum* plants,[188] steroid saponins and sapogenins of *Tamus communis*,[99] aloin and other components in a South African *Aloe*,[106] aromatic aldehydes of certain lichen species,[199] quaternary amines of beet-root sap,[244] colchicine of *Colchicum hungaricum*,[160] and to the pungent protoalkaloidal principles of the *Capsicum* genus.[121] The phenol carboxylic acids of *Sanicula europaea*;[102] the triterpenoids of *Ilex latifolia* leaves;[261] the dianthrone and anthraquinone glucosides of *Cassia tora*,[182] *C. angustifolia*, and *Rheum palmatum*;[263] and the sulfur-containing amino acids of *Allium sativum*[107] have been subjected to detailed TLC identification.

Examination of Column Chromatographic Fractions

Since its beginning paper chromatography has been extensively used for examination of the components of column chromatographic fractions, but recently it has been increasingly replaced by TLC. TLC is also preferred to other methods by which the various steps in isolation and purification of drugs are checked.

TLC is used to check the isolation of the anti-neoplasticly active β-solamarin of *Solanum dulcamara* after purification by Craig's countercurrent distribution followed by purification on an alumina column.[137] The so-called withanolides of *Withania somnifera* were isolated on an alumina column and the fractions analyzed on a layer of Silica Gel G.[77, 141, 142, 143] A similar method was applied when estrone was isolated from the seeds of *Phoenix dactylifera*[24] and partly applied when cucurbitacines were isolated from the drugs of *Bryonia dioica*.[57] Other authors have fractionated the aglucons of the steroid glucosides of *Convallaria majalis* on a Celite-Florisil column and have carried out identification by TLC on layers of Wakogel-B-5 silica gel.[129, 130] The glucoside mixture isolated from the roots of *Cynanchum wilfordi* and *Metaplexis japonica* of the *Asclepiadaceae* species and the aglucon mixture prepared by alkaline hydrolysis were fractionated on an alumina column with a solvent mixture of increasing polarity (methanol was added to methylene chloride). The fractions were checked by TLC on alumina.[170, 171] In isolating a new cytotoxic sesquiterpene lactone from *Gaillardia pulchella*[138] and three new eudesmane-type sesquiterpene lactones from the roots of *Inula helenium*,[126] the columns were packed with different sorbents; fractions containing the same components were collected by means of TLC tests for crystallization and investigation of their structures.

Other publications on the TLC analysis of fractions obtained by chromatography on an alumina column include reports on the lipids of the root and fruit of *Foeniculum vulgare*,[124] the condensed aromatics in *Tamus communis*,[231] the active ingredient of the petals of *Calendula officinalis*,[85] and the cholegenin analog in the root of *Solanum sisymbriifolium*.[240] It should be mentioned further that in the fractionated distil-

lation of essential oils the components of the distillate are identified by
TLC combined with gas chromatography.[168]

Application of Thin-Layer Chromatographic Separation
Conditions to Column Chromatography

For the isolation of larger quantities column chromatography, the
classical form of adsorption chromatography, has now been used for
decades. TLC may be considered a special type of open-tube column
chromatography, so that the near relationship between the "open" and
the "closed" columns is obvious immediately.[217] TLC is primarily suited
for the detection and identification of small quantities; this is the decisive
factor in its experimental arrangement. From TLC tests conclusions may
be drawn on separation possibilities in the closed column. However,
even if TLC and column chromatographic tests are carried out on the
same type of adsorbent, several factors can prohibit a direct comparison
of the two techniques. The most important of these factors is the possibility of solvent transfer between thin-layer and vapor phase during
separation (vapor impregnation of adsorbent, evaporation of mobile
phase) being dependent on the type and shape of the separation chamber used. Examples of other factors include different techniques (ascend-
ent TLC, descendent column chromatography), difficulties in the accurate reproduction of adsorbent activation, etc. For this reason TLC is
used only for preliminary examinations in isolation work and for following fractionation by column chromatography. In the preceding paragraphs several examples of the combination of TLC and classical column
chromatography in pharmacognosy were listed. One of the main advantages of TLC appears in the sharpness of separation, and its application in separation of the components of natural mixtures is particularly
justified. With the help of TLC it is possible to detect individual isomers
which previously were considered inseparable, and it seems obvious that
their production in larger quantities may be achieved by applying the
analytical method to the column.

It is further obvious that TLC experience will be applicable to the
conditions of column chromatography more easily as the conditions of
the two techniques become more alike. Here the role of the TLC tanks
is of particular importance. In the so-called sandwich chamber, such as
the S- or BN-chamber[12, 217, 218] or their modifications,[49, 115] the runs
resemble column chromatographic conditions. Recent experience has
shown that in the S-chamber separation will be successful, exploiting the
advantages due to solvent demixing, if the vertical sorbent plate is completely covered in such a way that the covering plate projects a few mm
beyond the solvent mixture (Figure 6). Here this arrangement is called
the ultramicrochamber (UM-chamber),[247] where the free volume results
from the grooves between the particles and the glass plates. This is a

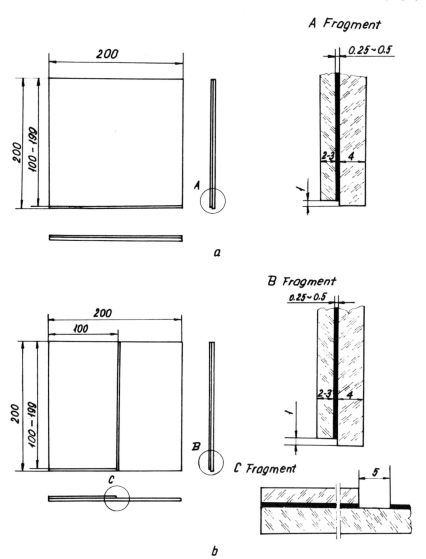

Figure 6. Ultramicrovolume sandwich chamber (UM-chamber).[247] Above: total thin-layer plate is covered by a glass plate; below: only half of the thin-layer plate is covered by a glass plate.

case between the "open" and the "closed" column where one of the main advantages of TLC—the simplicity of the method of identification—has not been lost. In the vertical position, chromatography may be carried out as follows: the mixture of substances is applied to the layer as desired either below or outside the covering plate. The layer is covered by a glass plate so that, *e.g.,* a 1-cm sorbent layer should remain free below the covering plate. The two plates are clamped together and placed in a large tank, and the run is carried out in the usual manner. Once the desired distance has been reached, the plates are dismantled and detection of spots is carried out as usual.

The construction of the UM-chamber is a technical problem that provides satisfactory chromatograms only if perfect covering is achieved— usually only with an even covering plate and a uniform layer surface. The solvents will run in all directions, otherwise, and the chromatogram will be useless.

Our initial results with the UM-chamber gave some interesting data on the relationship between closed and open columns. We separated methanolic fruit extracts from various *Capsicum* species, degreased in petrol ether, as well as isolated and synthetic capsaicin on layers of cellulose MN 300 in alkaline buffer solutions. In these experiments one half of the 20 × 20-cm glass plate was covered and the other half was run uncovered in a large tank (here referred to as T-chamber) without chamber saturation. No essential difference was observed between the

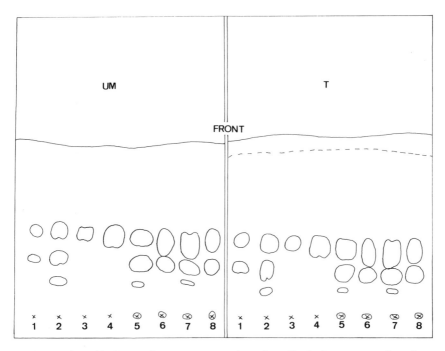

Figure 7. Thin-layer chromatograms of methanolic fruit extracts of various *Capsicum* species in UM-chamber (see Figure 6) and in a normal trough-chamber (T-chamber) without chamber saturation.[247] (1 and 2) 1 and 5 μg capsaicin; (3 and 4) 1 and 5 μg synthetic capsaicin; (5) *C. frutescens;* (6) *C. nigrum;* (7) *C. annuum;* (8) *C. angulosum.* Cellulose MN 300; 0.2M sodium acetate–0.2M NaOH– 0.3M sodium carbonate (1:2:3, v/v); detection: 0.5% $K_4Fe(CN)_6$–15% $FeCl_3$ (1:1, v/v).

two runs with the exception that in the UM-chamber diffusion was less pronounced and the spots were compact; hence, the separation in the T-chamber could be applied to column chromatographic conditions, at least in the case of capsaicin isomers (Figure 7). From this conclusion we arrived at the preparation of capsaicin isomers.[247] The same extracts and test substances were run on a Silica Gel G layer with a nonpolar solvent (petrol ether–benzene–methanol, 97:2:1, v/v) both in the UM-chamber and freely in a T-chamber (Desaga chamber without chamber saturation) using the above-described covering technique. In the T-chamber a very agreeable separation was obtained but, though the spots were

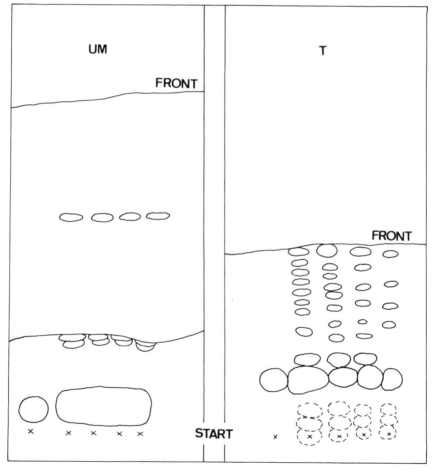

Figure 8. Thin-layer chromatograms of methanolic extracts of various *Capsicum* species in UM-chamber (see Figure 6) and in a normal trough-chamber (T-chamber) without chamber saturation.[247] From left to right: (1) 5 μg capsaicin; (2) *C. frutescens;* (3) *C. nigrum;* (4) *C. annuum;* (5) *C. angulosum.* Silica Gel G; petrol ether–benzene–methanol (97:2:1, v/v); detection: 0.5% $K_4Fe(CN)_6$–15% $FeCl_3$ (1:1. v/v).

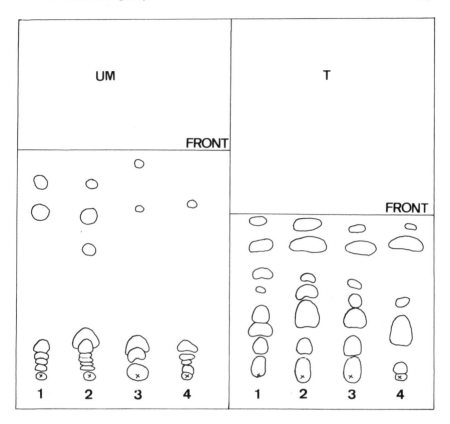

Figure 9. Thin-layer chromatograms of various essential oils in UM-chamber (see Figure 6) and in a normal trough-chamber (T-chamber) without chamber saturation.[254] (1) *Lemon;* (2) *Lavender;* (3) *Muscatel;* (4) *Rosemary*. Silica Gel G; cyclohexane–methanol (98:2, v/v); detection: 0.5% anisaldehyde in conc. H_2SO_4, 5 minutes at 105°C.

compact, the capsaicin did not separate into its components. In the UM-chamber capsaicin, and with it the bulk of the carotenoids, lagged behind at the start (Figure 8). Because conditions in the UM-chamber are entirely different in this case, the favorable separation obtained in the large tank cannot be applied to column chromatographic conditions. It should be further mentioned that certain components did run and that the migration of the solvent front was greatly accelerated in the UM-chamber. Similar results were obtained on other groups of substances— *e.g.,* essential oils—with the same type of solvent (Figure 9), where the migration rate of solvent front was two or three times higher. When amino acids were separated with polar solvents of low vapor pressure, the separation was almost the same in the T-chamber as in the UM-chamber (Figure 10). The conditions in the UM-chamber are obviously applicable to polyzonal TLC studies (Niederwieser and Brenner[175]); on the basis

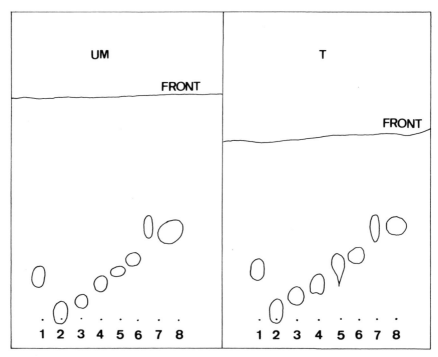

Figure 10. Thin-layer chromatograms of amino acids in UM-chamber (see Figure 6) and in a normal trough-chamber (T-chamber) without chamber saturation.[247] (1) DL-ε-N-Trimethyl lysine; (2) DL-*meso*-homocysteine; (3) L-asparagine; (4) L-homoarginine; (5) β-alanine; (6) γ-aminobutyric acid; (7) DL-5-methyl tryptophan; (8) DL-α-amino-*n*-butyric acid. Cellulose MN 300; chloroform–methanol–25% ammonia (4:4:1, v/v); detection: 0.2% ninhydrin and 0.05% $CdCl_2$ in acetone.

of these initial results and with improved UM-chamber techniques, we may expect new possibilities for clarifying relationships among the various chromatographic systems.

Experiences of recent years have proved that in several cases it is possible to apply the separation conditions worked out in a large chamber for TLC directly to column chromatography. Gmelin[79] succeeded in a satisfactory separation of a triterpene fraction obtained from the roots of *Bryonia dioica*. This author employed the same adsorbent (silica gel) and solvent for both TLC and column chromatography. He applied the same method for the isolation of the cucurbitacins of *Gratiola officinalis*.[82] From certain *Compositae* species the germacranolides were prepared on a silica gel column on the basis of TLC experience.[245] The L-α-bisabolol component of chamomile oil[113] and a lipophil flavone were obtained in pure state on a Silica Gel G column. The flavonoids of *Capsicum* fruits were separated on a polyamide layer with methanol–water (4:1, v/v), and the individual flavonoids were separated and isolated on a polyamide column with the same solvent.[188]

In certain cases it is neither possible nor advisable to apply the TLC conditions exactly as they are to column chromatographic conditions. To obtain the rapidly moving substances in adequate purity it is desirable to reduce the quantity of the polar component in the TLC solvent and then to increase this quantity gradually (gradient elution) to elute also the slowly moving substances in a reliable time.[79, 82, 176, 245]

Silica gel is the most widely used adsorbent in TLC technique. This explains the increasing use of silica gel as column packing, though not always in the form of fine powder or with binder as in TLC because a column packed with fine silica gel powder displays a rather high resistance. Columns packed with large silica gel granules were used for the analysis of the active ingredients of *Simaruba glauca*,[183] the furocoumarines of *Ruta graveolens*,[189] the triterpenoids of *Crossostephium chinense*,[201] the petrol ether-extracted root substances of *Taxus baccata*,[184] the photodynamic substances of *Dictamnus albus*,[230] and the tetracyclic triterpenes of *Bryonia dioica*.[57] The triterpenoids of *Sambucus ebulus* roots were separated on an impregnated silica gel column.[52]

Preparative Layer Chromatography

The "dismantable cell" constructed by Békésy[18] as early as 1942 for adsorption chromatography may be considered a transition between the column and the thick-layer plates for preparative purposes. Békésy used his cell primarily for the separation of ergot alkaloids.[19] The cell was later modified by Hall[90] and is in principle a closed chamber filled with adsorbent.

For the preparation of drugs today preparative layer chromatography, as modified by Ritter and Meyer,[190] Honegger,[105] and Halpaap,[91] is used. For the history and various techniques of preparative layer chromatography, we refer to the pertinent textbooks.[132, 179, 187, 217, 218]

Today preparative layer chromatography enjoys general use for the preparation of components which are present in small quantities in natural mixtures. The acceptance of the method in the preparative field is due to the favorable results obtained with analytical TLC, since it is desirable to prepare satisfactorily separated substances in larger quantities for the study of their structures or for preliminary biological tests. The quantity of substance which can be isolated by preparative layer chromatography is obviously limited, but in general it is possible to produce sufficient pure substance for structural research. For pharmacological tests, however, larger quantities are often required. Their preparation may involve difficulties, but generally for antibacterial and cytological trials the quantity of material obtainable by TLC will be sufficient.

Miller and Kirchner[166] were among the first who used thick-layers in pharmacognosy as we understand it today. With the chromato-strip technique it was possible to separate essential oils in quantities between

30 and 100 mg. In this respect the series of publications by Bohlmann *et al.* (see Table I) are particularly noteworthy, since they reported on a model preparation of polyines by methods that included preparative layer chromatography and on the subsequent investigation of the structure of the pure compounds. They used mostly Silica Gel HF_{254} (Merck) as the preparative layer, but carried out purification on an alumina column prior to preparative TLC. Preparative layer chromatography was employed also for purification of reaction products to prove the assumed structure of the thio ethers of *Anthemis carpatica*,[31] and these authors were able to separate the *cis-* and *trans-*isomers. The same method was used for the isolation and structure elucidation of the biogenetically important triacetylenes which are present in very small quantities in the various representatives of the *Compositae Anaphalis* and *Gnaphalium* genera.[33] To prepare some new acetylene compounds from the *Anthemis* genus, repeated preparative layer chromatography was applied leading to chromatographically pure substances.[34] A similar method was employed for the isolation of naturally occurring cumulenes and some other polyines.[37] Other authors studied the structure of sapogenins isolated from the roots of *Primula veris*[241] or of the steroids from *Dioscorea tenuipes;*[6, 7] some used preparative layer chromatography for the production of the Δ^7-sterols of the *Cucurbitaceae*,[229] of the photodynamic substances in *Dictamnus albus*,[230] or of the condensed aromatics in *Tamus communis*.[231] It was possible to produce pure β-bizabolol from the essential oil of *Gossipium hirsutum* on a thick-layer of silica gel.[169]

THIN-LAYER CHROMATOGRAPHY OF DRUGS

Up to now, a considerable part of official drugs included in the various pharmacopoeiae are still pharmaceutical raw materials. The advantages of TLC are being used more and more in pharmacopoeic specifications to establish the contents of active ingredients in official drugs and to detect impurities and falsifications.

A topical problem in this regard lies in presenting a survey of test methods and reliable data obtained by TLC experience collected to date in relation to the study of drug components from several aspects (chemotaxonomic, biogenetic, isolation and phytochemic, etc.) in a way which may be utilized by the pharmacopoeiae. In Luckner's book on the analysis of drugs[150] the application of chromatographic techniques including TLC is discussed in detail, in addition to the classical assay of the most important drugs, which include the official drugs. His suggestions, which were published in many papers (*e.g.,* References 151, 152, 153, and 154, among others listed in Table I), were also accepted by DAB 7. Ample data on the determination of the content of active ingredients in drugs may be found in pertaining chapters of TLC textbooks.[132, 187, 217, 218] Table I includes the most recent publications.

Accidental mixing of drugs, their falsification, or erroneous identification are everyday occurrences which necessitate a simple, reliable method for the identification of drug components. Háznagy *et al.*[95] have shown the applicability of TLC in detecting impurities and in revealing errors and falsifications on samples of some valuable drugs. Figure 11

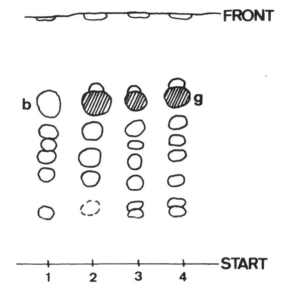

Figure 11. TLC of samples of leaves of *Digitalis lanata Ehrh.* adulterated with leaves of *Plantago lanceolata L.*[95] (1) Folia *Digitalis;* (2) Folia *Plantaginis* (3) Folia *Digitalis* + 5% Folia *Plantaginis;* (4) Folia *Digitalis* + 10% Folia *Plantaginis.* Silica Gel G; ethyl acetate–methyl ethyl ketone–formic acid–water (10:6: 2:2, v/v); detection: alcoholic lead acetate, UV. (Reproduced from Pharmazie by permission of the publisher.)

shows the thin-layer chromatographic evidence of a falsification of *Digitalis lanata* by the morphologically highly similar leaves of *Plantago lanceolata.*[95] Wartmann-Hafner[258] suggests for Pharmacop. Helv. VI the identification of the alkaloids of drug extracts and tinctures by TLC. He investigated aconitum, solanaceous, cinchona, Coca Cola, colchicum, ipecacuanha, opium, and strychnine alkaloids. For example, in investigating opium alkaloids, he used Silica Gel GF_{54} with ethyl acetate–94% ethanol–diethyl amine–dimethyl formamide (75:20:2:5, v/v) as solvent.

The test methods for essential oils as specified by the pharmacopoeiae

are rather cumbersome and inaccurate, generally giving unreliable results. Jaspersen-Schib[116] was among the first to suggest the introduction
of TLC for the assay of *Oleum menthae,* for example, and for the
detection of falsifications. By comparing data from GC and TLC of
genuine, extracted, and distilled essential oils in some *Mentha* species
Sticher and Flück[228] provided further information on the falsifications
and admixtures of *Oleum menthae* by the essential oils of some other
Mentha species. A thin-layer chromatogram of the essential oils of various *Mentha* species is shown in Figure 12.[228]

It should, however, be stressed that drug identification by TLC demands a great deal of experience, though the simplicity and sensitivity
of the technique make it possible to detect certain characteristics in the
case of the investigated drugs. In general, investigations so far suggest the
use of one-dimensional runs whose disadvantages are pronounced in the

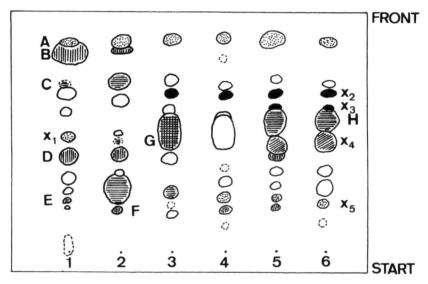

Figure 12. Thin-layer chromatogram of essential oils of various *Mentha*
species.[228] (1) Oleum *Menthae aquaticae;* (2) Oleum *Menthae piperitae;* (3)
Oleum *Menthae pulegii* (4) Oleum *Menthae crispae;* (5) Oleum *Menthae longi-
foliae;* (6) Oleum *Menthae rotundifoliae.* (A) Hydrocarbons; (B) menthofuran;
(C) menthyl acetate; (D) cineole; (E) menthol; (F) sabinene; (G) pulegone; (H)
piperiton oxide; (x_1–x_5) unknowns. Silica Gel G; benzene–ethyl acetate (95:5,
v/v); detection: anisaldehyde in conc. H_2SO_4. (Reproduced from Pharm. Acta
Helv. by permission of the publisher.)

case of total extracts or mixtures containing a large number of components. It appears justified, therefore, to suggest that the TLC technique
used for drug identifications should be improved by applying several
solvents and sorbents, and finally two-dimensional runs.

CONCLUSION

Largely because of TLC the number of investigated plant species and of isolated chemical compounds has greatly increased during the past decade. Nevertheless, the number of investigated plant species is still negligibly small compared to the tremendous number of species which make up the plant kingdom; consequently, the preparation of pure compounds also lags considerably behind the possibilities. Through further improvements in TLC technique it is hoped that considerable advances may be made with respect both to the investigated species and the isolated compounds—and consequently to one of the aims of medical plant and drug research: the preparation of plant substances capable of new therapeutical action.

REFERENCES

1. Abdel-Hay, F. M., E. A. Abu-Mustafa, B. A. H. El-Tawil, and M. B. E. Fayez. Planta Med. 1, 91 (1965).
2. Adcock, J. W., and T. J. Betts. J. Chromatog. 34, 411 (1968).
3. Aexel, R., S. Evans, M. Kelley, and H. J. Nicholas. Phytochemistry 6, 511 (1967).
4. Ahmed, Z. F., M. A. Rizk, and F. M. Hammouda. Pharm. Pharmacol. 17, 395 (1965).
5. Ahmed, Z. F., M. A. Erkeiy, M. A. Rizk, A. M. Hammouda, and F. M. E. F. Abdel-Bary. Planta Med. 16, 282 (1968).
6. Akahori, A., F. Yasuda, and T. Okanishi. Chem. Pharm. Bull. (Tokyo) 16, 498 (1968).
7. Akahori, A., F. Yasuda, I. Okuno, M. Togami, and T. Okanishi. Phytochemistry 8, 45 (1969).
8. Anton, R., and P. Duquénois. Ann. Pharm. Franc. 25, 589 (1967).
9. Arthur, H. R., S. N. Loo, S. Tung, and W. H. Hui. Trop. Sci. 8, 28 (1966).
10. Asen, S. J. Chromatog. 18, 602 (1965).
11. Audette, R. C. S., G. Blunden, J. W. Steele, and C. S. C. Wong. J. Chromatog. 25, 367 (1966).
12. Aurich, O., G. Osske, K. Pufahl, A. Romeike, H. Rönsch, K. Schreiber, and G. Sembdner. Kulturpflanze 13, 621 (1965).
13. Austin, D. J., and M. B. Meyers. Phytochemistry 4, 255 (1965).
14. Badawi, M. M., and M. B. E. Fayez. Planta Med. 15, 140 (1967).
15. Baisted, D. J. Phytochemistry 6, 93 (1967).
16. Barz, W., and G. Grisebach. Z. Naturforsch. 21b, 11, 1113 (1966).
17. Bauthorpe, D. V., and K. W. Turnbull. J. Chromatog. 37, 366 (1968).
18. Békésy, N. Biochem. Z. 312, 100 (1942).
19. Békésy, N. Private communication, 1969.
20. Bendz, G., J. Santesson, and C. A. Wachtmeister. Acta. Chem. Scand. 19, 1250 (1965).

21. Bendz, G., J. Santesson, and C. A. Wachtmeister.　Acta Chem. Scand. 19, 1776 (1965).
22. Bendz, G., J. Santesson, and L. Tibell.　Acta Chem. Scand. 20, 1181 (1966).
23. Bennett, R. D., and E. Heftmann.　J. Chromatog. 9, 353 (1962).
24. Bennett, R. D., S.-T. Ko, and E. Heftmann.　Phytochemistry 5, 231 (1966).
25. Bernasconi, R., S. Gill, and E. Steinegger.　Pharm. Acta Helv. 40, 246 (1965).
26. Bernasconi, R., S. Gill, and E. Steinegger.　Pharm. Acta Helv. 40, 275 (1965).
27. Beyrich, T.　J. Chromatog. 20, 173 (1965).
28. Blunden, G., C. J. Briggs, and R. Hardman.　Phytochemistry 7, 453 (1968).
29. Blunden, G., R. Hardman.　J. Chromatog. 34, 507 (1968).
30. Bohlmann, F., and H. Jastrow.　Chem. Ber. 95, 1742 (1962).
31. Bohlmann, F., and A. Seyberlich.　Chem. Ber. 99, 138 (1966).
32. Bohlmann, F., H. Mönch, and U. Niedballa.　Chem. Ber. 99, 586 (1966).
33. Bohlmann, F., C. Arndt, C. Zdero.　Chem. Ber. 99, 1648 (1966).
34. Bohlmann, F., K.-M. Kleine.　Chem. Ber. 99, 2096 (1966).
35. Bohlmann, F., M. Grenz.　Chem. Ber. 99, 3197 (1966).
36. Bohlmann, F., S. Köhn, E. Waldau.　Chem. Ber. 99, 3201 (1966).
37. Bohlmann, F., K.-M. Kleine, C. Arndt.　Liebigs Ann. Chem. 694, 149 (1966).
38. Bohlmann, F., H. Mönch, P. Blaszkiewicz.　Chem. Ber. 100, 611 (1967).
39. Bohlmann, F., H. Schulz.　Tetrahedron Letters 46, 4795 (1968).
40. Bolliger, H. R., in E. Stahl.　*Dünnschicht-Chromatographie* (Berlin-Heidelberg-New York: Springer-Verlag, 1965; and New York-London: Academic Press, 1965), p 210.
41. Bose, S., and S. Fröst.　Hereditas 58, 145 (1967).
42. Brenner, M., and A. Niederwieser.　Experientia 17, 145 (1961).
43. Calderwood, J. M., and F. Fish.　J. Pharm. Pharmacol. Suppl. 18, 1195 (1966).
44. Chafetz, L., A. I. Kay, and H. Schriftman.　J. Chromatog. 35, 567 (1968).
45. Challan, S. M., and M. Kucera.　J. Chromatog. 32, 53 (1968).
46. Copius-Peereboom, J. W., and H. W. Beekes.　J. Chromatog. 17, 99 (1965).
47. Danielak, R., and B. Borkowski.　Dissertationes Pharm. 20, 419 (1968).
48. Danielak, R., Z. Szmal, and B. Borkowski.　Dissertationes Pharm. 20, 431 (1968).
49. Davies, B. H.　J. Chromatog. 10, 518 (1963).
50. DeLoose, R.　Phytochemistry 8, 253 (1969).
51. DiTullio, N. W., C. S. Jacobs, Jr., and W. L. Holmes.　J. Chromatog. 20, 354 (1965).

52. Domagalina, E., S. Zareba. Dissertationes Pharm. **19**, 391 (1967).
53. Drawert, F., H. Gebbing, and A. Ziegler. J. Chromatog. **30**, 259 (1967).
54. Dreyer, D. L. Tetrahedron **23**, 4613 (1967).
55. Drozdz, B. Dissertationes Pharm. **20**, 93 (1968).
56. Drozdz, B. Dissertationes Pharm. **20**, 217 (1968).
57. Duncan, G. R., D. D. Levi, and R. Pyttel. Planta Med. **16**, 224 (1968).
58. Egger, K., and H. Voight. Z. Pflanzenphysiol. **53**, 64 (1965).
59. Egger, K., and M. Keil. Z. Anal. Chem. **210**, 201 (1965).
60. Eichenberger, W., and E. C. Grob. Helv. Chim. Acta **45**, 974 (1962).
61. Eichenberger, W., and E. C. Grob. Helv. Chim. Acta **45**, 1556 (1962).
62. Eichenberger, W., and E. C. Grob. Helv. Chim. Acta **46**, 2411 (1963).
63. Farnsworth, N. R., M. Hess, A. E. Fisher, R. E. Martello, and L. V. Cammararo. J. Pharm. Sci. **56**, 967 (1967).
64. Faugeras, G., and R. Paris. Chem. Geol. Biol. Nr. **3**, 235 (1966).
65. Fejér-Kossey, O. Acta Biol. Acad. Sci. Hung. **15**, 251 (1964).
66. Fischer, F., and R. Hertel. J. Chromatog. **38**, 274 (1968).
67. Földesi, D. Herba Hung. **4**, 63 (1965).
68. Frencel, I. Dissertationes Pharm. **17**, 577 (1965).
69. Friedrich, H., and J. Höhle. Planta Med. **14**, 363 (1966).
70. Geissman, T. A., S. Griffin, T. G. Waddell, and H. H. Chen. Phytochemistry **8**, 145 (1969).
71. Gerlach, H. Pharmazie **20**, 523 (1965).
72. Geyer, S., and R. Meyer. Z. Chem. **5**, 308 (1965).
73. Gibbons, G. F., L. J. Goad, and T. W. Goodwin. Phytochemistry **6**, 677 (1967).
74. Gill, S., and E. Steinegger. Pharm. Acta Helv. **39**, 508 (1964).
75. Gill, S., and E. Steinegger. Pharm. Acta Helv. **39**, 565 (1964).
76. Gill, S. Acta Polon. Pharm. **21**, 379 (1964).
77. Glotter, E., R. Waitman, and D. Lavie. J. Chem. Soc. **1966**, 1765.
78. Gmelin, R. Arzneimittel-Forsch. **13**, 771 (1963).
79. Gmelin, R. Arzneimittel-Forsch. **14**, 1021 (1964).
80. Gmelin, R., and J. B. Bredenberg. Arzneimittel-Forsch. **16**, 123 (1966).
81. Gmelin, R. Planta Med. Suppl. **1966**, 119.
82. Gmelin, R. Arch. Pharm. **300**, 234 (1967).
83. Grabaczyk, H. Dissertationes Pharm. **20**, 557 (1968).
84. Gracza, L., and K. Szász. Acta Pharm. Hung. **38**, 118 (1968).
85. Grau, W., and H. Endres. J. Chromatog. **17**, 585 (1965).
86. Grisebach, H., and H. Zilg. Z. Naturforsch. **23b**, 494 (1968).
87. Gupta, A. S., and S. Dev. J. Chromatog. **12**, 189 (1963).
88. Hänsel, R., H. Rimpler, and K. Walther. Naturwiss. **53**, 19 (1966).
89. Hais, E. M., and K. Macek. *Handbuch der Papierchromatographie,* Vol. 1 and 2 (Jena: VEB Gustav Fischer-Verlag, 1958 and 1960).
90. Hall, R. J. J. Chromatog. **5**, 93 (1961).
91. Halpaap, H. Chem. Jug. Tech. **35**, 488 (1963).
92. Harborne, J. B. Phytochemistry **7**, 1215 (1968).

93. Harborne, J. B.   Phytochemistry **8**, 177 (1969).
94. Háznagy, A., K. Szendrei, and L. Tóth.   Pharmazie **20**, 541 (1965).
95. Háznagy, A., K. Szendrei, and L. Tóth.   Pharmazie **20**, 651 (1965).
96. Háznagy, A., L. Tóth, and K. Szendrei.   Pharmazie **20**, 649 (1965).
97. Hecker, E.   Planta Med. Suppl. **1968**, 24.
98. Hefendehl, F. W.   Arch. Pharm. **300**, 438 (1967).
99. Held, G., D. Vágujfalvi.   Bot. Közlem. **52**, 201 (1965).
100. Held, G., D. Vágujfalvi, and F. Uresch.   Phytochemistry **8**, 493 (1969).
101. Hess, D., and C. Meyer.   Z. Naturforsch. **17b**, 853 (1962).
102. Hiller, K.   Pharmazie **20**, 9 (1965).
103. Hiller, K., M. Keipert, and B. Linzer.   Pharmazie **21**, 713 (1966).
104. Hiller, K., B. Linzer, S. Pfeifer, L. Tökés, and J. Murphy.   Pharmazie **23**, 376 (1968).
105. Honegger, C. G.   Helv. Chim. Acta **45**, 1409 (1962).
106. Hörhammer, L., H. Wagner, and G. Bittner.   Arzneimittel-Forsch. **13**, 537 (1963).
107. Hörhammer, L., H. Wagner, M. Seitz, and Z. J. Vejdelek.   Pharmazie **23**, 462 (1968).
108. Hultin, E.   Acta Chem. Scand. **19**, 584 (1965).
109. Hultin, E.   Acta Chem. Scand. **19**, 588 (1965).
110. Hultin, E.   Acta Chem. Scand. **19**, 591 (1965).
111. Hultin, E.   Acta Chem. Scand. **20**, 1588 (1966).
112. Ikan, R.   J. Chromatog. **17**, 591 (1965).
113. Isaac, O., H. Schneider, H. Eggenschwiller.   Deut. Apotheker-Ztg. **108**, 293 (1968).
114. Ismailov, A. N., and S. M. Schraiber.   Farmacia **3**, 1 (1938).
115. Jänchen, D.   J. Chromatog. **14**, 261 (1964).
116. Jaspersen-Schib, R.   Pharm. Acta Helv. **36**, 141 (1961).
117. Jentzsch, K., P. Spiegel, and R. Kamitz.   Sci. Pharm. **36**, 251 (1968).
118. Johne, S., and D. Gröger.   Pharmazie **23**, 35 (1968).
119. Johnston, E. J., and A. L. Jacobs.   J. Pharm. Sci. **55**, 531 (1966).
120. Jork, H.   J. Pharm. Belg. **1963**, 213.
121. Juhász, K., E. Tyihák.   Acta Agron. Acad. Sci. Hung. **18**, 113 (1969).
122. Kaneko, K.   Chem. Pharm. Bull. (Tokyo) **8**, 611 (1960).
123. Kartnig, T., H. Wagner, and L. Hörhammer.   Fette-Seifen-Anstrichmittel **67**, 10 (1965).
124. Kartnig, T., and G. H. Scholz.   Fette-Seifen-Anstrichmittel **67**, 19 (1965).
125. Kartnig, T., and A. Hiermann.   Planta Med. **16**, 109 (1968).
126. Kashman, Y., D. Lavie, and E. Glotter.   Isr. J. Chem. **5**, 23 (1967).
127. Kasprzyk, Z., and T. Kozierowska.   Bull. Acad. Polon. Sci. Classe III **14**, 645 (1966).
128. Kasprzyk, Z., Z. Grzelczak, and J. Pyrek.   Bull. Acad. Polon. Sci. Classe III **13**, 661 (1965).
129. Kimura, M., M. Tohma, and I. Yoshizawa.   Chem. Pharm. Bull. (Tokyo) **14**, 55 (1966).

130. Kimura, M., M. Tohma, and I. Yoshizawa. Chem. Pharm. Bull. (Tokyo) **15**, 226 (1967).
131. Kirchner, J. G., J. M. Miller, and G. J. Keller. Anal. Chem. **23**, 420 (1951).
132. Kirchner, J. G. *Thin-Layer Chromatography* (New York-London-Sidney: Interscience, 1967).
133. Kloss, P., and H. Schindler. Pharm. Ztg. Ver. Apotheker-Ztg. **111**, 772 (1966).
134. Klouwen, M. H., R. TerHeide, and J. G. J. Kok. Fette, Seifen, Anstrichmittel **65**, 414 (1963).
135. Korte, F., and H. Sieper. J. Chromatog. **13**, 90 (1964).
136. Korte, F., and H. Sieper. J. Chromatog. **14**, 178 (1964).
137. Kupchan, S. M., S. J. Barbautis, J. R. Knox, and C. A. Cam. Science **150**, 1827 (1965).
138. Kupchan, S. M., J. M. Cassady, J. Bailey, and J. R. Knox. J. Pharm. Sci. **54**, 1703 (1965).
139. Labadie, R. P., and A. B. Svendsen. Pharm. Weekblad **102**, 169 (1967).
140. Lassányi, S., and C. Lörincz. Acta Agron. Sci. Hung. **16**, 95 (1967).
141. Lavie, D., E. Glotter, and Y. Shvo. J. Org. Chem. **30**, 1774 (1965).
142. Lavie, D., E. Glotter, and Y. Shvo. J. Chem. Soc. **1965**, 7517.
143. Lavie, D., Y. Kashman, and E. Glotter. Tetrahedron **22**, 1103 (1966).
144. Lawrence, B. M. J. Chromatog. **38**, 535 (1968).
145. Leistner, E., and M. H. Zenk. Z. Naturforsch. **23b**, 258 (1968).
146. Lepage, M. J. Chromatog. **13**, 99 (1964).
147. Leung, A. Y., A. H. Smith, and A. G. Paul. J. Pharm. Sci. **54**, 1577 (1965).
148. Lossner, G. Pharmazie **22**, 51 (1967).
149. Lörincz, C., and E. Tyihák. Acta Agron. Acad. Sci. Hung. **17**, 303 (1968).
150. Luckner, M. *Prüfung von Drogen* (Jena: VEB Gustav Fischer-Verlag, 1966).
151. Luckner, M., O. Bessler, and R. Luckner. Pharmazie **21**, 620 (1966).
152. Luckner, M., O. Bessler, and R. Luckner. Pharm. Zhalle **105**, 711 (1966).
153. Luckner, M., O. Bessler, R. Luckner, and E. Korn. Pharm. Zhalle **107**, 28 (1968).
154. Luckner, M., O. Bessler, and R. Luckner. Arzneimittel-Standard **12**, 1 (1968).
155. MacLeod, W. M. D., Jr., and N. M. Buigues. J. Food Sci. **31**, 588 (1966).
156. MacMillan, J., and P. J. Suter. Nature **197**, 790 (1963).
157. MacSweeney, G. P. J. Chromatog. **17**, 183 (1965).
158. Malins, D. C., and H. K. Mangold. J. Am. Oil Chemists' Soc. **37**, 576 (1960).
159. Masschelein-Kleiner, I. Mikrochim. Acta **1967**, 1082.
160. Máthé, I., and E. Tyihák. Herba Hung. **2**, 35 (1963).

161. Máthé, I., D. Földesi, E. Szabó, l. Sárkány, and P. Tétényi. Herba Hung. 3, 295 (1964).
162. Máthé, I., and G. Held. Bot. Közlem. 52, 87 (1965).
163. Matsumoto, N. Chem. Pharm. Bull. (Tokyo) 11, 1189 (1963).
164. Maturová, M., D. Pavlásková, and F. Santavy. Planta Med. 14, 22 (1966).
165. Messerschmidt, W. Planta Med. 13, 56 (1965).
166. Miller, J. M., and J. G. Kirchner. Anal. Chem. 23, 428 (1951).
167. Miller, R. W., F. R. Earle, and I. A. Wolff. J. Am. Oil Chemists' Soc. 42, 817 (1965).
168. Minyard, J. P., J. H. Tumlinson, A. C. Thompson, and P. A. Hedin. Agricult. Food Chem. 15, 517 (1967).
169. Minyard, J. P., A. C. Thompson, and P. A. Hedin. J. Org. Chem. 33, 909 (1968).
170. Mitsuhashi, H., and T. Nomura. Chem. Pharm. Bull. (Tokyo) 13, 274 (1965).
171. Mitsuhashi, H., K. Sakurai, T. Nomura, and N. Kawahara. Chem. Pharm. Bull. (Tokyo) 14, 712 (1966).
172. Mullick, D. B. J. Chromatog. 39, 91 (1969).
173. Nakanishi, K., S.-I. Sasaki, A. K. Kiang, J. Goh, H. Kakisawa, M. Ohashi, M. Goto, J.-M. Watanabe, H. Yokotani, C. Matsumara, and M. Togashi. Chem. Pharm. Bull. (Tokyo) 13, 882 (1965).
174. Nakov, N., and A. Boychinov. Farmacia 17, 34 (1967).
175. Niederwieser, A., and M. Brenner. Experientia 21, 50 and 105 (1965).
176. Novák, I., G. Buzás, E. Minker, M. Koltai, and K. Szendrei. Planta Med. 14, 57 (1966).
177. Pakrashi, S. C. Indian Chem. Soc. 44, 887 (1967).
178. Pastuska, G., H.-J. Petrowitz. Chemiker Ztg. 86, 311 (1962).
179. Pataki, G. Dünnschichtchromatographie in der Aminosäure und Peptid Chemie (Berlin: W. de Gruyter-Verlag, 1966); *Techniques of Thin-Layer Chromatography in Amino Acid and Peptide Chemistry* (Ann Arbor: Ann Arbor Science Publishers, 1968).
180. Persinos, G. I., and H. W. Quimby. J. Pharm. Sci. 56, 1512 (1967).
181. Pfeifer, S. J. Chromatog. 24, 364 (1966).
182. Poethke, W., D. A. Rao, and K.-D. Löscher. Pharm. Zhalle 107, 571 (1968).
183. Polonsky, J., C. Fouquey, M. A. Gaudemer, Z. Baskevitch, N. Bourguignon, and F. Prestat-Gaudemer. Bull. Soc. Chim. Franc. 1964, 1827.
184. Preuss, F. R., and H. Orth. Planta Med. 13, 261 (1965).
185. Purdy, S. J., and E. V. Truter. Nature 190, 554 (1961).
186. Raffauf, R. F. Lloydia 25, 255 (1962).
187. Randerath, K. *Dünnschicht-Chromatographie* (Weinheim/Bergstr.: Verlag Chemie, 1962 and 1965).
188. Rangonwala, R., and H. Friedrich. Naturwiss. 54, 368 (1967).
189. Reisch, J., I. Novák, K. Szendrei, and E. Minker. Pharmazie 21, 628 (1966).

190. Ritter, F. J., and G. M. Meyer. Nature **193**, 941 (1962).
191. Rönsch, H., and K. Schreiber. J. Chromatog. **30**, 149 (1967).
192. Rothbächer, H. Farmacia **13**, 475 (1965).
193. Rothbächer, H., F. Suteu, and A. Kraus. Planta Med. **15**, 434 (1967).
194. Rothbächer, H., and H. Heltmann. Pharmazie **23**, 387 (1968).
195. Rozumek, K. E., and H. Sander. Arch. Pharm. **300**, 316 (1967).
196. Ruffini, G. J. Chromatog. **17**, 483 (1965).
197. Sandberg, F., K.-H. Michel, and B. Staf. Acta Pharm. Suecica **4**, 51 (1967).
198. Sander, H. Planta Med. **11**, 303 (1963).
199. Santesson, J. Acta Chem. Scand. **19**, 2254 (1965).
200. Santesson, J. Acta Chem. Scand. **21**, 1162 (1967).
201. Sasaki, S. I., S. Aoyagi, H.-Y. Hsü. Chem. Pharm. Bull. (Tokyo) **13**, 87 (1965).
202. Sauer, H. H., R. D. Bennett, and E. Heftmann. Phytochemistry **7**, 1543 (1968).
203. Schratz, E., and S. M. J. S. Quadry. Planta Med. **14**, 310 (1966).
204. Schreiber, K. Kulturpflanze **11**, 451 (1963).
205. Schulte, K. E., F. Ahrens, and E. Sprenger. Pharm. Ztg. Ver. Apotheker-Ztg. **108**, 1165 (1963).
206. Schulz, G. Z. Pflanzenphysiol. **56**, 209 (1967).
207. Schwarz, V. Pharmazie **18**, 122 (1963).
208. Seeboth, H. Monatsber. Deut. Akad. Wiss. Berlin **5**, 693 (1963).
209. Sieper, H., R. Longo, and F. Korte. Arch. Pharm. **296**, 403 (1963).
210. Sjöholm, I. Svensk. Farm. Tidskr. **66**, 321 (1962).
211. Slavik, J., L. Slaviková, and K. Haisova. Collection Czech. Chem. Commun. **32**, 4420 (1967).
212. Slavik, J. Collection Czech. Chem. Commun. **33**, 323 (1968).
213. Stahl, E. Pharmazie **11**, 633 (1956).
214. Stahl, E. Arch. Pharm. **292**, 411 (1959).
215. Stahl, E., and U. Kaltenbach. J. Chromatog. **5**, 458 (1961).
216. Stahl, E., and U. Kaltenbach. J. Chromatog. **5**, 458 (1961).
217. Stahl, E. *Dünnschicht-Chromatographie* (Berlin: Springer-Verlag, 1962).
218. Stahl, E. *Dünnschicht-Chromatographie, Zweite Auflage* (Berlin: Springer-Verlag, 1967).
219. Stahl, E., H. R. Bolliger, and L. Lehnert. Wiss. Veröffentl. Deut. Ges. Ernährung **9**, 129 (1963).
220. Stahl, E., and H. Jork. Arch. Pharm. **297**, 273 (1964).
221. Stahl, E., and J. Schmitt. Arch. Pharm. **297**, 385 (1964).
222. Stahl, E. Arch. Pharm. **297**, 500 (1964).
223. Stahl, E., and H. Jork. Arch. Pharm. **299**, 670 (1966).
224. Stahl, E., and D. Scheu. Arch. Pharm. **300**, 456 (1967).
225. Stahl, E., and D. Scheu. Arch. Pharm. **301**, 306 (1968).
226. Stahl, E., and J. Fuchs. Deut. Apotheker-Ztg. **108**, 1227 (1968).
227. Stecka, L. Dissert. Pharm. Pharmacol. **19**, 365 (1967).
228. Sticher, O., and H. Flück. Pharm. Acta Helv. **43**, 411 (1968).
229. Sucrow, W., and A. Reimerdes. Z. Naturforsch. **23b**, 42 (1968).

230. Szendrei, K., I. Novák, E. Varga, and G. Buzás. Pharmazie **23**, 76 (1968).
231. Szendrei, K., I. Novák, M. Báthory, E. Minker, M. Koltai, J. Reisch, and G. Buzás. Pharmazie **23**, 211 (1968).
232. Takeda, K., S. Hara, A. Wada, and N. Matsumoto. J. Chromatog. **11**, 562 (1963).
233. Takeda, K., H. Minato, and A. Shimaoka. Chem. Pharm. Bull. (Tokyo) **16**, 275 (1968).
234. Taylor, E. H. Lloydia **27**, 96 (1964).
235. Teichert, K. H., E. Mutschler, and H. Rochelmeyer. Deut. Apotheker-Ztg. **100**, 283 (1960).
236. Tétényi, P., E. Tyihák, I. Máthé, and J. Sváb. Pharmazie **17**, 463 (1962).
237. Tóth, L. Planta Med. **15**, 157 (1967).
238. Tóth, L. Planta Med. **15**, 371 (1967).
239. Tschesche, R., F. Lampert, and G. Snatzke. J. Chromatog. **5**, 217 (1961).
240. Tschesche, R., and K. H. Richert. Tetrahedron **20**, 387 (1964).
241. Tschesche, R., B. T. Tjoa, and G. Wulff. Liebigs Ann. Chem. **696**, 160 (1966).
242. Tswett, M. Ber. Deut. Botan. Ges. **24**, 316 (1906).
243. Tyihák, E., D. Vágujfalvi, and P. I. Hágony. J. Chromatog. **11**, 45 (1963).
244. Tyihák, E. Naturwiss. **51**, 315 (1964).
245. Tyihák, E., I. Pályi, and V. Pályi. Naturwiss. **52**, 209 (1965).
246. Tyihák, E., and D. Vágujfalvi. Planta Med. **15**, 269 (1967).
247. Tyihák, E. Unpublished data.
248. Vágujfalvi, D., and E. Tyihák. Bot. Közlem. **51**, 41 (1964).
249. Vágujfalvi, D., G. Held, P. Tétényi. Bot. Közlem. **53**, 125 (1966).
250. Vágujfalvi, D., G. Held, P. Tétényi. Arch. Pharm. **299**, 812 (1966).
251. Vágujfalvi, D., P. Tétényi, C. Lörincz. Klasse Chem. Geol. Biol. **1966**, 349.
252. Vágujfalvi, D., and G. Held. Herba Hung. **6**, 161 (1967).
253. Vágujfalvi, D. Unpublished data.
254. Vágujfalvi, D., and E. Tyihák. Unpublished data.
255. Verzár-Petri, G., R. Szentpétery, S. Sárkány. Acta Biol. Acad. Sci. Hung. **19**, 506 (1968).
256. Wagner, H., L. Hörhammer, and B. Dengler. J. Chromatog. **7**, 211 (1962).
257. Wall, M. E., C. R. Eddy, M. L. McClennan, and M. E. Klumpp. Anal. Chem. **24**, 1337 (1952).
258. Wartmann-Hafner, F. Pharm. Acta Helv. **41**, 406 (1966).
259. Willuhn, G. Planta Med. **16**, 462 (1968).
260. Wrolstad, R. E. J. Chromatog. **37**, 542 (1968).
261. Yamada, S. Bull. Chem. Soc. Japan **39**, 2313 (1966).
262. Zielinski, J., and J. Konopa. J. Chromatog. **36**, 540 (1968).
263. Zwaning, J. H. J. Chromatog. **35**, 562 (1968).

Chapter 7

The Investigation of
Aminoacidurias by TLC*

by F. J. Detterbeck and H. A. Lillevik

More than 60 inborn errors of amino acid metabolism are known to date,[1] and most of these aminoacidopathies have been discovered within the past ten years. With very few exceptions, they are all associated with mental retardation. The separation of amino acids from biological fluids, especially from the urine, has become an important diagnostic tool; recognition of these new disorders has been facilitated through the development of new techniques of amino acid separation.

Nearly all known techniques of amino acid separation and many of their numerous variations have been applied, at one time or another, to the study of the amino acid excretion pattern in the urine. Interest in this field of investigation was aroused through the pioneer work of Dent,[2, 3] who first applied paper chromatography (PC) to the amino acid analysis of urine. Other methods that followed include one-dimensional,[4, 5, 6] two-dimensional,[5, 6] and circular[7] PC; one-dimensional high-voltage paper

*This report represents investigation made possible through a grant from the Michigan Department of Mental Health.

We gratefully acknowledge the technical assistance of Mrs. E. S. Rimpau, Mr. M. T. McAuliffe, and Mr. D. B. Buchanan. We also acknowledge contributions made by the UpJohn Company in providing the Liprotein and by the Dow Chemical Corporation in furnishing laboratory materials. Our special thanks go to Dr. H. Halpaap for his direct communication and advice.

electrophoresis (PE);[8, 9, 10] PE + PC;[11, 9, 6, 12] one-dimensional thin-layer electrophoresis (TLE);[13] TLE + TLC;[14-19] two-dimensional TLC of free amino acids;[20-25] DNP-derivatives[26-38] and DNS-derivatives;[39] gas-liquid chromatography;[40] column chromatography;[41-45] and even microbiological assays.[46] The great variety of methods used for this purpose indicates that medical investigators are constantly on the lookout for new and better screening procedures. The ideal method must be an economical, high-resolution, highly sensitive, rapid technique. For a review, see Reference 50.

Economy

Since the combined incidence of all known aminoacidurias among the general population or even among the newborn is exceedingly small (at the most 1:10,000), a screening technique for aminoacidurias must be economical.[47] In fact, most of the methods available are still too costly to be used for screening the newborn population. Only methods for the detection of PKU (fortunately the most common of all aminoacido-pathies) have been applied so far on a statewide basis.

The incidence among the institutionalized mentally retarded is considerably higher and may exceed 5%. But if screening for amino-acidurias is limited to the mentally retarded, then the diagnosis is made too late to let the patient derive much benefit from any treatment that might be available. Even so, recognition of these diseases is invaluable in counseling the families of these patients and keeping a close check on any future offspring. Considerable progress has been made in the recognition of carriers.[48]

High Resolution

More than 170 ninhydrin-positive substances have been separated from urine by column chromatography.[49] It is unlikely that the same degree of resolution can ever be obtained by TLC, except perhaps by subfractionation and TLC of the subfractions. But TLC has already achieved an impressive resolution of urine into 45 DNP-derivatives from the ether-soluble fraction and 18 DNP-derivatives from the acid-soluble fraction.[33, 34] It appears to be the most likely candidate to meet the need for an inexpensive screening method.[50]

High Sensitivity

Since the concentration of amino acids in the urine is quite small (5 μmole of total amino acid per liter), the ideal screening method should be rather sensitive. But because the starting material is plentiful, high sensitivity means primarily a smaller sample volume, which in turn means that less time is required to apply the sample to the plate. A plate with a small sample volume may also give better resolution than one carrying a heavy amino acid load. With a sufficiently small sample, accompanying substances (notably salt and urea) are less likely to affect the separation and may not need to be removed.

Speed

Much emphasis has been placed on the speed of analysis. While speed is desirable, it is certainly the least important requirement for a screening technique. The amount of handling per specimen is of far greater significance than the time required for the analysis.

In our search for a screening technique capable of detecting a large variety of aminoacidurias, including those rare inborn errors of amino acid metabolism which are not commonly tested for, we have developed the following thin-layer chromatographic method. It is particularly well-suited for mass screening.

METHOD

Diet and Specimen Collection

A synthetic test meal containing 40% protein (Liprotein, UpJohn) is given to the patient in the morning, using 2 rounded tablespoons of Liprotein per 10 kg of body weight (equivalent to 1.1 g of protein per kg of body weight). A random urine specimen is then collected 2–6 hours after administration of the formula. If not immediately analyzed, the sample may be frozen.

Preparation of Sample

The amino acids of native urine can be obtained as a pure fraction by treating the sample on a small cation-exchange column, using a slight variation of a method by Harris *et al.*[51] A 5-ml aliquot of urine is centrifuged for 10 minutes at 2000 rpm. Then 2.0 ml of the supernatent is acidified to a pH of 3–4 with about 2 drops of glacial acetic acid and allowed to stand for 10 minutes to decompose any carbonates present. Meanwhile, a filter paper disc (Whatman No. 1) cut out with a paper hole-punch to measure 6 mm in diameter is inserted across the bottom of a miniature chromatography column (0.6 × 15 cm). It is then filled with 300 mg of moist cation-exchange resin (Dowex—50 × 8, 100–200 mesh) in the H^+ form. The acidified urine is gently poured over the column. The amino acids (with the exception of taurine) are retained by the resin along with the other cations whereas the anions, proteins, and neutral substances pass through the column. The sample becomes more acidic as the cations are exchanged against the H^+ ion of the resin. Care must be taken against overacidification of the sample since this leads to ionization and adsorption of urea. If, on the other hand, the effluent has not reached a pH of at least 2, it should be further acidified and recirculated over the column. The resin is then washed, first with 2 ml of 0.5N acetic acid and then with 2 ml of water. The effluent plus washings are discarded. Next the column is eluted with 2 ml of 2N triethylamine in 20% acetone, which removes all the amino acids and the ammonia while it liberates only traces of metallic cations. The recovery of the amino acids is essentially quantitative.[51]

The eluate, which is collected on a watch glass, is evaporated overnight *in vacuo* over H_2SO_4. It is redissolved next day with exactly 0.2 ml of distilled water, yielding a tenfold concentration of the amino acids (minus taurine) originally present in the urine specimen. After removal of 5 μl of the redissolved eluate for determining the α-amino nitrogen, cysteine and methionine are oxidized according to Hirs[52] by adding a few drops of performic acid to the sample and evaporating it over NaOH *in vacuo*.

Determination of α-Amino Nitrogen

According to Reference 53, exactly 5 μl of the tenfold concentrated amino acid solution is removed with an Eppendorf automatic micropipet and added to a small test tube containing 2.5 ml of distilled H_2O. In identical manner 5 μl of a 50-mM glycine solution is introduced into another small test tube with 2.5 ml of H_2O and used as a reference standard. In a third test tube 2.5 ml of H_2O are used as a blank. To each tube is added 2.5 ml of ninhydrin reagent (composed of 1.25 ml of stock + 1.25 ml of 4M sodium acetate buffer, pH 5.5); the reagents are made up according to Hsia.[54] All three tubes are simultaneously placed in a boiling water bath and heated for 15 minutes. After removing and cooling at room temperature for 10 minutes the absorbance for each at 570 nm is read in a spectrophotometer (Beckman DU-2) and recorded. A standard curve shows linear dependence of concentration vs absorbance in the range from 0.05 to 2.0 units.

Sample Application and TLC

The following day the oxidized sample is redissolved in enough 0.1N HCl to yield a concentration of 50 μmole of amino acid per ml (based on the α-amino nitrogen determination). The solvent may contain taurine as internal standard in a concentration of 5 μmole of taurine per ml of solvent. From this amino acid solution 13 μl is applied to a 20 × 20-cm thin-layer plate (Brinkmann precoated silica gel) 1.5 cm from the edge. A Shandon multiplate tank is used for the simultaneous chromatography of 12 plates: the five inner slots of the stainless steel plate holder contain two plates each (back to back) and the two outer slots contain one plate each (the coated side facing inward). Tongue depressors are used to keep the plates within the same slot from sticking to each other.

TLC is performed ascendingly at room temperature, using 300 ml of solvent per tank, for a distance of 15 cm in acetone–water–glacial acetic acid–formic acid (70:20:8:2, v/v). The procedure takes about 3–4 hours. After drying, the plates are run in the second direction in phenol–water–formic acid (75:24:1, v/v). This migration is performed at 40°C to lower the viscosity of the phenol–water, which reduces the time required for a 15-cm ascending run from 11 hours to 7 hours. We can confirm the finding of Niederwieser, that chromatography at this elevated temperature causes no significant changes in Rf-values.[55] The phenol must be redistilled if it is not colorless.

Detection

After the plates have been air-dried horizontally under the hood overnight, they are sprayed with a cadmium-ninhydrin reagent prepared according to Atfield and Morris[56] by freshly dissolving 1 g of ninhydrin in 112 ml of stock cadmium-acetate solution (1 g cadmium-acetate–100 ml water–20 ml acetic acid–1000 ml acetone). The plates are left at room temperature and as soon as they appear dry are stacked and stored in a refrigerator. The color develops gradually in the dark over several days. The amino acids appear as dark red spots on a white background (except for proline and hydroxyproline which are yellow). Care must be taken to avoid prolonged exposure to traces of NH_3 in the atmosphere because it will stain the background pink.

Interpretation and Documentation

Proline and hydroxyproline tend to show up early and are easily recognized by their yellow color. Since there are no color differences among the other amino acids, they must be identified entirely by their location using a two-dimensional map of known standards for comparison (Figure 1). The polychromatic spray of Moffat and Lytle[57] can facilitate identification of the standards on the map. The cadmium-ninhydrin reagent, however, is more sensitive than the Moffat-Lytle spray. For most amino acids the detection limit is less than 1 nmole.

A semiquantitative evaluation of the chromatogram is possible by comparing size and intensity of the various spots with an appropriate mixture of standards. The fact that the cadmium-ninhydrin reagent yields a colored compound with very nearly the same molar extinction coefficient for all the various amino acids (except proline and hydroxyproline)[58] facilitates the quantitation. Allowance must be made, however, for the degree of diffusion, which is more pronounced with the fast-running amino acids. For this reason, it is best that the mixture of

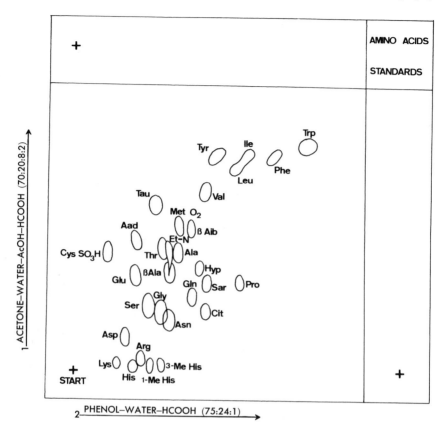

Figure 1. Two-dimensional map of amino acids and ethanolamine (Et-N).

standards used for comparison with the chromatogram of the sample be run in two dimensions as well. In analogy with the procedure of Rok-kones[60] the standards are divided into two groups, each group made up of a combination that will separate with little or no overlap. It is sufficient to apply these standards in only those proportions that are expected to occur in normal urine (Table I); 13 μl of these mixtures corresponds to the amino acid content of a normal sample load. In addition, an over-loaded (26 μl) and an underloaded (6.5 μl) plate are prepared. These reference chromatograms need not be run with each batch of samples: after some experience it is possible to perform a semiquantitation of the urine chromatogram entirely by comparison with its internal standard (taurine).

The excretion pattern is reported in the form of a bar graph (amino-gram) where the amino acids are arranged in order of their decreasing distribution in normal urine. This arrangement makes deviations from

Table I
Amino Acid Mixtures used for
Semiquantitation of Amino Acids in Urine

Mixture I *μmole/13 ml*		*Mixture II* *μmole/13 ml*	
Gly	160	Gln	80
His	80	Tau	80
1-MeHis	20	3-MeHis	40
Ala	20	Ser	40
Thr	20	Et-N	20
βAib	20	Asp	10
βAla	10	Asn	10
CysSO₃H	10	Leu	10
Val	10	Phe	10
Tyr	10	Aad	10
Ile	10	Glu	10
Lys	10	MetO₂	10
Arg	10	Orn	10

Solvent: 0.1N HCl with 10% isopropanol. Et-N means ethanolamine.

the norm stand out more clearly. Since all the plates are loaded with the same amount of total amino acid, the absolute quantities excreted in the urine are not apparent from either the plate or the aminogram but can be inferred from the α-amino–nitrogen content which is reported in mmole of amino acid per g of creatinine. The latter is determined by the Jaffe reaction as given in Oser.[59] Those amino acids which are not sufficiently separated for quantitation are reported together.

If permanent records are desired, the chromatograms can be photographed over an X-ray view box (Figures 2 and 3) or the spots may be traced. Since all amino acids other than proline and hydroxyproline absorb maximally at the same wavelength (505 nm), black-and-white photography renders a faithful record of the chromatogram. The visibility of weak spots is further enhanced by use of a blue filter for photography. Such records are valuable primarily when abnormal or unidentified spots are present. For normal chromatograms the bar graph is sufficient.

DISCUSSION

Although the method employed in this laboratory takes 7 days to complete an entire analysis, it requires less handling per sample than most other methods of amino acid separation. A new batch of up to 12 samples is started every day while earlier batches are continued through the various phases of analysis (see work schedule, Table II). Once the program is fully under way, every step of the analysis is carried out each

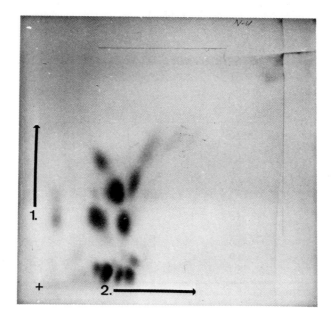

Figure 2.   Thin-layer chromatogram of normal urine.

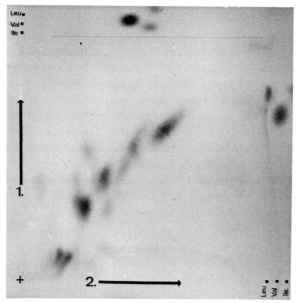

Figure 3.   Thin-layer chromatogram of urine from a
patient of branched-chain aminoaciduria (maple syrup
urine disease). Note the increased spots of leucine, isoleucine, and valine.

day but on different batches in various stages of completion. Indeed, this overlapping of seven batches contributes greatly to making the method economically feasible.

The application of the sample to a single thin-layer plate is a slow and tedious process if the spot is to be kept small. It takes no more time to load twelve plates than it takes to load one because of the intervening drying time. Indeed, the drying of the sample on the first plate is not complete even by the time the sample is applied to the twelfth plate, so that other steps of analysis can easily be performed between spotting. Proper integration of the various tasks is essential for an efficient flow of analysis.

The application of a 13-μl sample to 12 chromatography plates can be an extremely taxing chore for any technician. After some experimentation, we have found that the sample is most easily applied with a dressmaker's pin. The volume of the droplet adhering to the head of the pin is quite constant. It is not difficult to file the heads of a number of small pins to such a size that the droplet adhering to it will be about 0.5 μl. Calibration of the pins can be carried out by applying 10 "pinloads" of a 50-mM glycine solution to a strip of filter paper which is then analyzed for α-amino nitrogen as outlined above. We are willing to accept an error of ±20% in order to gain this simplicity of sample application. The head of the pin should be filed flat so that the droplet will adhere to this flat bottom. It is amazing how easily the sample can be applied in this manner without the pin's ever touching the plate.

In order to minimize evaporation of the dissolved sample, we place the watch glass containing the sample on a wet filter paper and cover it with a petri dish. A separate pin, of course, is used for each sample. It is convenient to leave the pin in a cork on top of the petri dish alongside the TLC plates. The samples can also be applied with a microsyringe. Although this is more accurate it is also more time-consuming, and much greater care must be taken to avoid damaging the silica gel layer.

Since the various amino acids occur in greatly different proportions in the urine (200 times as much glycine, for example, as ornithine),[41] underloading will not permit recognition of the trace amino acids whereas overloading will lead to excessive overlap of the spots. The optimal load appears to be about 0.6 μmole of total amino acid; we have adopted a total load of 640 nmole for ease of percentage calculation (see evaluation). Since it is known that the Rf-value of a given amino acid is to some degree influenced by the presence of other substances—even other amino acids—[61] in the sample, the uniformity of the load (640 nmole) should contribute to keeping the two-dimensional mapping more constant. In pathological specimens, however, certain amino acids in the

Table II
Working Schedule

	1st batch	2nd batch	3rd batch	4th batch	5th batch	6th batch	7th batch
1st day	desalt						
2nd day	α-amino N	desalt					
3rd day	spot	α-amino N	desalt				
4th day	solvent I	spot	α-amino N	desalt			
5th day	solvent II	solvent I	spot	α-amino N	desalt		
6th day	spray	solvent II	solvent I	spot	α-amino N	desalt	
7th day	read	spray	solvent II	solvent I	spot	α-amino N	desalt

sample may be drastically increased even though the total amino acid load remains constant. Such variations in the relative load of specific amino acid may quite noticeably affect the mapping, particularly if the substance is a fast-running amino acid.

A further precaution against inadvertent variation in sample load is the use of taurine as an internal standard. It is simply added to the 0.1N HCl which is used as the final solvent for the sample (5 μmole of taurine per ml of solvent).

Of the 2.0-ml urine sample, only a small fraction (on the average, about 1/20) is actually needed for spotting. The excess may be stored in a capillary tube, sealed with plasticine, and stored frozen for future use should the need arise for further investigation. A 2.0-ml sample is the smallest that can be conveniently handled since the volume of the re-dissolved eluate should not be less than 0.1 ml; this is to avoid excessive losses through evaporation during spotting. Larger specimens may be used although this increases the draining time of the column. The amount of resin must, of course, be varied accordingly to allow a resin capacity of 500 μEq per ml of urine. It is best to determine the resin capacity of one column by experiment; this is quickly done by treating the resin with an excess of NaCl and then titrating the HCl formed in the effluent. Subsequent columns can then be made up by weight or volume of resin. It was not found necessary to determine the total adsorbable cations (TAC) of each urine specimen, if 500 μEq of resin are used per ml of urine, although it can be done, according to Harris.[51] The eluant (TEA) need not be increased in proportion to the increase of the urine specimen. Since the metal ions (Na^+, K^+, etc.) remain on the column, the increase in TEA is primarily needed for additional interstitial space and the increment in unused resin. For a 5-ml specimen, 3 ml of TEA was found adequate.

Native urine can be used directly for TLC with this system as it has been done with many other solvents.[20, 21] However, good separation is obtained only if not more than 10 μl of native urine is applied. This represents about 10% of the amino acid load that can be applied after removal of salt and urea, and therefore it allows only the identification of the most predominant amino acids.

This method of separation is essentially a variation of a system used by Halpaap.[62] The original solvent was altered to achieve better separation of the basic amino acids. It is possible to separate the basic amino acids and tryptophan from the neutral and acidic amino acids first,[56] and then to separate the basic fraction with a different solvent: propanol–water (7:3) and phenol–water–formic acid (75:24:1); this, however, greatly increases the work.

It should be pointed out that to our knowledge this method of separation works only with precoated Brinkmann silica gel plates. A rather poor resolution is obtained when self-coated plates are used. Similarly, some of the methods yielding good results with self-coated plates[22] did not work well with precoated plates.

Since the amino acid excretion is very much dependent upon diet, the use of a synthetic test meal helps to standardize the protein intake. In addition, the problem of collecting a 24-hour urine specimen in an uncooperative patient has been circumvented. A random specimen taken 2–6 hours after the test meal is quite satisfactory if the amino acid content as determined by the α-amino nitrogen is related to the creatinine content of the urine.

Semiquantitation of the individual amino acids is possible only on a logarithmic scale (2, 4, 8 times a given amount). Finer graduation requires that the same specimen be run in at least two different sample loads which must be applied with a microsyringe. Determination of the area of each spot and consequent evaluation according to Purdy and Truter[63] may give considerably better quantitation but seem too tedious for our purpose.

The average chromatogram shows more than 20 ninhydrin-positive spots. Since all chromatograms are loaded with the same amount of total amino acid, the number of spots does not vary much from plate to plate. Tryptophan is not seen and is probably destroyed during the performic acid oxidation[52] and also during chromatography. Leucine and isoleucine are usually poorly separated, and ornithine and lysine do not separate at all.

The principal limitation lies in the unequal concentration of amino acids in the urine: 10 amino acids account for 85% of the total excretion.[41] More sensitive means of detection by dinitrophenylation or dansylation would not necessarily aid in the recognition of the trace amino acids. If the most predominant amino acids (Gly, Tau, His, Gln, Ala, Ser, 3-MeHis, 1-MeHis, βAib, Thr) could be selectively removed, the remaining amino acids could then be applied in considerably larger amounts. This problem has not yet been solved.

RESULTS

A new method for the separation by TLC of free amino acids from urine and other physiological fluids has been developed.[64] The method employed by us does not achieve the speed of many other TLC and TLE procedures described in the past, nor does it achieve the resolution or quantitation of column chromatography. It is, however, well-suited to large-scale screening of urine and other physiological fluids for many aminoacidopathies, including most of the rare types for which simpler screening tests are not available. It permits the simultaneous chromatography of 12–14 plates per tank, and the procedure requires a minimum of handling per specimen. The use of precoated plates not only eliminates a time-consuming preparatory step but also allows the stacking of these more abrasive-resistant plates; this in turn avoids the storage problem that would arise if such a large number of plates were to be processed. The method of detection employs a cadmium ninhydrin reagent which produces spots that remain stable for many weeks; thus, evaluation of the plates can be fitted with considerable latitude into the work routine. Although the entire analysis requires 7 days, the procedure can be interrupted any day and does not interfere with the usual work schedule of 40 hours per week. If carried out on a large scale, the procedure is reasonably economical.[64, 47]

Over 400 institutionalized mentally retarded patients have so far been screened with this method. Among this group, which was not selected at random, 8% showed some abnormality of amino acid metabolism. Approximately half of these could be diagnosed as to specific aminoacidopathy from the chromatogram. The method is useful in distinguishing from a large group of patients those on whom further biochemical investigations should be carried out.

REFERENCES

1. Detterbeck, F. J.   M.S. Thesis (in preparation), Michigan State University (1969).
2. Dent, C. E.   Biochem. J. **41**, 240 (1947).
3. Dent, C. E.   Biochem. J. **43**, 169 (1948).
4. Efron, M. L., D. Young, H. J. Moser, and R. A. MacCready.   New Eng. J. Med. **270**, 1378 (1964).
5. O'Brien, D.   *Rare Inborn Errors of Metabolism in Children with Mental Retardation* (Washington, D.C.: U.S. Dept. Health, 1965), p 74.
6. Hsia, D. Y., and T. Inouye.   *Inborn Errors of Metabolism, Part 2* (Chicago: Year Book Medical Publishers, 1966), p 60.
7. Turner, B., and M. Joster.   Med. J. Australia **1**, 152 (1964).
8. Mabry, C. C., and W. R. Todd.   J. Lab. Chem. **61**, 146 (1962).
9. Samuels, S.   Arch. Neurol. **10**, 322 (1964).
10. Juul, P.   Scand. J. Clin. Lab. Invest. **18**, 629 (1966).
11. Efron, M. L.   New Eng. J. Med. **72**, 692 (1959).
12. Bottomly, S. S.   Anal. Biochem. **18**, 472 (1967).
13. Young, D. S.   Clin. Chem. **14**, 418 (1968).
14. Samuels, S., and S. S. Ward.   J. Lab. Clin. Med. **67**, 669 (1966).
15. Walker, W. H., and M. Bark.   Clin. Chim. Acta **13**, 241 (1966).
16. Troughton, W. D.   Tech. Bull. Registry Med. Technologists **36**, 137 (1966).
17. Troughton, W. D., R. S. C. Brown, and N. A. Turner.   Am. J. Clin. Pathol. **46**, 139 (1966).

18. Farrelly, R. O., and W. B. Watkins.   Clin. Chim. Acta **20**, 291 (1968).
19. Ambert, J., C. Pechery, and C. Carpentier.   Ann. Biol. Clin. **24**, 17 (1966).
20. Opienska-Blauth, J., H. Kraczkowski, and H. Bruszikiewicz, in G.-B. Marini-Bettolo.   *Thin-Layer Chromatography* (Amsterdam: Elsevier, 1964).
21. Baron, D. N., and J. Economidis.   J. Clin. Pathol. **16**, 484 (1963).
22. Rokkones, T.   Scand. J. Clin. Lab. Invest. **16**, 149 (1964).
23. Crawhall, J. C., E. Saunders, and C. J. Thompson.   Abstract of 1st Meeting, Fed. European Biochem. Soc. (London, March 1964), p 91.
24. Frentz, R.   Ann. Biol. Clin. Paris **23**, 1145 (1965).
25. Hirano, K.   Osaka Shiritsu Daigaku Kaseigakubu Kiyo **12**, 115 *ca.* **63**, 15206D (1965).
26. Walz, D., A. R. Fahmy, G. Pataki, A. Niederwieser, and M. Brenner.   Experientia **19**, 213 (1963).
27. Pataki, G., and M. Keller.   Z. Klin. Chem. **1**, 157 (1963).
28. Keller, M., and G. Pataki.   Helv. Chim. Acta **46**, 1687 (1963).
29. Brenner, M., A. Niederwieser, and G. Pataki, in *New Biochemical Separations,* Ed. by A. T. James, and L. J. Morris (London: Van Nostrand, 1964).
30. Pataki, G.   Z. Klin. Chem. **2**, 129 (1964).
31. Bürgi, W., J. P. Colombo, and R. Richterich.   Klin. Wochschr. **43**, 1202 (1965).
32. Curtius, H. C., and F. Tancredi.   Quoted from Reference 50.
33. Pataki, G., and M. Keller.   Helv. Chim. Acta **47**, 787 (1964).
34. Keller, M., and G. Pataki.   Klin. Wochschr. **44**, 99 (1966).
35. Horstmann, H. Y., and A. Hennig.   Z. Physiol. Chem. **349**, 41 (1968).
36. Pataki, G., J. Borko, H. C. Curtius, and F. Tancredi.   Chromatographia **1**, 406 (1968).
37. Sunderman, W. F., Jr., in *Clinical Pathology of Infancy,* Ed. by W. F. Sunderman (Springfield, Illinois: C. C. Thomas Co., 1967), p 145.
38. Current Lab. Pract. **1**, 7 (1969).
39. Crowshaw, K., S. J. Jessup, and P. W. Ramwell.   Biochem. J. **103**, 79 (1967).
40. Gehrke, C. W., D. Roach, R. W. Zumwalt, D. L. Stalling, and L. L. Wall.   *Quantitative Gas-Liquid Chromatography of Amino Acids in Proteins and Biological Substances* (Columbia, Missouri: Analytical Biochemistry Laboratories, Inc., 1968).
41. Bigwood, E. J., R. Crocart, E. Schramm, P. Soupart, and H. Vis.   Advan. Clin. Chem. **2**, 201 (1959).
42. Efron, M. L.   *Technician Symp. 1965: Automation in Analytical Chemistry.* Ed. by L. T. Skeggs (New York: Mediad, Inc., 1966).
43. Shih, R. E., M. L. Efron, and G. L. Mechanic.   Anal. Biochem. **20**, 299 (1967).
44. Benson, J. V., Jr., J. Cormick, and J. A. Patterson.   Anal. Biochem. **18**, 481 (1967).

45. Benson, J. V. and J. A. Patterson, in *New Techniques in Amino Acid, Peptide, and Protein Analysis,* Ed. by A. Niederwieser and G. Pataki (Ann Arbor, Michigan: Ann Arbor Science Publishers, Inc., in press, 1970) p 1.
46. Guthrie, R.   Birth Defects Orig. Art. Ser. **4**, 92 (1968).
47. Stachnik, T. J., and T. G. DeLoach.   Mich. Mental Health Res. Bull. **2**, 3 (1968).
48. Hsia, D. T.   Birth Defects Orig. Art. Ser. **4**, 75 (1968).
49. Hamilton, P. B., quoted from Bio-Rad Lab. Price Bull. **July 1 ed.**, 28D (1968).
50. Pataki, G.   *Techniques of Thin-Layer Chromatography in Amino Acid and Peptide Chemistry* (Ann Arbor, Michigan: Ann Arbor Science Publishers, 1968).
51. Harris, C. K., E. Tigane, and G. S. Hanes.   Can. J. Biochem. Physiol. **39**, 439 (1961).
52. Hirs, D. H. W., in *Methods of Enzymology* **11**, 197 (1967).
53. Detterbeck, F. J., and H. A. Lillevik.   Submitted to Anal. Biochem. (1969).
54. Hsia, D. Y., and T. Inouye.   Reference 6, p 58.
55. Niederwieser, A.   Dissertation, University of Basle (1962).
56. Atfield, G. N., and C. J. O. R. Morris.   Biochem. J. **81**, 606 (1961).
57. Moffat, E. D., and R. L. Lytle.   Anal. Chem. **31**, 926 (1959); *cf.* also Pataki, Reference 50, p 92.
58. Blackburn, S., in Alexander, P., and H. Lundgren.   *A Laboratory Manual of Analytical Methods of Protein Chemistry,* Vol. 4 (London: Pergamon Press, 1968).
59. Oser, B. L.   *Hawk's Physiological Chemistry,* 14th ed. (New York: McGraw-Hill, 1966), p 1233.
60. Rokkones, T., as quoted in Reference 50.
61. Pataki, G., in Reference 50, p 45.
62. Halpaap, H.   Personal communication (1967).
63. Purdy, S. J., and E. V. Truter, as given in Reference 50, p 58.
64. Detterbeck, F. J., and H. A. Lillewik.   Mental Health Res. Bull. **2**, 17 (1968).

Index

absolute reflectance, 2
absorbance, 8
absorption band, particle size effect
    on reflectance, 4
absorption coefficient, 2
accuracy in reflectance spectroscopy,
    8ff, 27
acetolysis of phosphoglycerides, 160
acids
    fatty, 69, 86, 200, 106, 159
    organic, 207, 211
    phenolic, 39, 216
    resin, 203
    terpenes, 206
    wax, 200
activation temperature, effect on
    reflectance spectra, 27, 48, 51
active plant ingredients, 184
adsorbent-adsorbate interactions in
    reflectance spectroscopy, 11, 27,
    48
adsorbents, new, for TLC, 81
alcohols, 89, 132
    fatty, 132
    terpenes, 202, 206
    thujyl isomers, 88
    triterpenes, 209
aldehydes, 46, 89, 122, 202, 216 (*see
    also* fatty aldehydes)
    aromatic, 46, 216
    reflectance spectroscopy, 46
    stability in CS_2, 122
    terpenes, 202
alkaloids, 46, 94, 98, 99, 185, 187, 190,
    193, 194, 196, 209, 211, 225
    ergot alkaloids, 99
    reflectance spectroscopy, 46
alk-1-enyl diol lipids, 105ff (*see also*
    diol lipids and ether lipids)

alk-1-enyl diol lipids (*cont'd*)
    synthesis, 109
    TLC, 123ff, 128, 130
alk-1-enyl glyceryl ethers (*see also* ether
    lipids)
    acylation, 107
    alk-1-enyl silver complex, 158
    argentation TLC, 130–132, 147, 150,
    154ff, 158
    cleavage of ether bonds, 112
    diglyceride acetates, 162ff
    GLC, 118ff, 132–136
    GLC of aldehydes, 112, 122, 123
    hydrogenation of alk-1-enyl, 135
    IR spectra, 109, 162, 164
    phosphoryl-base transfer, 107
    stereospecific analysis, 118
    TLC, 123ff, 130–132, 143ff, 150,
    154ff, 162, 165, 167, 171ff
        alkenylacylglycerols, 126
        alkenyldiacylglycerols, 125, 128,
        158, 162ff
        monoalkenylglycerols, free, 127,
        131
        phospholipids, 129ff, 147ff, 155ff,
        171ff
alk-1-enyl phosphoglycerides, 106 (*see
    also* ether lipids)
    argentation TLC, 130, 147ff, 154,
    155, 177
    cleavage of ether bond, 112
    deacylation, 107, 113ff
    dephosphorylation, 113, 115, 129
    130, 145, 160, 161
    dimethylphosphatidates, 172, 173
    DNP-derivatives, methylated, 130,
    175ff
    enzymatic cleavage, 107, 112, 114,
    115, 145, 161

*This book was typeset at SSPA Typesetting,
Inc., Carmel, Indiana, in 10-point Times
Roman; and it was printed and bound by
LithoCrafters, Inc., Ann Arbor, Michigan*